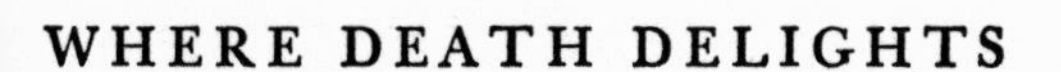

WHERE DEATH DELIGHTS

Books by Marshall Houts

FROM GUN TO GAVEL

FROM EVIDENCE TO PROOF

FROM ARREST TO RELEASE

THE RULES OF EVIDENCE

COURTROOM MEDICINE

COURTROOM MEDICINE: DEATH

TRAUMA *(8 volumes)*

PHOTOGRAPHIC MISREPRESENTATION

LAWYERS' GUIDE TO MEDICAL PROOF

WHERE DEATH DELIGHTS

WHERE DEATH DELIGHTS

The Story of Dr. Milton Helpern and Forensic Medicine

By MARSHALL HOUTS

COWARD-McCANN, INC.

NEW YORK

Library of Congress Catalog Card Number: 67-21513
Printed in the United States of America
by American Book–Stratford Press, Inc.

To *Be Helpern*

TACEANT COLLOQUIA. EFFUGIAT RISUS. HIC LOCUS EST UBI MORS GAUDET SUCCURRERE VITAE

("Let conversation cease. Let laughter flee. This is the place where death delights to help the living.")

—*Inscription on marble wall of Chief Medical Examiner's Office, City of New York*

Contents

WHERE DEATH DELIGHTS

CHAPTER 1

"The Body Seems to Defy Physical Laws"

For the past three years, whenever Dr. Milton Helpern has discussed the subject of bullet wounds in the body, he has been asked to give his opinion on President Kennedy's assassination.

Those who are knowledgeable about the subject of bullet wounds listen to what he has to say with a respect that borders on reverence. As Chief Medical Examiner of the City of New York, he has either performed or supervised approximately 60,000 autopsies; and 10,000 of these have involved gunshot wounds in the body. *The New York Times* has said that "he knows more about violent death than anyone else in the world."

No one can come close to matching his vast experience with bullet wounds. Dr. Helpern's book *Legal Medicine, Pathology and Toxicology* was cited as the standard reference work on the subject by Lieutenant Colonel Pierre Finck, one of the doctors who assisted in the autopsy on President Kennedy's body, in his testimony before the Warren Commission.

It now seems incredible that Dr. Helpern's opinion was not one of the first sought when the official investigation into the President's death was launched. It has not yet been asked for, either officially or unofficially, by anyone connected with the Warren Commission.

"The Warren Commission," Dr. Helpern says, shaking his head sadly, "was a tragedy of missed opportunities for forensic medicine.* Its entire approach to the problems of the President's wounds shows a total lack of familiarity with the subject. The Warren Commission had an opportunity to settle once and for all a great many of the confusing doubts, but because none of its members or its legal staff had any training or knowledge in forensic medicine, those opportunities fell by the wayside. It is tragic! Tragic!"

Almost every week Dr. Helpern plays host to some official visitor from a foreign country whose specialty is forensic medicine, and invariably the subject of the assassination comes up.

"I am continually amazed," he says, "at the refusal of the Europeans to accept the conclusions of the Warren Commission as being fact. Millions of Europeans apparently still feel strongly that the Commission report was nothing but a whitewash of some kind to cover up a vicious conspiracy. My friends in forensic medicine who have read the report in detail, and it seems that most of them have, simply cannot believe that the examination and evaluation of the President's bullet wounds could have been handled in the manner which the report describes.

"I am talking now only about the medical evaluation of the bullet wounds themselves, nothing else. The FBI certainly did a commendable job on the other phases of the case, but the FBI had to rely entirely on the medical information furnished it by the three doctors who performed the autopsy. The FBI does not have its own experts in forensic medicine. There is no reason for them to have. The FBI undoubtedly has had more experience with firearms identification, that is, matching a particular bullet to a particular gun, than any other agency in the world; but the FBI is seldom called upon to investigate a murder. Murder is a crime which usually involves a state jurisdiction only. Bullet wounds in the body are not the FBI's long suit."

Bullet wounds in the body, however, definitely are Dr. Helpern's long suit.

One of his most fascinating bullet wound cases goes back twenty-five years, when he was Assistant Medical Examiner. He

* Forensic medicine means medicine used in the courtroom, or in some step in the administration of justice.

received an urgent plea for help from a young attorney by the name of Robert Meyner, who was beginning a law practice in western New Jersey. Meyner's client was charged with first degree murder for shooting his father with deliberation and premeditation.

From Meyner's point of view, the situation was grim. He met Helpern at the railroad station late one evening and drove him to his mother's house where they would spend the night. The depressed young lawyer and the beginning forensic pathologist analyzed the facts of the case over a late supper, graciously served by Mrs. Meyner.

The defendant was thirty-seven-year-old Edoardo Bonifacio, a tall, handsome, first-generation Italian. His mother and father, Marina and Raulo Bonifacio, had emigrated to the United States some forty years earlier, to settle in the productive vegetable country of western New Jersey. The father and his many sons and sons-in-law worked long, back-breaking hours together as truck farmers in something of a communal family business. They were an expansive, close-knit group, who not only worked together but played together, danced together, schooled and churched together. Their family parties and reunions were legendary, even in an area saturated with foreign-born and first-generation Italian families.

There was, however, one cloud that always hovered threateningly over these family gatherings. When Papa Raulo got too much *vino,* he underwent a radical change in personality. He became intractable, stubborn, belligerent, abusive, and sometimes physically violent. The family had learned to live with this flaw in his makeup. They would humor him, stay out of his way, and even urge him on to a greater consumption of *vino* so that he would eventually pass out quietly and silently in a corner chair. The party could then safely reach crescendo and continue on into the early morning hours without his threatening interruptions.

The task of getting him home and to bed was a family joke. It was assigned and parceled out among the children in turns, just like any other domestic chore such as sweeping the floor or washing the dishes.

The next morning, routinely and on schedule, Papa Raulo

would awake with a massive hangover, total amnesia about most of the preceding evening, and in a funk of apologetic depression, knowing from past experience that his conduct undoubtedly had failed to pass even the minimum standard of civility imposed by Emily Post.

Mama Marina and all of the kith and kin would perfunctorily grant him forgiveness. He would passionately and in great sincerity swear off *vino* for the rest of his life, and would meticulously hold to his pledge until the next family gathering, usually no more than two weeks in the future. He would then sit restlessly for the first thirty minutes after all the clan had assembled.

"Well," he would begin, "Mama, I just take one little glass of *vino,* just one. That's all. No more. Just one little glass. See, no more than two fingers of *vino.*"

The two fingers of *vino* would always spread to a full hand, and then two hands, and finally a full arm. The rosary of events was in full swing. Papa Raulo would become loud, sometimes profane, threatening, and violent. He would soon pass out in his chair in the corner. The proper child or children would cart him home and put him to bed; the following morning would see his remorseful prayers and pledge of total abstinence.

Then one evening the clan gathered at Edoardo's house. It was a special occasion, Mama Marina's sixty-eighth birthday; and Papa Raulo treated it with proper respect.

"Mama," he said on the way to Edoardo's, "for you especially, I take no *vino* tonight. Not two fingers, not one finger, not even a fingernail of *vino* do I take tonight. For you this is the special night."

"That's great," she replied, gently squeezing his hand. "This will be our best party ever."

Papa Raulo was firm and strong for a longer time than usual, and he did start out with only one finger of *vino* instead of the usual two.

"Just a drop to toast your mother," he announced to all the assembled Bonifacios. "Just a little toast to the most wonderful mama in the world."

One toast to the most wonderful mama in the world could not possibly be enough. Even half a dozen more were inadequate, and soon Papa Raulo had become abusive and belligerent. This time, as frequently happens, Papa Raulo vented his outbursts against the one he loved and held most dear, Mama Marina. He berated her unmercifully for her deficiencies as a mother, grandmother, wife, and woman.

Edoardo finally reached the breaking point. He walked over to his father, took him firmly by the arm, marched him into the kitchen, and sat him down in a kitchen chair.

"We will absolutely not listen to any more, Papa," Edoardo said forcefully. "You have gone too far. I will understand when you get mad at me or any of the other children, but with Mama, no. She's too sacred. She's different."

Now another inhibition burst, releasing a flare that none of the family had ever seen before.

"I will kill you, Edoardo," Papa Raulo screamed. "I am your papa. You will obey me. You will not talk to me like that."

By this time, two of Edoardo's brothers were also in the kitchen, and they gently held Papa Raulo in the chair. Edoardo's wife was genuinely alarmed, and suggested that her husband leave for about thirty minutes. They would continue to pour wine into Papa Raulo. He would pass out in the chair in the corner, and the party could go on uninterruptedly.

Edoardo kissed his mother and told her that he would be back in half an hour. He got into his car and drove aimlessly around town, but when he returned, Papa Raulo had not passed out. He was swaying drunkenly in the middle of the living room, still berating Mama Marina unmercifully.

Edoardo's reappearance triggered an even more violent tirade of invective, so he retired again and drove around for another thirty minutes.

The stories as to exactly what happened upon his second return became varied and fragmented.

The family all agreed that by this time they had retired to the dining room and kitchen areas of the house to eat their pasta, leaving Papa comfortably passed out in his usual place in the living room.

Edoardo claimed that when he came in through the front door, Papa was alone in the living room but far from passed out. He was holding Edoardo's double-barreled 12-gauge shotgun across his knees, and Edoardo knew that this gun was loaded. Edoardo instinctively reached into the top drawer of a desk which stood just inside the door, and took out a loaded .38 caliber pistol.

By this time, Papa Raulo was standing unsteadily on his feet and was pointing the shotgun at his son. The first barrel of the shotgun fired and missed Edoardo, and he saw and heard his father cock the hammer of the second barrel. Edoardo now fired a shot from the pistol at his father's feet, in an effort to quiet him and make him realize the seriousness of what he had attempted to do. The bullet ricocheted upward from the floor, entered Papa's abdomen, and continued its course all the way through his body.

By the time other members of the family raced into the living room, Papa Raulo was lying face down on the floor, motionless and silent.

They rushed him to the hospital, where the doctors performed an abdominal operation, but it was too late. The bullet from Edoardo's pistol had perforated the liver and one of the major blood vessels of the body. Internal hemorrhage was the immediate cause of death, although it is doubtful that Papa Raulo could have recovered even if the doctors had been able to stem the hemorrhage. The coiled intestines had been perforated in twenty-one different places. It was the era before the sulfa and other wonder drugs, and multiple perforations of the intestines resulted in death from infection more often than not.

The coroner ordered an autopsy, which was performed by a young hospital pathologist who had encountered only one previous bullet wound case. He correctly observed the bullet wound in the back, slightly to the right of the midline and just under the end of the rib cage. There was no bullet wound to be seen in the abdomen since the surgeon's incision had cut it away.

The autopsy pathologist immediately concluded that the bullet wound in the back was a wound of entrance.

If this were true, the prosecuting attorney reasoned, and he had no cause to doubt the opinion of the doctor who performed the autopsy, the conclusion was clear. Edoardo Bonifacio had suffered under the drunken taunts and insults of his father all of his life. His built-in resentments, particularly the scene before the shooting in which his mother was the pathetic, innocent victim of his father's drunken rage, had flamed to the boiling point. He had clearly shot his father in the back intentionally and with malice and premeditation. True, there may have been extenuating circumstances and some reasonable provocation; but these were questions for the jury to decide. If they wanted to reduce the charge of murder in the first degree to murder in the second degree, or to manslaughter, this was their prerogative.

This was the evidence that challenged Edoardo Bonifacio's attorney, the challenge that had prompted his desperate call to Dr. Helpern.

"If I could have seen that wound in Papa's back," Dr. Helpern said discouragingly that morning at breakfast, "I am reasonably sure that I could have told you whether it was a wound of entrance or a wound of exit. Generally speaking, each type of wound has its own characteristics; but a given case may cause the inexperienced observer some trouble. This is especially true if one of the wounds has been altered or obliterated by surgery. It's not the job for the beginner working alone or the general pathologist whose knowledge of bullet wounds comes only from a textbook. Reliable interpretation of bullet wounds comes from constant practice at the autopsy table and through the careful study of each case, regardless of how simple it may seem."

"I didn't know enough," the young attorney replied sadly, "to even question this doctor's medical appraisal at the time he saw the wound at the autopsy. I assumed that an autopsy was an autopsy."

"And that any doctor who could write 'M.D.' after his signature was competent to perform it?" Dr. Helpern said, shaking his head and frowning.

Robert Meyner nodded: "Especially if he was a pathologist."

It was the old familiar refrain. Dr. Helpern had heard it day in and day out for ten years, and he wondered seriously when, if ever, the barrier would be broken so that the specialty of forensic medicine could be recognized and finally given an opportunity to grow and develop.

"What about the clothes that Papa Raulo was wearing?" Dr. Helpern asked in a final desperate move.

"Well, I don't know. I guess we can find them if they haven't been thrown away. You want me to see what I can do?"

"Yes, by all means. Let's see if we can find those clothes. I'm not too hopeful, but it looks like our only chance at this stage of the game."

The sheriff still had Papa Raulo's clothes tied up in a loose string bundle. He reluctantly agreed to let Meyner and Dr. Helpern examine them, reluctantly because he dared not do anything that might help the defense and harm the State's first degree murder case. This is the way of the confraternity of police officers and prosecuting attorneys.

Dr. Helpern carefully unwrapped the bundle and reassembled the bloodstained garments, item by item.

At the time Papa Raulo was shot, he wore a sleeveless cotton undershirt next to his body. Then came his dress shirt. Next, a long-sleeved wool sweater. Then a vest, and finally the jacket of his suit.

"Here's the answer you're looking for right here," Dr. Helpern said after a few minutes study.

"Where? What? I don't see it," Meyner said expectantly.

As Dr. Helpern carefully explained, Meyner literally jumped with excitement. There was a hole through the front of each layer of clothing—the suit jacket, the vest, the sweater, the dress shirt, and the undershirt. There was a hole, however, in the back of only the undershirt. The back of each of the other garments was completely intact.

"You see," Dr. Helpern continued his explanation, "the bullet from Edoardo's pistol entered the body from the front. You can trace it through these matching perforations in the articles of clothing that Papa Raulo wore. In the back, only the undershirt is perforated. The bullet spent its force in passing through the body and pierced only the undershirt. As far as I am concerned, this proves that the bullet wound in the back was a wound of exit. The entrance wound in the abdomen was obliterated by the surgeon's incision at the time the operation was performed in an effort to save Papa Raulo's life."

It was also enough as far as the jury was concerned. They deliberated only a few minutes before acquitting Edoardo Bonifacio of murdering his father.

"The subject of bullet wounds in the body," Dr. Helpern says, the dancing sparkle in his eyes telegraphing his interest in a field in which he has no peer, "is fascinating. At times, the body seems to defy physical laws as it responds to the trauma of a bullet projected from a gun. We know, of course, that this simply can't be so. There is a physical explanation for the bizarre paths that some bullets take; but those who haven't had any substantial experience with bullet wounds in the body can be completely misled.

"You could really write volumes on the meanderings and wanderings of bullets," Dr. Helpern continues, warming to his subject. "If the bullet encounters only soft tissues as it passes through the body, it will follow a relatively straight line. On the other hand, if it strikes bone, it is hard to predict just where it will go."

He illustrates his premise by pointing out that probably no more than 50 percent of the people who attempt to commit suicide by shooting themselves in the heart are successful. There is a physical explanation for the failures. The bullet strikes the breastbone at just the right angle and is deflected so that it continues around the rib cage, between the bone and the skin. It may come out at the back of the body after causing nothing more than superficial injury; or it may lodge just under the skin, between the skin and the backbone.

Next to bone, the skin offers the greatest resistance to the penetration of a bullet. There are literally thousands of reported cases where the bullet passes all the way through the entire body, only to come to rest just underneath the skin on the side opposite the point where it entered. It has spent so much of its force that it cannot make its exit through the thin but tough barrier of the skin.

Dr. Helpern has solved the problem of locating the missing bullet hundreds of times for police, detectives, and investigators by simply running his hand along the side of the body opposite the wound of entrance, feeling the bullet, taking a scalpel and making a tiny incision, and pulling out the bullet and handing it to the grateful officers.

"About 20 percent of the cases of bullet wounds of the head," he continues, "involve the bullet which enters and passes through the cranial cavity, only to ricochet inside the skull and bounce off the inner table of the skull, and then continues to travel in a completely different direction. It may carom around inside the skull just like a billiard ball bouncing against the cushions of a billiard table."

He describes an unusual ricochet case where a bullet was fired into the back of the head. It traveled up through the brain, forward and to the right, until it hit the inner table or layer of the skull just above the right eye. It was then deflected downward, backward, and to the left through the brain, and returned almost to the point of entrance in the same manner that a jai alai ball is caught in a scoop and returned to the wall by the player.

A particularly sad case of murder and attempted suicide involved the estranged husband of a woman who had left him to live with a Lesbian. He arranged a meeting with his wife in an effort to effect a reconciliation, but the effort was utterly futile. As they were sitting in the front seat of a pick-up truck, his wife began to taunt him over his sexual impotence, told him that she would never return to him, and that the only sexual satisfaction she had ever had in her entire life came from the woman with whom she was now living. The husband reached across to the glove compartment of the truck and pulled out a .38 caliber revolver. He fired four shots in rapid succession into his wife's body. She slumped forward and died shortly thereafter.

He then placed the pistol squarely in the center of his forehead and pulled the trigger; but instead of joining his wife in death, he awoke several hours later in a hospital. The bullet had merely penetrated the skin over the forehead and coursed around between the skin and the bones of the skull, down the cheek, to pass all the way through the larynx (voice box) in the neck. The man's ability to speak was permanently destroyed. Otherwise he had no physical injuries of any kind.

All the other writers in this field report similar experiences.

Dr. LeMoyne Snyder describes one case in which he was called into consultation by a urologist who was examining a fifty-year-old man with a severely swollen and enlarged left testicle. Dr. Snyder palpated the testicle and found what he thought felt like a bullet. After injecting Novocain into the scrotum, he made a small incision and removed a .38 caliber bullet from the testicle. Reluctantly, the man finally explained its history. Ten days earlier, he had attempted to shoot himself in the heart; but when he regained consciousness some minutes later on the floor, he realized that he was still alive. He had a pain in the bone in the center of his chest but could see only a small gash with a minimum amount of blood coming from it. He thought that his life had been miraculously spared and that the bullet had glanced off his body without doing him any real harm. He spent more than an hour searching the room for the bullet. Somehow, this bullet went between the bone and the skin and passed through the front body wall, without penetrating the belly cavity, to lodge in his left testicle. After the bullet was removed, the swelling and pain in his testicle subsided, and he recovered uneventfully.

Another of Dr. Helpern's remarkable cases concerned a policeman whose love affair with a woman was shattered when she threw him over for a taxi driver. The policeman waited for her in front of her apartment and strangled her in broad daylight. He commanded a passing car to drive him to his home, with his brother officers in hot pursuit. He rushed into the bathroom of his apartment, locked the door, and answered commands to surrender by shooting himself with his .38 caliber service revolver. The bullet entered his head through the roof of his mouth and exited through the top of his skull. He was taken to a hospital in a coma, where he was treated symptomatically without surgery because of the expected fatal outcome. He did not die, however, but recovered miraculously without any disability and was convicted of murdering his estranged girlfriend.

Even allowing for the vagaries of individual bullet wounds, it has been possible to formulate some general principles which permit the *experienced* forensic pathologist to be reasonably accurate in his calculations. Regardless of the number or position of the bullet wounds in the body in a given case, the first step is to determine whether each wound is a wound of entrance or a wound of exit.

When a bullet strikes the skin, it first produces a simple indentation, because the skin is both tough and elastic, and the tissues underneath are not rigid and resistant. This stretches the skin immediately under the nose of the bullet. The bullet, which is rotating as well as moving forward, is definitely slowed up at the point of first contact, but it then more or less bores its way through the skin and the tissues underneath, and courses on into the body. The skin is stretched by the bullet at the point at which it passes through; it then returns to its former condition, so that the size of the wound of entrance appears to be smaller than the diameter of the bullet which made it. Usually, there is only a small amount of bleeding from wounds of entrance, since tissue destruction at this point is not great. These rules apply to bullet wounds that are the result of the gun being fired at distances in excess of fifteen to eighteen inches. A different set of rules applies when the gun is held in direct contact with the skin or is fired from a distance less than fifteen to eighteen inches.

Wounds of exit, on the other hand, are usually larger than the bullet, since the bullet tends to pack tissues in front of it. These wounds are ragged, torn, and sometimes have shreds of fat or other internal tissues extruding out of them. As a result, wounds of exit may bleed far more extensively than wounds of entrance. This, however, is not invariably the case.

"You always are guided by the general rules that apply to bullet wounds," Dr. Helpern says, "but you must also be on guard for the bizarre, the unusual, the once-in-a-million case, the wounds that to the novice seem to defy physical laws. It is not a job for the beginner or the man whose knowledge is limited to a lecture or two, or to what he has read in some article or textbook."

To fully appreciate the gravity of Dr. Helpern's observations on the medical facets of President Kennedy's death, it is necessary to go back to the historic day of Friday, November 22, 1963.

Sometime between 12:30 P.M., when the tragedy struck in Dallas, and the arrival of *Air Force One* at Andrews Air Force Base just outside Washington at 5:58 P.M., Mrs. Kennedy decided that the autopsy on her husband's body should be performed at the Naval Medical School in Bethesda, Maryland. She was given two choices: either the Army's Walter Reed Hospital or Bethesda. She selected the Naval Medical School because of the President's World War II service in the Navy.

Certainly, Mrs. Kennedy could not be expected to have any knowledge of forensic medicine; and in her hour and the nation's hour of shock and bereavement, she made a logical choice. The point that disturbs Dr. Helpern, however, is the fact that the choice was left to her. It was not only an unpleasant, additional personal burden which should have been spared her, but it indicates the total lack of understanding of the subject of forensic medicine.

"It shows," he says, "that we are still laboring under the delusion that an autopsy is a computerized, mathematical type of procedure, and that *any* doctor is capable of performing it, especially if he is a pathologist. If he can run a correct urinalysis, ergo, this automatically qualifies him as an expert on bullet wounds in the body."

There can be no doubt but that this fallacious assumption was the real spawning ground for the contagious rash of anti-Warren Commission books that have poured out during the past three years. Their genesis can be traced directly to what was done and not done in a single operating room in the Naval Medical School in the evening hours of Friday, November 22, 1963.

The onus of performing the autopsy on the President's body, with the entire world expectantly watching, fell on James Joseph Humes, who described his qualifications in his subsequent testimony before the Warren Commission:

MR. SPECTER (assistant Commission Counsel). And what is your profession or occupation, please?

COMMANDER HUMES. I am a physician employed by the Medical Department of the United States Navy.

MR. SPECTER. What is your rank in the Navy?

COMMANDER HUMES. Commander, Medical Corps. United States Navy.

MR. SPECTER. Where did you receive your education, Commander Humes, please?

COMMANDER HUMES. I had my undergraduate training at St. Joseph's College at Villanova University in Philadelphia. I received my medical degree in 1948 from the Jefferson Medical College of Philadelphia.

I received my internship and my post-graduate training in my specialty field of interest in pathology in various naval hospitals, and at the Armed Forces Institute of Pathology at Walter Reed in Washington, D. C.

MR. SPECTER. What do your current duties involve?

COMMANDER HUMES. My current title is Director of Laboratories of the Naval Medical School at Navy Medical Center at Bethesda. I am charged with the responsibility of the overall supervision of all of the laboratory operations in the Naval Medical Center, two broad areas, one in the field of anatomic pathology which comprises examining surgical specimens and postmortem examinations and then the rather large field of clinical pathology which takes in examination of the blood and various body fluids.

MR. SPECTER. Have you been certified by the American Board of Pathology?

COMMANDER HUMES. Yes, sir; both in anatomic pathology and in clinical pathology in 1955.

MR. SPECTER. What specific experience have you had, if any, with respect to gunshot wounds?

COMMANDER HUMES. My type of practice, which fortunately has been in peacetime endeavor to a great extent, has been more extensive in the field of natural disease than violence. However, on several occasions in various places where I have been employed, I have had to deal with violent death, accidents, suicide, and so forth. Also I have had training at the Armed Forces Institute of Pathology. I have completed a course in forensic pathology there as part of my training in the overall field of pathology.

MR. SPECTER. Did you have occasion to participate in the autopsy of the late John F. Kennedy on November 22nd, 1963?

COMMANDER HUMES. Yes, sir; I did.

MR. SPECTER. What was your specific function in connection with that autopsy?

COMMANDER HUMES. As the senior pathologist assigned to the Naval Medical Center, I was called to the Center by my superiors and informed that the President's body would be brought to our laboratories for an examination, and I was charged with the responsibility of conducting and supervising this examination; told to also call upon anyone whom I wished as an assistant in this matter, that I deemed necessary to be present.

MR. SPECTER. Who did assist you, if anyone, in the course of the autopsy?

COMMANDER HUMES. My first assistant was Commander J. Thornton Boswell, whose position is Chief of Pathology at the Naval Medical School, and my other assistant was Lt. Col. Pierre Finck, who is in the Wound Ballistics Section of the Armed Forces Institute of Pathology.

In short, Commander Humes was a "hospital" pathologist. By any charity of imagination, he could not be considered a "forensic" pathologist or a "medico-legal" pathologist. The distinction between the two types of pathology is basic to a proper evaluation of the Warren Commission Report.

Pathology is the branch of medicine which concerns itself with the nature of disease, the causes of disease, its process of development, and its effects on the tissues and organs of the body. As Commander Humes indicated, the broad field of pathology breaks itself down into sub-fields and sub-specialties. One of these is forensic pathology. "Forensic" in this sense implies anything that has to do with the courtroom or some step in the administration of justice. The term "medico-legal" has the same meaning.

The "hospital" pathologist performs his autopsies on cases where death occurs in a hospital, usually as a result of some natural disease process. The cause of death is *presumed* in the great majority of cases because the patient has been under medical treatment. The autopsy is performed to confirm the diagnosis, or for research or other academic purposes.

The "forensic" or "medico-legal" autopsy has an entirely different setting. The death is usually not attended by a physician. The exact cause of death is crucial because of the legal implications. There may or may not be a suggestive or presumptive lead to guide the autopsy surgeon. If there is a lead, it is frequently insidious and misleading. The hospital pathologist is as much out of his field when he attempts a medico-legal autopsy as is the chest surgeon who attempts a delicate brain operation.

This analogy must be given a practical qualification. The chest surgeon would not attempt a delicate excursion into a living patient's brain for fear of killing him. Unfortunately, hospital pathologists are not fettered by any such fears.

Assistant Commission Counsel Specter did not consider it either necessary or advisable to attempt to establish Commander Boswell's expertise in the field of forensic pathology, or to ascertain whether he had any experience with bullet wounds in the body. The answer is that he had absolutely none worthy of mention.

Colonel Finck's professional qualifications were presented in an interesting fashion to the Warren Commission.

MR. SPECTER. What is your profession, sir?

COLONEL FINCK. I am a physician.

MR. SPECTER. And by whom are you employed?

COLONEL FINCK. By the United States Army.

MR. SPECTER. And what is your rank?

COLONEL FINCK. I am a Lieutenant Colonel in the Medical Corps.

MR. SPECTER. Where did you obtain your medical degree?

COLONEL FINCK. At the University of Geneva Medical School in Switzerland.

MR. SPECTER. And in what year did you obtain that degree?

COLONEL FINCK. In 1948.

MR. SPECTER. What has your experience been in the medical profession subsequent to obtaining that degree?

COLONEL FINCK. I had 4 years of training in pathology after my internship, 2 years, including 2 years of pathology at the University Institute of Pathology in Geneva, Switzerland, and 2 years at the University of Tennessee Institute of Pathology in Memphis, Tenn.

MR. SPECTER. And how long have you been in the United States Army?

COLONEL FINCK. Since 1955.

MR. SPECTER. And what have your duties consisted of in the Army?

COLONEL FINCK. From 1955 to 1958 I performed approximately two hundred autopsies, many of them pertaining to trauma including missile wounds, stationed at Frankfurt, Germany, as pathologist of the United States Army Hospital in Frankfurt, Germany.

MR. SPECTER. Have you had any additional, special training or experience in missile wounds?

COLONEL FINCK. For the past 3 years I was Chief of the Wound Ballistics Pathology branch of the Armed Forces Institute of Pathology and in that capacity I reviewed personally all of the cases forwarded to us by the Armed Forces, and some civilian cases from the United States and our forces overseas. The number of these cases amounts to approximately 400 cases. I was called as a consultant in the field of missile wounds for this particular case, and also last year in February 1963, the Surgeon General of the Army sent me to Vietnam for a wound ballistics mission. I had to testify in a murder trial, involving a 30/30 rifle in the first week of March of this year, and I came back yesterday after one week in Panama where I had to testify. I was sent to Panama by the Secretary of the Army regarding the fatalities of the events of 9–10 in January of 1964.

MR. SPECTER. Have you been certified by the American Board of Pathology, Doctor Finck?

COLONEL FINCK. I was certified in pathology anatomy by the American Board of Pathology in 1956, and by the same American Board of Pathology in the field of forensic pathology in 1961.

Of the two hundred autopsies he performed in Frankfurt, Germany, Colonel Finck did not give the number that involved bullet wounds in the body. He used the vague term "many." As to the four hundred cases that had come to his attention during his tenure as Chief of the Wound Ballistics Pathology branch of the Armed Forces Institute of Pathology, he says, "I reviewed personally." Colonel Finck's four hundred "reviewed" cases clearly are not four hundred cases in which he presided at the autopsy table and attempted a personal determination as to whether a bullet wound in the body is a wound of entrance or a wound of exit. His duties at the Armed Forces Institute of Pathology were administrative and supervisory. They did *not* include the performance of autopsies. He mentioned specifically only two bullet wound cases in which he had personally testified.

These were the three men charged with the responsibility of evaluating President Kennedy's gunshot wounds. They were all officers and gentlemen, and accomplished in their respective fields of general pathology. Regrettably, their field was not bullet wounds in the body. This particular autopsy was forced on them by circumstances over which they had no control. They dared not refuse it.

As a matter of fact, Colonel Finck's summons to Bethesda was something of an afterthought. He arrived well after the autopsy had begun and after a fragment of bullet had been removed from the President's head. He would not have been there at all except that General Blumberg, the commanding officer of the Armed Forces Institute of Pathology, telephoned Commander Humes to offer Colonel Finck's services. Colonel Finck was relegated to a back-row position.

The natural discomfort of the three autopsy surgeons who were working in an area in which they were basically unfamiliar—personally evaluating bullet wounds in the body at the autopsy table—was intensified by the goldfish-bowl atmosphere that enveloped their historic operations. The arena was jammed with FBI and Secret Service agents and various other persons. Commander Humes describes it:

MR. SPECTER. Tell us who else in a general way was present at the time the autopsy was conducted in addition to you three doctors, please?

COMMANDER HUMES. This, I must preface by saying it will be somewhat incomplete. My particular interest was on the examination of the President and not the security measures of the other people who were present.

However, the Surgeon General of the Navy was present at one time or another. Admiral Galloway, the Commanding Officer of the National Navy Medical Center; my own Commanding Officer, Captain John Stover of the Naval Medical School; Dr. John Ebersole, one of the radiologists assigned to the Naval Hospital, Bethesda, who assisted with the X-ray examinations which were made. These are the chief names, sir; that I can recall.

MR. SPECTER. What time did the autopsy start approximately?

COMMANDER HUMES. The President's body was received at 25 minutes before 8, and the autopsy began at approximately 8 P.M. on that evening. You must include the fact that certain X-rays and other examinations were made before the actual beginning of the routine type autopsy examination.

MR. SPECTER. Precisely what X-rays or photographs were taken before the dissection started?

COMMANDER HUMES. Some of these X-rays were taken before and

some during the examination which also maintains for the photographs, which were made as the need became apparent to make such.

However, before the postmortem examination was begun, anterior, posterior and lateral X-rays of the head, and of the torso were made, and identification type photographs, I recall having been made of the full face of the late President. A photograph showing the massive head wound with the large defect that was associated with it. To my recollection all of these were made before the proceedings began.

Several others, approximately 15 to 20 in number, were made in total before we finished the proceedings.

The taking of X-rays was a promising beginning and should be done in any gunshot or bullet wound case. The wanderings of bullets inside the human body both before and after death are often so bizarre that the only practical way to locate them is through the use of diagnostic X-rays. One case from Dr. Helpern's vast personal experience is sufficient to illustrate the need for X-rays. A .38 caliber lead bullet entered a man's right subclavian vein, a major vein just under the collarbone. It somehow made its way down through the right auricle, the right lower chamber of the heart, through the inferior vena cava, one of the two principal veins that return the blood from the body to the heart, finally to come to rest in the common iliac vein down in the region of the right hip. Without X-rays, the bullet would probably never have been found.

The autopsy on the President's body continued until 11 P.M., when it was released to those who would prepare it for burial and take it to the White House, where it arrived at four o'clock Saturday morning, November 23.

The weeks following the President's death flowed into months as the FBI and Secret Service painstakingly and thoroughly assembled the evidence, item by item, for formal presentation to the Warren Commission. The world waited expectantly for clarification of the bullet wounds.

An aura of confusion clouded the picture—due primarily to statements made by some of the doctors at Parkland Memorial Hospital in Dallas at a press conference a short time after the Presidential party left for the return trip to Washington. These doctors, who had worked skillfully at the impossible task of restoring life to the dead President, had observed a wound in the front part of the President's neck, just below the Adam's apple. Dr. Malcolm Perry described it as approximately 5 millimeters (1/5 of an inch) in diameter. It was exuding blood which partially hid edges which were "neither clearcut, that is, punched out, nor were they very ragged." This wound had been *extended* by Dr. Perry's tracheotomy. A tracheotomy is a surgical procedure of forming an opening in the trachea (windpipe) for the purpose of providing an artificial breathing vent in cases where the natural opening in the area of the larynx (voice box) is obstructed.

At no time during the interval that the President's body was in Parkland Memorial Hospital did any of the doctors turn it so that the back portion of the body could be viewed or examined. They, therefore, interpreted the wound in the front part of the neck as being a wound of entrance.

No legitimate criticism whatsoever can be directed against the doctors in Dallas. They performed their futile tasks creditably. None of them had any great experience with bullet wounds in the body, and they could not be expected to make a definitive interpretation of whether the neck wound was a wound of entrance or a wound of exit.

The principal burden of enlightening the Warren Commission on the President's wounds fell upon Commander Humes. In the military hierarchy, he was the senior officer charged with this responsibility, although Colonel Finck had more experience in the field of bullet wounds than the other two doctors combined, and his first-hand autopsy-table case experience was limited.

Commander Humes brought with him several drawings to assist his presentation. He described these drawings:

MR. SPECTER. Dr. Humes, before you identify what that represents let me place Commission Exhibition No. 385 on it so it may be identified.

(The drawing was marked Commission Exhibit No. 385 for identification).

COMMANDER HUMES. When appraised of the necessity of our appearance before this Commission, we did not know whether or not the photographs which we had made would be available to the Commission. So to assist in making our testimony more understandable to the Commission members, we decided to have made drawings, schematic drawings, of the situation as we saw it, as we recorded it and as we recall it. These drawings were made under my supervision and that of Dr. Boswell by Mr. Rydberg, whose initials are H. A. He is a hospital corpsman, second class, and a medical illustrator in our command at Naval Medical School.

MR. SPECTER. Did you provide him with the basic information from which these drawings were made?

COMMANDER HUMES. Yes, sir.

MR. SPECTER. Distances, that sort of thing?

COMMANDER HUMES. Yes, sir. We had made certain physical measurements of the wounds, and of their position on the body of the late President, and we provided these and supervised directly Mr. Rydberg in making these drawings.

MR. SPECTER. Have you checked the drawings subsequent to their preparation to verify their accuracy?

COMMANDER HUMES. Yes, sir.

MR. SPECTER. And proportion?

COMMANDER HUMES. I must state these drawings are in part schematic. The artist had but a brief period of some 2 days to prepare these. He had no photographs from which to work, and had to work under our description, verbal description, of what we had observed.

MR. SPECTER. Would it be helpful to the artist, in re-defining the drawings if that should become necessary, to have available to him the photographs or the X-rays of the President?

COMMANDER HUMES. If it were necessary to have them absolutely true to the scale. I think it would be virtually impossible for him to do this without the photographs.

MR. SPECTER. And what is the reason for the necessity for having the photographs?

COMMANDER HUMES. I think that it is most difficult to transmit into physical measurements by the—by word the—exact situation as it was seen to the naked eye. The photographs were—there is no problem of scale there because of the wounds, if they are changed in size or changed in size and proportion to the structures of the body and so forth, when we attempt to give a description of these findings, it is the bony prominences, I cannot, which we used as points of reference, I cannot transmit completely to the illustrator where they were situated.

Most medical illustrations in articles and textbooks that relate to anatomy are schematic or diagrammatic in nature. In medico-legal situations, however, where the ultimate in accuracy as to the path of a bullet is the goal, the better procedure is certainly to work from the photographs themselves rather than from a schematic medical illustration prepared not from the photographs which the medical illustrator views, but from a secondhand, hearsay description that is related to him orally. The fact of the matter is that in the case of the assassination the security regulations imposed were so stringent that the real investigative purpose of taking the photographs and the X-rays was completely obscured. As to their use, Commander Humes first testified:

MR. SPECTER. Were the photographs made available then, Dr. Humes, when Exhibit 388 was prepared?

COMMANDER HUMES. No, sir.

MR. SPECTER. All right.

COMMANDER HUMES. The photographs, to go back a moment, the photographs and the X-rays were exposed in the morgue of the Naval Medical Center on this night, and they were not developed, neither the X-rays or the photographs. They were submitted to the, and here, if I make a mistake I am not certain, to either the Federal Bureau of Investigation or to the Secret Service. I am not sure of these.

MR. SPECTER. Did you submit those yourself immediately after they were taken, Dr. Humes?

COMMANDER HUMES. Again, one of the senior people present, I believe my own Commanding Officer, Captain Stover, took care of turning this material over to these authorities, and receiving a receipt for this information, for this material. It was—I supervised the positioning of the body for various of these examinations but as far as beyond that, I did not consider that my responsibility. . . .

The X-rays, however, do make their appearance later on in Commander Humes' testimony:

. . . In further evaluating this head wound, I would refer back to the X-rays which we had previously prepared. These had disclosed to us multiple minute fragments of radio opaque material traversing a line from the wound in the occiput to just above the right eye, with a rather sizable fragment visible by

X-ray just above the right eye. These tiny fragments that were seen dispersed through the substance of the brain in between were, in fact, just that extremely minute, less than 1 mm. in size for the most part.

MR. SPECTER. Will you proceed now, Dr. Humes, to continue your description of the head wound.

COMMANDER HUMES. Head wound—a careful inspection of this large defect in the scalp and skull was made seeking for fragments of missile before any actual detection was begun. The brain was greatly lacerated and torn, and in this area of the large defect we did not encounter any of these minute particles.

I might say at this time that the X-ray pictures which were made would have a tendency to magnify these minute fragments somewhat in size and we were not too surprised at not being able to find the tiny fragments detected in the X-ray.

MR. SPECTER. Approximately how many fragments were observed, Dr. Humes, on the X-ray?

COMMANDER HUMES. I would have to refer to them again, but I would say between 30 or 40 tiny dustlike particle fragments of radio opaque material, with the exception of this one I previously mentioned which was seen to be above and very slightly behind the right orbit.

. . . I mentioned previously that X-rays were made of the entire body of the late President. Of course, and here I must say that as I describe something to you, I might have done it before or after in the description but for the sake of understanding, we examined carefully the bony structures in this vicinity as well as the X-rays, to see if there was any evidence of fracture or of deposition of metallic fragments in the depth of this wound, and we saw no such evidence, that is no fracture of the bones of the shoulder girdle, or of the vertical column, and no metallic fragments were detectable by X-ray examination.

The ambiguous status of the X-rays is not entirely cleared up even in this portion of the transcript:

MR. SPECTER. Did you search the body to determine if there was any bullet inside the body?

COMMANDER HUMES. Before the arrival of Colonel Finck we had made X-rays of the head, neck and torso of the President, and the upper portions of his major extremities, or both his upper and lower extremities. At Colonel Finck's suggestion, we then completed the X-ray examination by X-raying the President's body in toto, and those X-rays are available.

MR. SPECTER. What did those X-rays disclose with respect to the possible presence of a missile in the President's body?

COMMANDER HUMES. They showed no evidence of a missile in the President's body at any point. And these were examined by ourselves and by the radiologist, who assisted us in this endeavor.

The question that is left dangling is whether the X-rays were developed and available to guide the surgeons during the autopsy, or whether, as Commander Humes first testified, the exposed but *undeveloped* X-rays were turned over to FBI or Secret Service agents, so that they were not studied until after the autopsy was completed and the President's body prepared for burial.

The next routine step in any competent medico-legal autopsy involving bullet wounds, after the external examination and the X-rays, is to probe the track of the bullet. A stainless steel rod of small diameter is gently inserted and carefully guided through the wound track. This permits an exact determination of the course of the bullet through the body, its point and angle of entrance, and its point and angle of exit.

The futile, inexperienced efforts to probe the wound track in the body, one end of which was in the neck area, are described by Commander Humes:

. . . Attempts to probe in the vicinity of this wound were unsuccessful without fear of making a false passage. . . .

MR. SPECTER. Now, Doctor Humes, at one point in your examination of the President, did you make an effort to probe the point of entry with your finger?

COMMANDER HUMES. Yes, sir; I did.

Commander Humes was detailing a pathetic, fumbling effort to probe with his finger a wound track that had an entrance perforation of no greater than one-quarter of an inch in diameter. While it is readily understood that not all bullet wounds can be probed, particularly those that strike bone, the wound tracks of bullets that course directly through the body and strike only soft tissue can usually be probed by an experienced forensic pathologist.

There are complicating factors that confuse the novice. The bullet expends considerable energy as it moves from side to side through the body, so that the initial track is larger than the bullet itself. In most areas of the body, the wound track then collapses, although its original dimension is more or less fixed if it passes through brain tissue. The structures of the neck area are of varying densities which means that a single wound track here may have a different "feel" as the probe is advanced from the point of entry to the point of exit. Finally, the direction of the wound track may make an apparent change when the body moves. If, as Dr. Helpern believes, President Kennedy received his neck wound while his right hand and arm were raised in a wave to the crowd, the apparent wound track may have been altered slightly when his body was rotated on the autopsy table.

All three of the autopsy surgeons were unanimous in their opinions that the wound through the President's body and neck area did not strike any bony structures. Their lack of experience, compounded by the pressures of this particular autopsy situation, prevented them from ever successfully probing the President's wound. Their conclusions, therefore, as to the exact route of the bullet through the body are mathematical projections based upon measurements of the position of the two external wounds, one at each end of the track. Because of the tracheotomy which *extended* the wound in the front of the neck, just below the Adam's apple, the exact location of the wound made by the bullet had to be estimated or approximated.

These projections, in turn, were relayed *verbally* to Hospital Corpsman Second Class Rydberg so that he could incorporate them into his schematic drawings. The photographs and X-rays were never made available to him as he constructed the official illustrations which served as the demonstrative aids for the medical testimony. The synthetic character of the drawings is further exaggerated by the artist's arrows, complete with arrowhead and nock, to illustrate the paths of the bullets. They made it appear that the President was shot by bow and arrow.

We *must* accept the fact that these rather amateurish illustrations were *not* drawn to scale. Otherwise, the Commission's report and conclusions are patently inconsistent and obviously invalid. The size and shape of the bullet wound in the back of the President's neck is presented by the artist in such a way in Commission Exhibit 388 that it must either be a wound of exit or, if a wound of entrance, one made by a bullet of considerably larger caliber than the one fired from the rifle found on the sixth floor of the Texas School Book Depository Building.

To set the stage for the conclusions he would draw, Commander Humes described *four* wounds in the President's body, two in the head and two in the region of the neck. To avoid confusion in studying his testimony, it is necessary to remember that *each* bullet that passes through the body is said to create *two* wounds. One is the wound of entry; the other, the wound of exit. Commander Humes, therefore, in discussing *four* wounds was talking about the damage done by *two* bullets only, each of which created its own wound of entry and its wound of exit.

One of the head wounds was located 2.5 centimeters (approximately 1 inch) to the right and slightly above the large bony protrusion (external occipital protuberance) which juts out at the center of the lower part of the back of the skull. It measured 6 by 15 millimeters (1/4 of an inch by 5/8 of an inch).

The second head wound was massive, measuring approximately 13 centimeters (5 inches) in its greatest diameter. It was difficult to measure accurately because multiple crisscross fractures of the skull radiated from the large defect. It involved the right and frontal portion of the skull, which had been exploded off by the force of the bullet. During the autopsy, Federal agents brought the surgeons three pieces of bone recovered from Elm Street in Dallas and from the Presidential automobile. When put together, these fragments accounted for approximately three-quarters of the missing portion of the skull.

There was another wound near the base of the back of the President's neck, slightly to the right of his spine. It was described as being approximately 14 centimeters (5 1/2 inches) from the tip of the acromion (right shoulder joint) and approximately 5 1/2 inches below the tip of the right mastoid process, the bony point immediately behind the ear. This wound measured 7 by 4 millimeters (approximately 1/4 by 1/7 of an inch). It had clean edges and was sharply delineated.

The fourth wound was the one in the front part of the neck, just below the Adam's apple, which Commander Humes describes:

> Now, as the President's body was viewed from anteriorly in the autopsy room, and saying nothing for the moment about the missile, there was a recent surgical defect in the low anterior neck, which measured some 7 or 8 cm. in length or let's say a recent wound was present in this area.
>
> This wound was through the skin, through the subcutaneous tissues and into the larynx. Or rather into the trachea of the President.
>
> MR. SPECTER. To digress chronologically—
>
> COMMANDER HUMES. Yes.
>
> MR. SPECTER. Did you have occasion to discuss that wound on the front side of the President with Dr. Malcolm Perry of Parkland Hospital in Dallas?
>
> COMMANDER HUMES. Yes, sir; I did. I had the impression from seeing the wound that it represented a surgical tracheotomy wound, a wound frequently made by surgeons when people are in respiratory distress to give them a free airway.
>
> To ascertain that point I called on the telephone Dr. Malcolm Perry and discussed with him the situation of the President's neck when he first examined him . . .

Some of the difficulties and discomfort experienced by the autopsy surgeons are explained when it is understood that this telephone conversation between Commander Humes and Dr. Perry did not take place until the following morning, at which time the President's body was already resting in the White House. Lacking the medical history of what had transpired in Parkland Hospital in Dallas, the autopsy surgeons during the time that they had the President's body in front of them labored under the impression that they were working with only three bullet wounds, the two in the head and the one in the back of the neck. They attributed the wound in the front of the neck to the tracheotomy.

This caused them grave concern and anguish. Their inexperienced efforts to probe the neck wound were made at a time when they assumed that the bullet must still be in the President's body since there was no separate wound of exit.

Commander Humes explains their perplexity:

MR. SPECTER. Now, Dr. Humes, at one point in your examination of the President, did you make an effort to probe the point of entry with your finger?

COMMANDER HUMES. Yes, sir; I did.

MR. SPECTER. And at about the time that you were trying to ascertain, as you previously testified, whether there was any missile in the body of the President, did someone from the Secret Service call your attention to the fact that a bullet had been found on a stretcher at Parkland Hospital?

COMMANDER HUMES. Yes, sir; they did.

MR. SPECTER. And in that posture of your examination, having just learned of the presence of a bullet on a stretcher, did that call to your mind any tentative explanatory theory of the point of entry or exit of the bullet which you have described as entering at point "C" on Exhibit 385?

COMMANDER HUMES. Yes, sir. We were able to ascertain with absolute certainty that the bullet had passed by the apical portion of the right lung, producing the injury which we mentioned.

I did not at that point have the information from Dr. Perry about the wound in the anterior neck, and while that was a possible explanation of the point of exit, we also had to consider the possibility that the missile in some rather inexplicable fashion had been stopped in its path through the President's body and, in fact, then had fallen from the body onto the stretcher.

MR. SPECTER. And what theory did you think possible, at that juncture, to explain the passing of the bullet back out of the point of entry; or had you been provided with the fact that external heart massage had been performed on the President?

COMMANDER HUMES. Yes, sir; we had, and we considered the possibility that some of the physical maneuvering performed by the doctors might have in some way caused this event to take place.

MR. SPECTER. Now, have you since discounted that possibility, Doctor Humes?

COMMANDER HUMES. Yes; in essence we have . . .

The autopsy surgeons were considerably relieved by the receipt of this information. It permitted them to end their futile search for the missing bullet which was not in the President's body. They now believed that the bullet accidentally found on *a* stretcher in Parkland Hospital had been recovered from the stretcher on which the President's body had rested. This assumption, in all probability, was correct, even though the final report tortured the evidence, on Assistant Counsel Specter's persuasion, to conclude that the bullet was fortuitously found on the stretcher which held Governor Connally during his period in the emergency room at the hospital.

The truth of the matter is that no one will ever know for sure which stretcher held the bullet. Its discovery, however, did affect the course of the autopsy. The doctors thankfully abandoned their search, "presumed" with the self-assurance of the "hospital" autopsy atmosphere to which they were accustomed that they had solved the mysteries of the bullet wounds, and continued with a routine, systematic examination of the body cavities.

They experienced no obvious discomfort in adopting the theory that the wound in the back of the neck area was *both* a wound of entry and a wound of exit. Until the following morning, when Commander Humes telephoned Dr. Perry in Dallas, they still regarded the opening in the front of the neck as a surgical wound only.

The stubborn, persistent search of the President's body for a bullet that was not in it, a search which was abandoned only after information was relayed from Dallas that a bullet had been found in the hospital, sheds considerable light on the initial X-rays. Either the surgeons did not have them available, or for some reason, they doubted their own ability to read and interpret them. Whatever the reason, they elected to pursue a physical, manual attempt to probe for the missing bullet instead of confidently relying on the X-rays to tell them that no bullet was present.

The preliminaries were now established for the task of explaining the President's bullet wounds to the world, through the artificial, administrative forum of the Warren Commission; and Commander Humes rose to the demands of the occasion. Although his experience had been "more in the field of natural disease than violence," he succumbed to the intoxicating vapors and endemic infections of the witness-box. He developed a full-blown case of "witness-chairitis" which magically transformed him into an expert on every phase of the subject of bullet wounds in the body. Having had the final look, he proceeded to his biblical right of the final word.

How could there be two separate wound tracks or paths made by a single bullet through the President's brain? Commander Humes had his answer:

MR. SPECTER. Dr. Humes, would you elaborate on the differences in the paths, especially why the bullet went in one direction in part and in part in the second direction, terminating with the fragment right over the right eye?

COMMANDER HUMES. Yes, sir.

I will make a drawing of the posterior portion of the skull showing again this beveling which we observed at the inner table of the skull.

Our impression is that as this projectile impinged upon the skull in this fashion, a small portion of it was dislodged due to the energy expended in that collision, if you will, and that it went off at an angle, and left the track which is labeled 388, which is labeled on Exhibit 388 from "A", point "A" to the point where the fragment was found behind the eye.

Why a fragment takes any particular direction like that is something which is difficult of scientific explanation. Those of us who have seen missiles strike bones, be it the skull or a bone in the extremity, have long since learned that portions of these missiles may go off in various directions and the precise physical laws governing them are not clearly understood.

Had dumdum bullets been used? Commander Humes expounded on this:

MR. SPECTER. Do you have an opinion, Dr. Humes, as to whether there were dumdum bullets used specifically on the wound which struck point "A" on the head, on 388?

COMMANDER HUMES. I believe these were not dumdum bullets, Mr. Specter. A dumdum bullet is a term that has been used to describe various missiles which have a common characteristic of fragmenting extensively upon striking.

MR. SPECTER. Would you characterize the result and effect on this bullet as not extensive fragmenting?

COMMANDER HUMES. Yes. Had this wound on point "A" on Exhibit

388 been inflicted by a dumdum bullet, I would anticipate that it would not have anything near the regular contour and outline which it had. I also would anticipate that the skull would have been much more extensively disrupted, and not have, as was evident in this case, a defect which quite closely corresponded to the overlying skin defect, because that type of a missile would fragment on contact and be much more disruptive at this point.

What was the physical mechanism of the brain injury? Commander Humes continued:

. . . When the brain was turned over and viewed from its basular or inferior aspect, there was found a longitudinal laceration of the mid-brain through the floor of the third ventricle, just behind the optic chiasm and the mammillary bodies.

The laceration partially communicates with an oblique 1.5 cm. tear through the left cerebral peduncle. This is a portion of the brain which connects the higher centers of the brain with the spinal cord which is more concerned with reflex actions.

There were irregular superficial lacerations over the basular or inferior aspect of the left temporal or frontal lobe. We interpret that these later contusions were brought about when the disruptive force of the injury pushed that portion of the brain against the relatively intact skull.

This has been described as contre-coup injury in that location.

The fragments recovered were what proportion of the bullet?

MR. DULLES. Could one say as to what portion of the bullet was found in all these fragments, I mean arrive at an estimate, was it a tenth of the bullet, was it, how much was it, assuming the type of bullet that we believe was used in this particular rifle?

COMMANDER HUMES. Sir, I have not had an opportunity to personally examine the type of bullet which is believed to have been represented by this injury.

However, I would estimate—if I understand you correctly the total amount that was present in the President's skull and brain?

MR. DULLES. Yes.

COMMANDER HUMES. Including the fragments?

MR. DULLES. Including all the fragments.

COMMANDER HUMES. Including all these minute particles, I would say there was something less than one-tenth of the total volume of the missile.

Could the diameter of the bullet (its caliber) have been different from one fired from the rifle found on the sixth floor of the Texas School Book Depository Building? Commander Humes had an authoritative answer:

MR. McCLOY. Perhaps this was something that Colonel Finck could testify to exactly, but, he would be quite competent. Is there anything to indicate that this was, might have been a larger than a 6.5 or smaller than a 6.5?

COMMANDER HUMES. The size of the defect in the scalp, caused by a projectile could vary from missile to missile because of elastic recoil and so forth of the tissues.

However, the size of the defect in the underlying bone is certainly not likely to get smaller than that of the missile which perforated it, and in this case, the smallest diameter of this was approximately 6 to 7 mm., so I would feel that there would be the absolute upper limit of the size of this missile, sir.

MR. McCLOY. Seven would be the absolute upper limit?

COMMANDER HUMES. Yes, sir; and, of course, just a little tilt could make it a little larger, you see.

Again, on the mechanism of the massive head injury, Commander Humes rises to the occasion:

MR. DULLES. I have one other question, if I may?

Is the incidence of clean entry as indicated there, and then great fragmentation on exit, is that a normal consequence of this type of wound?

COMMANDER HUMES. Sir, we feel that there are two potential explanations for this.

One, having traversed the skull in entrance in the occiput as depicted on 388, the missile begins to tumble, and in that fashion it presents a greater proportion of its surface to the brain substance and to the skull as it makes its egress.

The other and somewhat more difficult to measure, and perhaps Colonel Finck will be able to testify in greater detail on this, is that a high velocity missile has tremendous kinetic energy, and this energy is expanded against the structures which it strikes, and so that much of this defect could be of the nature of blast, as this kinetic energy is dissipated by traversing the skull.

Is that the sense of the question, sir?

MR. DULLES. Yes.

The trajectory of the bullets? Commander Humes gave a long, rambling answer to conform to the preestablished theory of the Commission that all the shots were fired from the window of the Texas School Book Depository Building. When boiled down, it was:

COMMANDER HUMES. The degree of angle?

SENATOR COOPER. The angle, yes, the degree of angle of the missile from the building.

COMMANDER HUMES. Yes, sir; there is one difficulty, and that is the defect of exit was so broad that one has to rely more on the inclination of the entrance than they do connecting in this instance entrance and exit because so much of the skull was carried away in this fashion.

SENATOR COOPER. That was my second question.

My first question was would it be possible physically to establish the degree of angle of the trajectory of the bullet?

COMMANDER HUMES. Within limited accuracy, sir?

SENATOR COOPER. Within limited accuracy.

That being true then my second question was whether the point of entry of the bullet, point A, and the, what you call the exit—

COMMANDER HUMES. Exit.

SENATOR COOPER. Did you establish them so exactly that they could be related to the degree of angle of the trajectory of the bullet?

COMMANDER HUMES. Yes, sir; to our satisfaction we did ascertain that fact.

What about holes and defects in the clothing which the President wore and which Commander Humes only saw for the first time the preceding day? It was an uncomfortable question, but he did the best he could to make the holes in the clothing correspond to the wound in the back of the neck. He thought it a difficult hurdle, since the holes in the clothing were actually lower than the neck wound:

MR. SPECTER. Now, how, if at all, do the holes in the shirt and coat conform to the wound of entrance which you described as point "C" on Commission Exhibit 385?

COMMANDER HUMES. We believe that they conform quite well. When viewing—first of all, the wounds or the defects in 393 and 394 coincide virtually exactly with one another.

They give the appearance when viewed separately and not as part of the clothing of a clothed person as being, perhaps, somewhat lower on the Exhibits 393 and 394 than we have depicted them in Exhibit No. 385. We believe there are two reasons for this.

385 is a schematic representation, and the photographs would be more accurate as to the precise location, but more particularly the way in which these defects would conform with such a defect on the torso. It would depend on the girth of the shoulders and configuration of the base of the neck of the individual, and the relative position of the shirt and coat to the tissues of the body at the time of the impact of the missile.

MR. SPECTER. As to the muscular status of the President, what was it?

COMMANDER HUMES. The President was extremely well developed, an extremely well-developed muscular young man with a very well-developed set of muscles in his thoraco and shoulder girdle.

MR. SPECTER. What effect would that have on the positioning of the shirt and the coat with respect to the position of the neck in and about the seam?

COMMANDER HUMES. I believe this would have a tendency to push the portions of the coat which show the defects here somewhat higher on the back of the President than on a man of less muscular development.

MR. SPECTER. . . . Will you describe, Dr. Humes, the position of President Kennedy's right hand in that picture?

COMMANDER HUMES. Yes. This exhibit, Commission Exhibit No. 396, allegedly taken just prior to the wounding of the late President, shows him with his hand raised, his elbow bent, apparently in saluting the crowd. I believe that this action—

MR. SPECTER. Which hand was that?

COMMANDER HUMES. This was his right hand, sir. I believe that this action would further accentuate the elevation of the coat and the shirt with respect to the back of the President.

MR. SPECTER. Now, Dr. Humes, would you take Commission Exhibit No. 395—

MR. MCCLOY. Before you go, may I ask a question?

In your examination of the shirt, I just want to get it in the record, from your examination of the shirt, there is no defect in the collar of the shirt that coincides with the defect in the back of the President's coat, am I correct?

COMMANDER HUMES. You are correct, sir. There is no such defect.

The point of fire?

MR. DULLES. So then the shot would have been fired from some point above the head of the person hit?
COMMANDER HUMES. Yes, sir.

Commander Humes experienced no difficulty in girding up his loins so that he could discuss Governor Connally's wounds in great detail. He expounded on the bullet, its path through the President's body, its velocity after it passed through, the bullet's metal jacket, all in support of the premise that Governor Connally was struck by the same bullet that passed through the President's neck.

On the question of greatest concern to the Warren Commission, which were the wounds of entrance and which were the wounds of exit on the President's body, Commander Humes first quoted a few of the textbook criteria for making such a determination. He then confidently expressed his opinions:

MR. SPECTER. Dr. Humes, as to points of entry on the body of the late President, how many were there in total?
COMMANDER HUMES. Two, sir, as depicted in 385-C and 388-A.
MR. SPECTER. As to points of exit, how many were there?
COMMANDER HUMES. Two, sir, as depicted on 385-D and the vicinity of 388-B. I make the latter remark as was developed earlier, in that the size of the large defect in the skull was so great and the fragmentation was so complex that it was impossible to accurately pinpoint the exit of the missile in the head wound.
MR. SPECTER. Now as to that last factor, would the X-rays be of material assistance to you in pinpointing the specific locale of the exit?
COMMANDER HUMES. I do not believe so, sir. The only path that the X-rays show in any detail are of the minor fragments which pass from point A to point B.

In other words, the bullet through the head entered at the back of the head and made its exit somewhere toward the front and right portion of the skull.

As to the wound through the neck, Commander Humes continues:

We reached the conclusion that point "C" was a point of entry.

MR. SPECTER. What characteristics of that wound led you to that conclusion?

COMMANDER HUMES. The characteristics here were basically similar to the characteristics above, lacking one very valuable clue or piece of evidence rather than clue, because it is more truly a piece of evidence in the skull. The skull as I mentioned before had the bone with the characteristic defect made as a missile traverses bone.

The missile, to the best of our ability to ascertain, struck no bone protuberances, no bony prominences, no bone as it traversed the President's body. But it was a sharply delineated wound. It was quite regular in its outline. It measured, as I mentioned, 7 by 4 mm. Its margins were similar in all respects when viewed with the naked eye to the wound in the skull, which we feel incontrovertibly was a wound of entrance.

The defect in the fascia, which is that layer of connective tissue over the muscle just beneath the wound, corresponded virtually exactly to the defect in the skin.

And for these reasons we felt that this was a wound of entrance.

MR. SPECTER. What conclusion, if any, did you reach as to whether point "D" on 385 was the point of entrance or exit?

COMMANDER HUMES. We concluded that this missile depicted in 385 "C" which entered the President's body traversed the President's body and made its exit through the wound observed by the physicians at Parkland Hospital and later extended as a tracheotomy wound.

MR. SPECTER. Does the description "ragged wound" which is found in the Parkland report shed any light in and of itself as to whether point "D" is an exit or entry wound?

COMMANDER HUMES. I believe, sir, that that statement goes on, ragged wound in the trachea. I don't believe that refers to the skin and you might say that it is a ragged wound is more likely to be a wound of exit.

However, the trachea has little cartilaginous rings which have a tendency, which would be disrupted by this, and most wounds of the trachea unless very closely incised would perhaps appear slightly ragged.

But had Dr. Perry called this a "ragged wound"?

Dr. Malcolm Perry had observed it as exuding blood which

partially hid edges which were "neither clean-cut, that is, punched out, nor were they very ragged."

Although this wound in the front of the President's throat, as it appeared initially, was seen only by the doctors at Parkland Hospital before they *extended* it in performing the tracheotomy, there was absolutely no doubt in Commander Humes' mind but that it was a wound of exit:

MR. DULLES. Just one other question.

Am I correct in assuming from what you have said that the wound is entirely inconsistent with a wound that might have been administered if the shot were fired from in front or the side of the President: It had to be fired from behind the President?

COMMANDER HUMES. Scientifically, sir, it is impossible for it to have been fired from other than behind. Or to have exited from other than behind.

Toward the end of Commander Humes' substantive testimony about the President's wounds, Commission member Gerald Ford voiced his misgivings as to the pictures and X-rays.

REPRESENTATIVE FORD. May I ask what size are the pictures to which you refer?

COMMANDER HUMES. We exposed both black and white and color negatives, Congressman. They were exposed in the morgue during the examination. They were not developed. The Kodachrome negatives when developed would be 405. They were in film carriers or cassettes as were the black and white. Of course, they could be magnified.

REPRESENTATIVE FORD. Have those been examined by personnel at Bethesda?

COMMANDER HUMES. No, sir. We exposed the negatives; we turned them over. Here I must ask the counsel again for advice—to the Secret Service.

MR. SPECTER. Yes; it was the Secret Service.

COMMANDER HUMES. They were turned over to the Secret Service in their cassettes unexposed, and I have not seen any of them since. This is the photographs. The X-rays were developed in our X-ray department on the spot that evening, because we had to see those right then as part of our examination, but the photographs were made for the record and other purposes.

REPRESENTATIVE FORD. But they had never been actually developed for viewing.
COMMANDER HUMES. I do not know, sir.

Commander Humes had completely reversed his earlier testimony that "neither the X-rays or the photographs" were developed the night of the autopsy but were turned over to the FBI or Secret Service, exposed but not developed.

Assistant Commission Counsel Specter next proceeded to tidy up the record. He introduced approximately fifteen pages of longhand notes which Commander Humes had made during the performance of the autopsy. The transcript continues:

MR. SPECTER. Are there any notes which you made at any time which are not included in this group of notes?
COMMANDER HUMES. Yes, sir; there are.
MR. SPECTER. And what do those consist of?
COMMANDER HUMES. In privacy of my own home, early in the morning of Sunday, November 24th, I made a draft of this report which I later revised, and of which this represents the revision. That draft I personally burned in the fireplace of my recreation room.

There is no way of knowing at this stage just exactly what Commander Humes' initial, independent conclusions were. The transcript, however, does contain this interesting exchange:

MR. SPECTER. Now, just one point on the notes themselves. Page 14 of your rough draft, Doctor Humes, as to the point of origin, the notes showed that there was a revision between your first draft and your final report.
COMMANDER HUMES. Yes, sir.
MR. SPECTER. Will you first of all read into the record the final conclusion reflected in your final report.
COMMANDER HUMES. I would rather read it from the final report. The final report reads:
"The projectiles were fired from a point behind and somewhat above the level of the deceased."
MR. SPECTER. And what did the first draft of that sentence as shown on page 14 of your rough draft state?
COMMANDER HUMES. It read as follows:

"The projectiles were fired from a point behind and somewhat above a horizontal line to the vertical position of the body at the moment of impact."

MR. SPECTER. Now would you state the reason for making that modification between draft and final report, please?

COMMANDER HUMES. This examination, as I have indicated, was performed by myself with my two associates. The notes which we have just admitted as an exhibit are in my own hand and are my opinion, was my opinion at that time, as to the best way of presenting the facts which we had gleaned during this period.

Before submitting it to the typist, I went over this with great care with my two associates. One or the other of them raised the point that perhaps this sentence would state more than what was absolutely fact based upon our observations, pointing out that we did not know precisely at that time in what position the body of the President was when the missiles struck, and that therefore we should be somewhat less specific and somewhat more circumspect than the way we stated it. When I considered the suggestion, I agreed that it would be better to change it as noted, and accordingly, I did so.

All told, Commander Humes' testimony consumes less than thirty pages of transcript. Commander Boswell's contribution is less than a page. He merely corroborated Commander Humes' opinion and stated that he had nothing of value to add.

Colonel Finck's testimony runs for seven pages. His major contribution was in the form of an illustrated lecture as to how he could determine wounds of entrance and wounds of exit:

MR. SPECTER. Have you had occasion to conduct any experiments on the effect of missile penetration of the brain reflected in the chart which you have brought with you here today?

COLONEL FINCK. No, sir.

MR. SPECTER. Of the skull—let me phrase the question this way: What does the test which is depicted on the document before you relate to?

COLONEL FINCK. It is based on my observations, not on experiments.

MR. SPECTER. Would you pass that to me, sir, so that I may mark that as a Commission Exhibit, and then I will ask you to identify it, please?

Mr. Chief Justice, may I mark this Commission Exhibit No. 400 a document?

THE CHAIRMAN. It may be marked.

(The document was marked Commission Exhibit No. 400 for identification.)

MR. SPECTER. I will ask Dr. Finck to describe it for us, please.

COLONEL FINCK. This is a scheme which I prepared before the 22nd of November. It is a teaching scheme, but it does apply to the case in discussion. It will be a help in understanding how I could identify the entrance and the exit by examination of bone. "A" represents the bony portion of the skull. "B" represents the cavity of the head, the cranial cavity. "C" represents the entrance and "D" represents the exit. The arrows indicate the missile path.

This scheme is based upon observation of through and through wounds of bone, and the same differences apply to a pane of glass. The surface struck first by the missile in relation to the surface struck next by the missile, this one, shows a smaller diameter, which means that if you look at the route of entrance in this case here, "C" from the outside you will not see a crater. If you examine it from the inside, you will see a crater corresponding to the beveling, coning, shelving, previously described by Commander Humes.

In the case we are discussing today, it was possible to have enough curvature and enough portion of the crater to identify positively the wound of entrance at the site of the bone.

MR. SPECTER. Relating then your evaluation of the situation with respect to President Kennedy, and turning to Commission Exhibit No. 388, what is your opinion as to whether the point "A" is a wound of entrance or exit?

COLONEL FINCK. My opinion as regards Exhibit 388, letter "A" is that this wound is a wound of entrance.

MR. SPECTER. And what are the characteristics of that wound which leads you to that conclusion?

COLONEL FINCK. The characteristics were that seen from the inside of the skull, I could see a beveling in the bone, a beveling that could not be seen when the wound was seen from outside the skull.

MR. SPECTER. Are there any other individual characteristics that led you to conclude "A" was the wound of entrance?

Although he does not state it in so many words, it is obvious that Colonel Finck's theory concerning the head wound is that the bullet split into at least two parts when it crashed into the President's skull:

MR. SPECTER. One more question, Mr. Chief Justice.

On 388, point A to B, what is your view, Doctor Finck, as to whether or not this is represented by a straight line going back to the point of origin of the weapon?

COLONEL FINCK. The difficulty in interpreting the path in line A-B of Commission's Exhibit 388 is that, one, there is, as stated before, a large wound of exit, and two, there is a secondary path as indicated by the fragments recovered. So we can have an assumption and state that the general direction, the general path, the general angle of this missile was from behind and above, and that the bullet markedly fragmented, went out of the President's head on the right side, but that a portion of this bullet which badly fragmented was recovered within the skull.

Colonel Finck did have sufficient familiarity in the field of bullet wounds in the body to know the name of the authoritative text on the subject.

REPRESENTATIVE FORD. How many cases did you investigate to develop this theory shown by Commission Exhibit 400?

COLONEL FINCK. Among the more than four hundred cases I have reviewed, several of them—I cannot give you an exact figure, I do not tabulate them, but many of them had through-and-through wounds of the skull as well as of flat bones, as, for instance, the sternum, the bone we have in front of our chest, and this would apply also to a through-and-through wound of the sternum. I have had cases like that.

There was a specific case in which I was able to identify the entrance at the level of the sternum on the same basis as the criteria I have given for the skull. Whenever a bullet goes through a flat bone, it will produce that beveling, that cratering, shelving, and that I have seen in numerous cases.

REPRESENTATIVE FORD. Is this a generally accepted theory in the medical profession?

COLONEL FINCK. Yes, sir; it is. Am I allowed to quote a standard textbook?

THE CHAIRMAN. You may; yes, sir.

COLONEL FINCK. The textbook of legal medicine, pathology and toxicology by Gonzalez, Vance, Halpern and Umberger does not give a scheme like I have shown to you today, but describes similar criteria.

As you know, one of the authors of the book I mentioned is still chief medical examiner of New York City, with 20,000 medical-examiner cases a year.

This was the evidence on which the Warren Commission issued its official, authoritative report as to the medical nature of the bullet wounds which killed the President.

One continuing theme permeates the entire final work. It is the demand that the medical evidence be interpreted so as to be consistent with the already well-established theory that all of the bullets involved were fired from a single rifle found in the sixth-floor room of the Texas School Book Depository Building. This theme is clearly illustrated by an excerpt from the final Commission summary:

"The findings of the doctors who conducted the autopsy were consistent with the observations of the doctors who treated the President at Parkland Hospital. Dr. Charles S. Carrico, the resident surgeon at Parkland, noted a small wound approximately 1/4 of an inch in diameter (5 to 8 millimeters) in the lower third of the neck below the Adam's apple. Dr. Malcolm O. Perry, who performed the tracheotomy, described the wound as approximately 1/5 of an inch in diameter (5 millimeters) and exuding blood which partially hid edges that were 'neither clean-cut, that is, punched out, nor were they very ragged.' Dr. Carrico testified as follows:

Q. Based on your observations on the neck wound alone did you have a sufficient basis to form an opinion as to whether it was an entrance or an exit wound?

A. No, sir; we did not. Not having completely evaluated all the wounds, traced out the course of the bullets, this wound would have been compatible with either entrance or exit wound depending upon the size, the velocity, and the tissue structure and so forth.

The same response was made by Dr. Perry to a similar query:

Q. Based on the appearance of the neck wound alone, could it have been either an entrance or an exit wound?

A. It could have been either.

Then the doctor was asked to take into account the other known facts, such as the autopsy findings, the approximate distance the bullet traveled, and tested muzzle velocity of the assassination weapon. With these additional factors, the doctors commented on the wound on the front of the President's neck as follows:

DR. CARRICO. With these facts and the fact as I understand it no other bullet was found this would be, this was, I believe, was an exit wound.

DR. PERRY. A full jacketed bullet without deformation passing through the skin would leave a similar wound for an exit and entrance wound and with the facts which you have made available and with these assumptions, I believe that it was an exit wound."

This was the testimony that satisfied the Commission and permitted it to conclude that "the findings of the doctors who conducted the autopsy were consistent with the observations of the doctors who treated the President at Parkland Hospital."

"The tragic, tragic thing," Dr. Helpern explains in summarizing his comments on the medico-legal aspects of President Kennedy's death, "is that a relatively simple case was horribly snarled up from the very beginning; and then the errors were compounded at almost every other step along the way. Here is a historic event that will be discussed and written about for the next century, and gnawing doubts will remain in many minds, no matter what is done or said to dispel them."

What were these step-by-step errors?

"I've already touched on the gravest of them all—the selection of a 'hospital' pathologist to perform a medico-legal autopsy. This stemmed from the mistaken belief that because a man can supervise a laboratory or perform a hospital autopsy to see whether a patient died from emphysema or heart disease, he is qualified to evaluate gunshot wounds in the body. It's like sending a seven-year-old boy who has taken three lessons on the violin over to the New York Philharmonic and expecting him to perform a Tchaikovsky symphony. He knows how to hold the violin and bow, but he has a long way to go before he can make music."

Does this observation apply to Lieutenant Colonel Pierre Finck?

"Colonel Finck's position throughout the entire proceeding was extremely uncomfortable. If it had not been for him, the autopsy would not have been handled as well as it was; but he was in the role of the poor bastard Army child foisted into the Navy family reunion. He was the only one of the three doctors with *any* experience with bullet wounds; but you have to remember that his experience was limited primarily to 'reviewing' files, pictures, and records of finished cases. There's a world of difference between standing at the autopsy table and trying to decide whether a hole in the body is a wound of entrance or a wound of exit, and in reviewing another man's work at some later date in the relaxed, academic atmosphere of a private office. I know, because I've sweated out too many of these cases during the past thirty-five years. Colonel Finck is extremely able in the type of administrative work which has been assigned him over the years."

Are there any crucial steps that should have been taken that were omitted that Friday evening in the autopsy room at the Naval Medical School?

"The major problem in any gunshot case, of course, is to determine which is the wound of entry, and the wound of exit. This is basic. All the so-called critics of the Warren Commission Report would be left dangling in mid-air with their mouths gaping unless they can suggest or argue that the hole in the front of the President's throat was a wound of entrance. Deprive them of this opportunity for speculation and you pull the rug right out from under them. Give it to them, and they now have it, and they can bring in all kinds of unreliable eyewitness reports of shots coming from the bridge across the underpass, or from behind the screen of trees in Dealey Plaza, and puffs of blue smoke that remained suspended in the air with police officers scrambling up the bank to investigate these illusory puffs of smoke. Smoke from gunshots just doesn't behave like that!"

Specifically, how could a positive determination have been made at the time of the autopsy that the throat wound was a wound of exit or a wound of entrance?

"In a great many cases, the only safe way to reach a conclusive decision is to compare the size and characteristics of each wound on the end of the wound track. It's easy for textbook writers and their readers to assert pontifically that the wound of exit is *always* larger than the wound of entrance, and the wound of exit is ragged whereas the wound of entry is smooth, so that you have no difficulty in taking a gross, eyeball look and saying 'this is the entry wound' or 'that is the exit wound.' This isn't true at all. The difference between the entry wound and the exit wound is frequently a lot more subtle than that. Many of the wounds require careful and painstaking study before you can reach a decision."

But wasn't the throat wound gone at the time of the autopsy? In one place, the Warren Commission Report states: "At that time they [the autopsy surgeons] did not know that there had been a bullet hole in the front of the President's neck when he arrived at Parkland Hospital because the tracheotomy incision had completely eliminated that evidence." At another point the report says: ". . . since the exit wound was obliterated by the tracheotomy."

"No, you see, the staff members who wrote that portion of the report simply did not understand their medical procedures; and they did not know enough to seek medical guidance. Here's what the autopsy protocol says about this throat wound: '. . . it was extended as a tracheostomy incision and thus its character is distorted at the time of autopsy.' The key word here is *extended.* That bullet wound was not 'eliminated' or 'obliterated' at all. What Dr. Perry did was to take his scalpel and cut a clean slit away from the wound. He didn't excise it, or cut away any huge amount of tissue, as the report writer would have you believe."

What about the description in the autopsy protocol that "its character is distorted"?

"Certainly, its character is distorted in the sense that the original wound was *extended* in length by Dr. Perry's scalpel; but this throat wound could still have been evaluated. Its edges should have been carefully put back together and restored to their original relationships as nearly as possible. It should have then been studied, and finally photographed. By comparing this throat wound with the wound in the back of the neck, there should have been no room for doubt as to which wound was of entry and which of exit. This would automatically establish the course of the bullet, whether from front to back, or back to front."

Why wasn't this procedure followed?

"I can't crawl into the minds of the surgeons and answer for them. I can only offer my own speculative opinion. In the first place, their lack of experience deprived them of the knowledge of what should have been done. Secondly, it appears from every facet of the evidence now available that at the time they finished their autopsy and closed the body so that it could be prepared for burial, they labored under the illusion that the hole in the back of the neck was *both* a wound of entrance and a wound of exit. They thought the throat wound was nothing more than a surgical wound, so there was no need to pay it any special attention."

Are there any other procedures followed by the autopsy surgeons that have furnished ammunition to the critics of the Warren Commission Report?

"Unfortunately, there are. The phraseology in the formal autopsy protocol itself implies or suggests that the doctors still harbored doubts and uncertainties at the time it was written. In speaking of the neck wounds, the protocol describes them as 'presumably of entry' and 'presumably of exit.' It says: 'As far as can be ascertained this missile struck no bony structures in its path through the body.' Well, that just doesn't read like the work of men in confident command of their ship.

"On the other side of the coin, the writers of the Warren Commission Report went to the opposite extreme when they tried to force a unanimity of opinion on all the doctors at Parkland Hospital in support of the autopsy surgeons that the throat wound had to be a wound of exit. When you put too much tension on the evidence, by pulling and tugging it, in an effort to mold it to the shape of a preconceived conclusion, you leave yourself pretty vulnerable."

What about Commander Humes burning his original notes of his draft of the autopsy protocol?

"It's extremely unfortunate that he did; but I interpret this only as further evidence of his lack of experience in medico-legal situations. I can't believe that there's anything sinister about it as some of the critics would have you believe. Commander Humes simply did not appreciate that this was not just another hospital autopsy, and that every note or memorandum should be saved for later scrutiny."

Some of the critics of the Warren Commission Report have attempted to bolster their attacks by alleging that Commander Boswell's drawing (a portion of Commission Exhibit 397) shows the bullet wound in the back of the neck as being down about the level of the shoulder blades. Is this significant?

"It's significant in that it demonstrates the total ignorance of the critics in the matter of autopsy procedures. We don't need to spend any time on trivia like this; but for their information, this is simply part of the work sheet. It contains two purely schematic drawings of the human figure, one front and one rear, in what is known as the 'quasi-anatomic position.' The doctor doing the autopsy uses them as a shorthand way of making notes on what he observes during his external examination of the body. Commander Boswell sketched in a number of observations including the surgical wounds, the old scar from the President's back operation, and the bullet holes. No one ever pretends that these markings are drawn to scale. To take the time to do this would defeat the entire purpose of this shorthand way of making notes. The written material in the autopsy protocol is what matters."

Some critics have alleged some sort of duplicity because an FBI report dated December 9, 1963, and another one dated January 13, 1964, apparently contain information which is not consistent with the formal autopsy protocol.

"This is more trivia and underbrush. What difference does it make what these two FBI reports said? The controlling factor insofar as the medico-legal phase of the investigation is concerned is the autopsy protocol itself. There was undoubtedly conversation going on in the autopsy room. The FBI agent there probably heard the doctors agonizing over their inability to find the bullet. He observed them trying to probe the neck wound. He heard their speculations that the hole in the back of the neck was *both* a wound of entrance and a wound of exit. To me, all these particular FBI reports show is exactly what we have mentioned before: at the time the autopsy was finished, the doctors thought they were dealing with only three bullet holes, two in the head and one in the *back* of the neck."

Where did the Warren Commission, as distinguished from

the autopsy surgeons, fail to clarify the medical issues of the President's death?

"It failed tragically because it did not have sufficient knowledge in the field of forensic medicine to even appreciate the need to call in an expert with experience in bullet wounds in the body. This lack of knowledge is evident in the official report itself. For example, it contains thousands of exhibits in eleven volumes. They include all sorts of meaningless pictures of Marina Oswald, Oswald's mother, Oswald as a young boy, Jack Ruby's employees or girl friends in varying states of attire, and nine X-rays of Governor Connally's body.

"The X-rays of President Kennedy's body, however, were not considered significant enough to the entire investigation to be filed as exhibits to the report. The same holds true of the black and white and the color pictures of the bullet wounds. These were never seen by the Commission members, its staff, or even the autopsy surgeons before the report was finalized. The Commission said it would not 'press' for the X-rays and photographs because these would merely 'corroborate' the findings of the doctors, and that considerations of 'good taste' precluded these from being included.

"Well, you see, there was nothing that offended 'good taste' in the nine X-rays of Governor Connally's body [Commission Exhibit 691]; so this great curtain of secrecy that was pulled down on the X-rays and pictures of the President's body added more explosive fuel to the fire of doubt. There have been intimations that these X-rays and pictures had gone the way of Commander Humes' notes; and it was only after considerable public pressure built up that the pictures and X-rays were turned over to the National Archives by the Kennedy family in November of 1966; but they are still shrouded by this great curtain of secrecy. Secrecy is the natural culture medium for suspicion."

Why didn't the examination by the Navy doctors of the X-rays and pictures in November 1966 still the doubts of the critics?

"Let's come back to our analogy of the seven-year-old violin player. We sit him down in front of an electronic microscope and ask him what he sees on a slide. He says: 'I don't see anything.' We then jump to the conclusion that there is nothing there because an inexperienced eye can't see anything there."

What might these X-rays show to an experienced observer that could have been completely overlooked by the nonexpert expert?

"Who knows? Probably absolutely nothing. I don't like to engage in rank, blind speculation; so I can only explain how I would approach them. My first interest would be to see whether there could be another bullet or fragment of bullet in the body which has not been accounted for.

"Remember that the Warren Commission concluded that the preponderance of the evidence indicated that three shots altogether were fired. Only one relatively intact bullet and the fragments of a second bullet were found. This leaves a missing third bullet. I definitely do not agree with the Commission's conclusion that only two bullets caused all the wounds suffered by both President Kennedy and Governor Connally; but we'll pass that for the moment.

"Since the X-rays of the President's body were not filed as exhibits, we must rely entirely upon the observations of the Navy doctors that they skillfully eliminated the possibility that a third bullet, or a fragment of some bullet, did not enter the body and somehow meander down to come to rest in some illogical, remote spot. Apparently, the doctors did not feel confident enough to rely on the X-rays during the autopsy when they went probing, or rather tried to go probing, for the bullet that was found on the stretcher in Parkland Hospital. They have now been quoted publicly as saying that they did have the X-rays available to them that night. Bullets do have a funny habit of showing up in the most astounding places in the body.

"I would also look for trace flecks of metal that might indicate another head wound. This possibility is extremely remote; but it still exists. Often, quite often, wounds of entrance in the head are completely overlooked because they are covered naturally by the hair. The wound may barely bleed at all. If you don't take a comb and go over the entire scalp inch by inch, separating the hair carefully and meticulously, it's easy to miss a head wound entirely. There is no evidence that this type of examination was made."

Would the X-rays help establish whether the two wounds in the neck area were wounds of entrance or of exit?

"No, I would not expect them to be of help on this question. An X-ray film is nothing more than a photographic record of the different densities of tissues through which the X-ray beam has passed. It will not record defects in the skin and soft tissue caused by a bullet passing through."

What about the black and white and the color photographs?

"These could be of considerable interest and value. A lot would depend on their quality and how they were exposed. Hopefully, they could shed considerable light on the neck wounds. I would, of course, be interested in what the pictures of the rear neck wound would show; but I would be particularly interested in seeing whether the pictures of the throat wound are good enough to permit it to be evaluated and possibly reconstructed."

Where else can the Warren Commission be faulted for what it did or failed to do?

"Again, it committed a grievous error of omission by failing to call in someone who knew something about bullet wounds in the body. This led them into the final trap of buying Assistant Counsel Arlen Specter's theory that the same bullet which passed through the President's neck was the bullet that also wounded Governor Connally, shattering his fifth rib, fracturing a bone in the wrist, and finally going on to slash his thigh. Now, this bizarre *path* is perfectly possible. When you are working with bullet wounds, you must begin with the premise that *anything* is possible; but Mr. Specter and the Commission overlooked two important ingredients.

"In the first place, the original, pristine weight of this bullet before it was fired was approximately 160–161 grains. The weight of the bullet recovered on the stretcher in Parkland Hospital (Commission Exhibit 399) was reported by the Commission as 158.6 grains. This bullet wasn't distorted in any way. I cannot accept the premise that this bullet thrashed around in all that bony tissue and lost only 1.4 to 2.4 grains of its original weight. I cannot believe either that this bullet is going to emerge miraculously unscathed, without any deformity, and with its lands and grooves intact.

"Secondly, Mr. Specter and the Commission have asked too much from this bullet. You must remember that next to bone, the skin offers the greatest resistance to a bullet in its course through the body than any other kind of tissue. The energy of the bullet is sometimes so spent that it can't quite get out through the final layer of skin, and it comes to rest just beneath the outside layer of skin. If it does get through the skin, it may not have enough energy to penetrate even an undershirt or a light cotton blouse. It has exhausted itself, and just more or less plops to a stop.

"This single bullet theory requires us to believe that this bullet went through seven layers of skin—tough, elastic, resistant skin. It passed through the back of the President's neck, then out through his throat; it entered the Governor's back and out through his chest; it next entered the skin on the back of his wrist; it came out through the layer of skin on the inside of his wrist; and it apparently penetrated the layer of skin on his left thigh. In addition to these seven layers of tough human skin, this bullet passed through other layers of soft tissue; and then these shattered bones!

"I just can't believe that this bullet had the force to do what Mr. Specter and the Commission have demanded of it; and I don't think they have really stopped to think out carefully what they have asked of this bullet for the simple reason that they still do not understand the resistant nature of human skin to bullets."

Do these conclusions shed any light on the order of the shots?

"In my opinion, this beautifully preserved bullet that was found in the Hospital was the first bullet that was fired. It passed through the President's neck, exited from the throat wound, and was stopped by his clothing, or just plopped out of his neck into his clothing. I've seen this exact thing happen hundreds of times."

What about the Commission's conclusion that this bullet was found on Governor Connally's stretcher in Parkland Hospital?

"It's based on tortured evidence, or inconclusive evidence, to say the least. No one will ever know for sure which stretcher this bullet came from. In my opinion, the probabilities are that it fell out of the President's clothing while the doctors were administering to him in the hospital. For the sake of argument, however, let's assume that it was found on the Governor's stretcher. This still does not rule out the premise that it was the first bullet that passed through the President's neck. That spent bullet could just as easily have taken an erratic jump out of the President's clothing and lodged in Governor Connally's clothing. These things happen with bullets. Sometimes they get through the final layer of skin and hop limply about it all arcs of the circle and at all angles to the wound of exit."

Do you agree with Governor Connally that he was struck by the *second* bullet?

"Yes, I definitely do. His testimony is most persuasive. I just can't buy this theory that this beautifully preserved first bullet is going to have power enough to pass all the way through the *seven* layers of skin of the two men, plus other soft tissue, plus rib and wrist bone, and end up losing no more than 2.4 grains of its weight. In my opinion, the second bullet that wounded Governor Connally is the one that is missing."

Shouldn't this bullet have been found during the careful search of the Presidential limousine?

"Not necessarily. It is not unusual at all for spent bullets that have passed through a human body to become lost. Most long-time homicide detectives can spin off several tales of cases of lost bullets. If I had to venture a guess as to what happened to the bullet that wounded Governor Connally, I would suggest that it fell out of his pants leg while he was being removed from the car and placed on the stretcher; or it could have fallen out at any stage of his hospital experience."

And the third?

"The third one quite obviously is the one that caused the President's massive head wound, and his death. Also, either a fragment from this bullet, or a piece of skull, caused the cracking of the windshield and the dent in the windshield chrome on the interior of the limousine, provided these marks on the car were not already present at the time the shooting began."

Assistant Counsel Arlen Specter's creation of the theory that a "single bullet" passed through the President's neck and went on to inflict all of Governor Connally's wounds has been hailed by a prominent Commission staff member as the one significant contribution of the Warren Commission to the solution of the assassination. It was at odds with the FBI reports of December 9, 1963, and January 13, 1964. The FBI concluded: ". . . three shots rang out. Two bullets struck President Kennedy, and one wounded Governor Connally. . . ."

Mr. Specter thought that he needed the "one bullet" theory because of the Zapruder movie, and the "one bullet" theory is perhaps the most amateurish conclusion in the entire Commission Report. Regrettably, it permits the brand of "doubtful" to cloud the genuine, bona fide Commission findings.

Abraham Zapruder is now undoubtedly the most famous amateur movie photographer in all history. As he stood in Dealey Plaza aiming his home movie camera in an easterly direction, he caught and recorded the Presidential motorcade as it proceeded north on Houston Street, to make its turn west onto Elm Street. This innocent, famous home movie ended up by leading Mr. Specter and the Warren Commission into an unfortunate trap.

Even those who have purported to study the work of the Commission in considered hindsight are still mesmerized by the beguiling and misleading power of the Zapruder movie. For example, in its November 25, 1966 issue, *Life* magazine innocently perpetuates the error. Its article reads: "Of all the witnesses to the tragedy, the only unimpeachable one is the 8-mm. movie camera of Abraham Zapruder, which recorded the assassination in sequence. Film passed through the camera at 18.3 frames a second, a little more than a 20th of a second (.055 seconds) for each frame. By studying individual frames one can see what happened at every instant and measure precisely the interval between events."

The error that trapped the Warren Commission as well as *Life* magazine is that there is nothing at all *precisely* measured by the Zapruder film.

The nearest thing to a *precise,* objective event which the film records is at Frame 313, which shows the President's skull exploding as a result of the bullet that passed through his head. Every other item purportedly measured by the Zapruder film is *imprecise* because it must be evaluated and speculated upon through factors and calculations which involve unknown quantities.

One of the most common pitfalls in any investigation is the "timetable trap." The investigator becomes mesmerized by either a clock or a calendar and ends up with a conclusion that two and two are five, or that some Florida oranges are red because Washington Delicious apples are also red. This is exactly what happened to Mr. Specter who, unfortunately, was able to sell his erroneous theory to the Warren Commission.

Some time after the investigation into the President's death began, the FBI staged a mock reenactment of the assassination, which was geared to and scripted by the Zapruder movie. An FBI agent was stationed in the sixth-floor window of the Texas School Book Depository Building with a camera geared to the telescopic lens of the Mannlicher-Carcano rifle found at this same window minutes after the assassination. An effort was made to *synchronize* the Zapruder movie with what the assassin presumably saw from his point of vantage at the sixth-floor window as the Presidential caravan moved along its historic route.

It had previously been determined that the Zapruder camera ran at the speed of 18.3 pictures or frames per second. The timing of certain events, therefore, could be calculated by allowing 1/18.3 seconds for the action depicted from one frame to the next. Other tests had also determined that this Mannlicher-Carcano rifle required a minimum of 2.3 seconds between each shot fired.

Each frame of the Zapruder film was given a number, Number 1 beginning where the motorcycles leading the motorcade came into view on Houston Street. Combining the FBI reenactment with the Zapruder movie, it was concluded that the assassin had a clear view of the President from his sixth-floor window as the limousine moved up Houston Street, and for an additional one hundred feet as the Presidential car proceeded west on Elm Street. At a point denoted as Frame 166 on the Zapruder film, the assassin's view of the President became obstructed by the foliage of a large oak tree.† The President's back reappeared into view through the telescopic lens on the rifle for a fleeting instant at Frame 186. This momentary view was permitted by an opening in the leaves of the tree; but they closed to again obscure the view of the President's back through the telescopic sight until the car emerged from behind the tree at Frame 210.

The Commission implies that one of the difficulties in interpreting the Zapruder film is that the President's car begins to disappear behind a road sign reading "Stemmons Freeway Right Lane" at approximately Frame 193. At Frame 206, the President's hand is still raised as he disappears behind the street sign. He reappears in the film at Frame 225. As a matter of fact, it is really not essential to the evidential value of the film whether the President was or was not out of sight for some 30 to 32 frames.

There are those who viewed the Zapruder movie who *thought* that the President *looked like* he was hit through the neck when he reappeared from behind the street sign at Frame 225. They *think* that Governor Connally appeared to be hit at Frame 230. Governor Connally *believes* that he was hit around Frame 234. *Life* magazine summarizes the *subjective* factor of interpretation by saying: "Specter sees Connally wincing in Frame 230. *Life*'s photo interpreters think he looks unharmed, as does Connally himself."

Still, Mr. Specter labored under the illusion that the Zapruder movie gave him a stopwatch precision measurement of events that took place *not in the Presidential limousine but in the Texas School Book Depository Building over one hundred feet back up Elm Street.*

Mr. Specter did not believe that he could solve the problem of orienting the Zapruder movie to the minimum time required to fire two shots from the Mannlicher-Carcano rifle without adopting the "one bullet" theory. The 2.3 seconds required to

† One of the most incredible statements of the entire report appears on page 97: "On *May 24, 1964,* agents of the FBI and Secret Service conducted a series of tests to determine as precisely as possible what happened on *November 22, 1963.* . . . The agents ascertained that the foliage of an oak tree that came between the gunman and his target along the motorcade route on Elm Street was approximately the same as on the day of the assassination."

fire two shots from the rifle worked out to 42.09 frames of the Zapruder movie. Even assuming that the President had been hit in the neck while he was behind the street sign at, say, Frame 210, it would not be possible for a second shot to be fired until Frame 252.09.

This presented a difficult impasse, provided the "timetable" supplied by the Zapruder movie was correct. Mr. Specter assumed that this "timetable" was accurate, and then adopted the "one bullet" theory to get around its limitations. Otherwise, he was faced with the awkward admission that *two* guns were used instead of one.

His better procedure would have been to carefully analyze his "timetable" in an effort to understand exactly what he was working with. By beginning with Frame 313, the only objective point of reference in the entire film where the picture of the President's exploding skull was recorded, it is possible to set up a *reverse timetable* by *working backward:*

Frame	Description of Event	Elapsed Frames	(Seconds) Elapsed Time
313	President's skull explodes	—	—
230	Governor Connally's "reaction" (earliest estimate)	83	4.5
210	President possibly hit while behind street sign	103	5.6
186	Momentary reappearance of President through leaves of oak tree	127	6.9
166	Disappearance of President from assassin's view caused by foliage of oak tree	147	8.0

What does this *reverse timetable* prove? It proves exactly the same thing as the *forward timetable* of the Zapruder film, which is exactly nothing. Nothing is proved because we do not know when the President and Governor Connally were struck by the first and second bullets. There is absolutely nothing in the frames of the movie to give us any precise measurement. In the first place, we are in a quandary of uncertainty as to when the President and the Governor "reacted" to their respective wounds. It has already been clearly established that different observers of the Zapruder film have reached different opinions as to when these "reactions" took place. We are dealing with *subjective* evaluation which completely kicks out the concept of any *precise* "timetable."

The next great error that was committed in attempting to use the Zapruder film as a "timetable" was the assumption that the President and the Governor would have some visible reaction to their wounds at almost the *exact instant* that the wounds were sustained. There is absolutely nothing in medicine to indicate that this assumption is correct. As a matter of fact, what is known about reaction-time generally indicates that the assumption may *not* be correct.

It must readily be admitted that the reaction-time of any person to a bullet wound is a purely speculative entity. No one has yet conducted a series of experiments so that a set of rules governing reaction-time to bullet wounds can be formulated.

Studies have been made of certain other types of reaction-time in the field of automobile accident reconstruction where elaborate tests have been given to drivers under controlled conditions. It has been established that between the time the driver perceives a dangerous event and the time that he applies his brakes or begins other evasive action, an average reaction period of two-thirds to three-quarters of a second elapses. In some individuals, this reaction-time is well over one full second. There is always some "drag" or reaction-time involved between the stimulus and the reaction to the stimulus. This is true, even though this type of stimulus is something that the driver has been conditioned to expect and which he must anticipate by the nature of the testing situation.

No one knows whether there is an analogy between driver reaction-time and bullet wound reaction-time. It can be argued plausibly that driver reaction-time involves a conscious thinking process, whereas the reaction of the body to a bullet is more nearly analogous to an autonomic, reflex type of action. There are, however, hundreds of reported cases in which the person shot apparently does not realize that he has been shot for a period of several minutes. He may continue to perform a number of complex, highly coordinated functions for a substantial period of time before collapsing to lose consciousness or to die.

Furthermore, Governor Connally's reaction-time to his wounds may have been more rapid than the President's reaction-time to his first neck wound. This is true because the Governor's wounds were far more severe than the President's neck wound. The Governor may have been hit at Frame 230 of the Zapruder film. He may have "reacted" immediately, so that his "reaction" can still be observed by viewers of the movie. This does not mean at all that the President could *not* have been shot through the neck *before* Frame 166 when his back disappeared behind the leaves of the oak tree, or at Frame 186 when his back reappeared momentarily, and the President's observable physical reactions appeared in the movie only *after* Frame 225 when the President emerges from behind the road sign.

There is absolutely nothing in the "open end" Zapruder movie "timetable" to rule out the possibility or even the probability that the President was shot through the neck before Frame 166. The error in using the Zapruder film was in the assumption that the President would have to "react" instantaneously to the neck wound in such a manner that his reaction could be observed in the movie. The Zapruder film is not really a "timetable" after all, because it can help establish the "location" of only one "station" along the "railroad." It does not help us pinpoint the other two important stations, nor does it tell us when the train got there. We can use the Zapruder "timetable" to conclude that the train got to one station *probably* no later than Frame 225. It reached the second station no later than Frame 234. We cannot tell from the Zapruder film what the train was doing before these two locations, or even where our "floating" stations one and two are located.

It was not necessary for Mr. Specter to devise, nor for the Commission to buy, the "one bullet" theory to eliminate the necessity of adopting the embarrassing premise that *two* rifles were used to do the shooting instead of one.

Dr. Helpern's theory of three separate bullets causing three separate wounds, two in the President's body and one in Governor Connally, is not at all inconsistent with the Zapruder movie when the movie is properly interpreted as being nothing more than an open-end, one-station timetable where the separate and distinct elements of time, distance, and location have been confused.

Mr. Specter also failed to reckon with a creature called chance, or fate, or luck and to consider the possibility that the assassin may have fired a first shot blindly, without taking careful aim. Dr. Helpern recalls the case of a spectator who suddenly plunged forward out of his seat at the Polo Grounds while watching a baseball game. He was dead from a .45 caliber bullet hole through the middle of his forehead. Police subsequently traced the firing location to the roof of a house several blocks away, where a man, without intent or purpose, had pointed the gun into the air and pulled the trigger. The least likely result that he could have anticipated was the death of an innocent baseball fan.

What about the "wound ballistics experiments" conducted at the Edgewood Arsenal?

"Well," Dr. Helpern responds, shaking his head in disbelief, "the mere fact that they felt constrained to perform these tests in the first place shows a total lack of knowledge on the subject of bullet wounds in the body. They went down there and tried to rig up dummies that would simulate the President's head and neck area. They took human skulls, filled them with gelatin, and covered them with goatskin and hair. They rigged up a dummy with gelatin and animal meat to simulate the neck area of his body. Then they got a goat to simulate Governor Connally's body. They took the rifle found in the Texas School Book Depository Building and began firing into these dummies. All they proved was that they proved absolutely nothing. One of the experts was utterly surprised that a bullet could cause the massive wound in the President's head. His surprise alone clearly indicates his limited experience.

"We have all kinds of cases in our files that show what bullets can and have done in the human body. So does everyone else who is active in the field of forensic medicine. For example, Dr. LeMoyne Snyder has a case that almost duplicates the President's head wounds in every respect. It arose out of a bank holdup in Michigan. A dentist who had his office on the second floor of a building directly across the street from the bank went to the window to see what the trouble was. He saw one of the bandits running down the street with people yelling after him. The dentist was quite a deer hunter and kept a rifle in his office. He reached for his rifle, raised the window, and hit the bandit in the back of the head with a single shot. By that time, the bandit was just about the same distance away as the Presidential limousine was from the sixth-floor window of the Texas School Book Depository Building when the third shot struck. The head wounds this bank bandit sustained were almost identical in every respect to those of President Kennedy.

"Nevertheless, the Commission chose to rely on the synthetic tests at the Edgewood Arsenal to support its conclusion that a single bullet probably caused the wound through the President's neck and all of Governor Connally's wounds. This was done even though one of the three experts, Dr. Light, testified that the anatomical findings alone were insufficient for him to 'formulate a firm opinion on whether the same bullet did or did not pass through the President's neck wound first before inflicting all the wounds on Governor Connally.' "

Is there anything in the overall picture to cast serious doubt on the principal conclusions reached by the Warren Commission?

"Of course, I haven't seen the pictures and the X-rays of the President, but on the basis of the evidence that has been made public, the Commission reached the correct opinion that all three bullets were fired by one rifleman from the sixth-floor window of the Texas School Book Depository Building. The unfortunate autopsy and other procedures have merely opened the door and invited the critics to enjoy a full-blown Roman holiday at the expense of the dignity and prestige of the country as a whole.

"The fact that a rigorous cross-examination of the three autopsy surgeons would have ripped their testimony to shreds does not necessarily mean that their conclusions were *totally* wrong. The fact that the Commission may have erred in concluding that the same bullet that struck the President also wounded Governor Connally does not mean that the Commission was *totally* wrong in its opinion that all the shots came from the Depository Building. What it means is that the Commission members themselves set the stage for the aura of doubt and suspicion that has enveloped their work."

The Commission, of course, was an unusual creature. It was itself a synthetic entity. It was extrajudicial, extraexecutive, and extralegislative. It was supposed to be a public forum for taking evidence because the normal forum of the courtroom was wiped out when Jack Ruby killed Oswald. If Oswald had lived, all the evidence about the President's death could have been aired in the courtroom and all the witnesses would have been open to cross-examination. In its procedures, the Commission failed to supply anything that would fill the disastrous void left when the right or motive to cross-examine the witnesses was wiped out. They did not provide for the essential 'Devil's Advocate.'

The biblical saying that "a man is judged by his work" may be appropriate. The Commission's work opened the door and invited the critics to flood in.

Is there anything specifically that Dr. Helpern would like to see done at this point?

"It may well be too late to do anything, since the primary evidence is gone. There is a possibility, however, that the X-rays and photographs of the President's wounds might contain some clarifying information. I would certainly feel more comfortable about the Warren Commission's findings if a group of experienced men, who have had a great deal of practical work in bullet wound cases, could take a look at these X-rays and pictures. I have in mind men like Dr. LeMoyne Snyder, author of *Homicide Investigation,* Dr. Russell Fisher, the medical examiner for the State of Maryland, Dr. Frank Cleveland in Cincinnati, and Dr. Richard Myers in Los Angeles. These men are all members of the American Academy of Forensic Sciences. These pictures and X-rays *might,* and I emphasize *might,* settle the questions raised by the critics once and for all.

"The tragic thing is that a greatly loved President was not given the same type of expert medical attention and medical respect in death that he received in life. When he was having his back problems, he properly consulted the leading experts in the field of orthopedic surgery; but, you see, in death, the task of evaluating his bullet wounds was not given to experienced experts in this field. It was still the old saw that an autopsy is an autopsy is an autopsy, and anyone can do it, particularly as long as he is a general or 'hospital' pathologist."

What about the portions of the autopsy protocol that have not been released to the public?

"These, I think," Dr. Helpern answers, "are personal matters that should be left entirely to the family, although I do think that the public is entitled to the most expert and definitive determination possible on the bullet wounds that caused death."

It has been argued that since the question of whether the President did or did not have Addison's disease was injected as an issue into the 1960 Presidential campaign, the public is entitled to know whether there were any findings at autopsy that tended to substantiate this allegation.

Some of Dr. Helpern's colleagues also argue that if the autopsy findings did show a deterioration of the adrenal glands, which would be evidence of Addison's disease, it is a missed opportunity for showing the progress of medicine in general to fail to disclose it. A person suffering from Addison's disease can now be placed on medication so that the disease can be controlled in much the same manner that diabetes is controlled by insulin. This, of course, was not true a generation ago. These doctors continue that it would dramatically show medicine's progress if a man with Addison's disease could be treated so successfully that he could function well enough to perform the duties demanded by the office of President of the United States.

"I still go along with the feeling," Dr. Helpern concludes, "that any disclosure in the autopsy findings over and above the bullet wounds which produced the President's death must be considered a private matter for the family to do with as they personally desire."

It is not difficult to understand the bewilderment of the Europeans as they attempt to evaluate the medico-legal features of the Kennedy autopsy and the Warren Commission report. Respected chairs in forensic medicine have been held by outstanding professors in all the European universities for many generations. It is a well-established medical specialty.

If President Kennedy had been assassinated in a European country, the Minister of Justice would have immediately designated the leading professor of forensic medicine in the country to perform the autopsy. He would have been assisted by three or four heads of medico-legal institutes. Men experienced in evaluating bullet wounds *at the autopsy table* would have appraised the head and neck wounds. The wounds of entry and of exit would have been clearly identified and labeled. There would have been nothing left over for the critics to chew on.

In private conversations, Dr. Helpern seriously wonders just how much progress has been made in acquainting the public with the needs and possibilities of forensic medicine since that day he traveled down to western New Jersey to testify in the Edoardo Bonifacio case over a quarter of a century ago.

The Bonifacio case had an interesting personal sequel for Dr. Helpern which he enjoys relating.

The years passed by after Bonifacio's acquittal. World War II came and went. Names by the hundreds, and then the thousands, clouded Dr. Helpern's memory.

He was on his way to work one morning when he opened *The New York Times*. A four-column picture in the middle of the front page caught his eye. In it, a man and a woman were embracing. He immediately recognized the face of the woman with its friendly expression, the warm eyes, and the beautiful white hair. It was the mother of the young defense attorney in western New Jersey who had been so proud of her son, and who had graciously served as Dr. Helpern's hostess.

There was something slightly familiar about the man's face as well, but Dr. Helpern could not immediately identify him. He hurriedly turned to the caption under the picture. The man was attorney Robert Meyner, just elected governor of the State of New Jersey, and later a leading contender for the Democratic nomination for the office of President of the United States.

CHAPTER 2

Voir Dire

"Your name is Dr. Milton Helpern?" Defense Attorney Harry Schmuck began his voir dire examination in the first degree murder trial of *State of Ohio vs. Domer.*

"That is correct."

"Are you a duly licensed physician and surgeon?"

"Yes, I am."

"In what state?"

"In the State of New York."

"How long have you been licensed to practice medicine?"

"Since 1926."

"Are you presently engaged in the practice of your profession?"

"Yes. I am the Chief Medical Examiner for the City of New York."

The judges saw a powerfully built man in his mid-sixties, sitting comfortably in the witness-box. His gray herringbone jacket draped thick and sloping shoulders, but could not conceal the expanding waist. The full head of stubborn hair, which was once quite dark, threatened to break out of its long Ivy League cut at any time. The Ben Franklin half-spectacles caused him to incline his large head downward as he looked over the missing top halves of the lenses, which in turn tended to exaggerate the fullness of his jowls.

The critical audience was not a jury, as would be expected in most first degree murder cases. Because of the complicated legal and medical issues involved, Attorney Schmuck had elected to waive a jury. Instead, defendant Domer's fate rested squarely upon the human whims, prejudices, impartiality, and judicial acumen of three trial judges who composed a panel of "professional" jurors appointed to hear the evidence. In this respect, Ohio procedure is somewhat unique.

Both Attorney Schmuck and defendant Domer were to agonize over this decision in the days to come.

The prosecuting attorney had used up the better part of three weeks in presenting his damning evidence. It was now the defendant's turn, a desperate turn since his life was seriously threatened. The ground for maneuvering was soft and mushy—the illusory area of expert opinion.

The ordinary lay witness is not permitted to express an opinion in the courtroom. He cannot say that he thinks or believes the defendant in a murder trial is guilty or innocent, or that the driver of an automobile was cautious or negligent. He can only report what he saw or heard, or more accurately, what he thinks he saw or heard.

There are matters, of course, which are not within the common knowledge of the average person, and the law recognizes that the judge and jury need someone to explain and interpret these facts. Medicine is one of the areas where help is needed, and this help is supplied in the form of a doctor's opinion.

For the past thirty-five years, in courtrooms all around the United States, Dr. Milton Helpern has been called as a medical witness well over three thousand times, to help juries and judges interpret medical facts that involve some aspect of death. His opinion is easily the most universally respected opinion in forensic medicine today; and it is for this reason that Attorney Schmuck used him as the principal defense witness in the Domer murder trial.

The law has a procedure called the voir dire (to see, to hear; to speak the truth) which Defense Attorney Schmuck was launching into. It permits the attorney who calls an expert witness to introduce the witness to the jury or judge to help them decide whether they want to pay any attention to what the witness says. Neither judge nor jury is compelled to accept the testimony of any witness. If they choose, they may completely ignore it and toss it out as so much moldy bread.

The voir dire is the lawyer's selling opportunity. The product he wants the judge or jury to buy is the *opinion* of the expert witness. They will not buy this opinion until they have bought the witness as an individual.

"Dr. Helpern, I'd like to have you tell us where you received your medical training," Attorney Schmuck continued.

"I graduated from the Cornell University Medical College in New York in 1926," Dr. Helpern answered in a deep voice. "I then interned at Bellevue Hospital in New York for two and a half years, at which time I was given a residency in pathology. In 1931, I joined the office of the Chief Medical Examiner of the City of New York as an assistant medical examiner."

"Will you please tell us what your duties are as Medical Examiner for the City of New York?"

"The medical examiner is charged with the responsibility of investigating all deaths of persons who die suddenly and unexpectedly who are not attended by another physician. This includes all DOA's at hospitals, all—"

"Pardon me, Doctor, what do you mean by DOA's?"

"This abbreviation stands for 'dead on arrival.' "

"Will you please continue with your answer?"

"The duties include the investigation of all deaths from accident or injury; those who die from poisoning, alcoholism, narcotic addiction, abortion; those who die in hospitals while under an anesthetic, or during or immediately following a surgical procedure; and those who die from unknown causes in which some negligence or criminal means is suspected."

Dr. Helpern did not specifically mention burned and incinerated bodies with which the Domer case was greatly concerned. This would come later, at its proper time.

"Would I be correct in stating that you are required by law to investigate all sudden, unexpected, and unexplained deaths, as well as suspicious and violent deaths?"

"Yes, that sums it up nicely."

"Is the function of a medical examiner similar to that of the coroner in some states?"

"Yes, but with this important difference. The medical examiner must be a doctor of medicine with special training and experience in the field of pathology. The coroner is not required to have any specialized training or professional qualifications. He may be, and often is, a funeral director or mortician, a furniture dealer, a barber, or a merchant. Sometimes he is the elected sheriff of a county."

"Does your work include the performance of autopsies?"

"Yes, it does."

"During your experience in the medical examiner's office in the City of New York, how many autopsies have you performed?"

"None of us keeps a personal scorecard; but in the past thirty-five years, I have performed approximately sixteen or eighteen thousand autopsies myself. I have also been present at, and supervised, and taken an active part in approximately forty-two to forty-five thousand additional autopsies."

Jurors and judges at this point of the voir dire usually engage in skeptical, mathematical computations. Sixty thousand autopsies sound like an unbelievable number.

"Can you break down those figures in a little more detail, Dr. Helpern?"

"Yes. At the present time, New York City has approximately ninety thousand deaths each year. Thirty thousand of these are referred to my office for investigation. Of this number, we autopsy approximately seventy-five hundred cases. Our mortuary facilities permit us to have as many as twelve autopsies in progress at the same time."

"Will you please continue with your background in the Medical Examiner's office?"

"From 1931 to 1943, I was an assistant medical examiner. In 1943, I was promoted to Deputy Chief Medical Examiner. In 1954, I was named Chief Medical Examiner, which is the position I hold at the present time."

"Are you on the staff, or are you affiliated with any universities or academic institutions?"

"Yes. I am Professor and Chairman of the Department of Forensic Medicine for the New York University Post-Graduate Medical School. I am also Visiting Professor of Pathology at the

Cornell University Medical College. I have also lectured regularly at the Homicide Seminar in the Department of Legal Medicine at Harvard Medical School, and at various other seminars in different parts of the United States."

Attorney Schmuck did not pursue this line of inquiry further. Both the attorney and the witness walk something of a precarious tightrope in a good voir dire examination. The accomplishments of the witness must be presented modestly and without the slightest air of ostentation. The judge or jury will not buy a pompous, haughty witness. If he had thought it tactically wise, Attorney Schmuck could have asked Dr. Helpern to describe the eighty-odd lectures he gives each year to coroners, prosecuting attorneys, defense attorneys, and medical groups in every part of the United States.

"Do you specialize in any particular branch or field of medicine?" Schmuck continued.

"I am a specialist in pathology."

"Would you tell us just exactly what pathology involves?"

"Pathology is the branch of medicine which deals with the nature, cause, and development of disease. It includes a study of the effects of disease upon the body, and the changes in structure of the affected tissues and organs. It is also concerned with the effects of traumatic injury and poisons."

"Are you a member of any specialized medical or scientific groups or associations?"

"I am a Fellow of the College of American Pathologists, a member of the American Association of Pathologists and Bacteriologists, a member and past president of the New York Pathological Society, and a Fellow of the International Academy of Pathology. There are several others."

Here again, Attorney Schmuck elected not to pursue this subject in greater depth. Dr. Helpern is actually a member, honorary or otherwise, of approximately forty professional groups, societies, and associations, but the three-judge panel would undoubtedly react adversely if they were all catalogued.

"Doctor, I do not want your modesty to prevent you from letting these judges know all about your accomplishments. Have you been elected to office by any of these medical and scientific groups?"

"There are quite a few. I am past president of the American Academy of Compensation Medicine, past president of the American Academy of Forensic Sciences, past president of the International Association of Forensic Medicine, past president of the Medical Society of the County of New York, and also president of the Society of Medical Jurisprudence. I believe that is all that is necessary."

"You've overlooked, Doctor, the American Board of Pathology which, I believe, has certified you as a Diplomate?"

"Yes, I have been certified by the Board as a Diplomate in forensic pathology."

"Now, Dr. Helpern, we have mentioned forensic pathology. Would you tell us what this means?"

Most jurors and judges welcome this question. Their interest is piqued by the word "forensic," which they relate to debates and oratorical contests. They are confused to hear it given a medical connotation.

"Forensic pathology is a sub-specialty or sub-branch of general pathology. Forensic, in this sense, covers anything that relates to law, the courtroom, and the administration of justice. This branch of medicine is sometimes called legal medicine. It is also referred to as forensic medicine. Regardless of the term used, we are talking about medicine or pathology that is used in court, or in some step in the administration of justice, in our efforts to arrive at the truth."

"Have you written any books in the field of forensic medicine?"

"I am the co-author of the textbook *Legal Medicine, Pathology and Toxicology.*"

"When was that book first published, please, Doctor?"

"1937, I believe."

"And it has been revised and kept up-to-date ever since?"

"Yes."

Attorney Schmuck could not keep the voir dire within the bounds of good taste and modesty by asking the witness to say that the book is 1349 pages in length, with several hundred illustrations, and that it is considered the most authoritative treatise on the subject ever published in the United States.

"I believe you are also the author of a great many papers and articles on legal medicine or forensic medicine, which have been published in the scientific and medical journals?"

"Yes. I do not know how many. There are probably between fifty and seventy-five."

Attorney Schmuck ended his voir dire at this point, hopeful that the three-judge panel had bought Dr. Helpern as a witness, and that they would listen to his expert opinion on the only real question involved in the contest between the State of Ohio and the defendant Domer. It was a deceptively complicated and complex issue which, presumably, a panel of three judges could grapple with more realistically than twelve lay jurors.

The Domer case had its official beginning at 2:20 A.M. on April 23, 1963, a cold, blustery Tuesday near County Line Road 103, approximately seven miles west of Massillon, fifty-five miles south of Cleveland. It obviously began much earlier in the defendant's unstable mind; and who can say with certainty whether any man actually sows the seeds of his own destruction or whether he merely reaps the malignant fruit.

Pennsylvania Railroad's eastbound passenger train Number 50 was struggling through the desolate hills, rolling under their dirty snow, about half a mile west of the Deerfield crossing, when an exploding fireball almost blinded the engineer and fireman. Frantically braking the train to a stop, they discovered that the burning meteor was an automobile.

The engineer's radio call to the Orrville Control Tower turned the first official wheel that finally stopped in the Canton courtroom. The Orrville Tower called the Wayne County sheriff's office and reported the burning automobile. Sheriff Joseph Figura arrived at the scene at 2:49 A.M. He had difficulty with his car radio, so that the North Lawrence Fire Department, the first unit to respond, did not receive its initial call until 3:15 A.M., fifty-five minutes after the fire was first observed by the train crew. Another thirty minutes sped by before the North Lawrence Fire Department could awaken and assemble its crew and reach the flaming car; by this time, the smoldering ruins of what had once been a white 1959 Buick sedan, Ohio license number M-491-R, had virtually burned themselves out.

All told, an interval of approximately two hours elapsed between the time the fire was first observed by the train crew, and the time the gutted wreck of an automobile cooled down sufficiently so that its interior could be inspected.

The investigators at the scene were not particularly startled to find a human body, grotesquely contorted and twisted, in the right front seat of the car. The face was almost totally destroyed, the arms and legs burned off, the chest wall and abdomen burned away, and the sex organs gone. The intense heat had cracked the bones of the head, which had become friable and brittle.

These physical remains, charred beyond all possibility of recognition, of what had once been a live human body that walked and talked, felt pain and pleasure, elation and heartache, were carefully lifted from the still smoldering car and placed in a plastic sheet. At a nearby funeral home, the plastic sheet was then wrapped in an additional rubber sheet, and the grisly package was transported to the Cuyahoga County coroner's office in Cleveland, where it arrived at approximately 2 P.M. Shortly thereafter, Dr. Lester Adelson, Chief Deputy Coroner and Pathologist for Cuyahoga County, began his autopsy.

This is not an unusual procedure, since the coroner's office and Western Reserve University collaborate in operating a law-medicine center designed to upgrade the practice of forensic medicine, with facilities available to law enforcement agencies throughout the State of Ohio.

Between twelve and thirteen hours had elapsed since the blazing automobile was first observed by the train crew. This time interval subsequently became a vital medico-legal consideration.

Back at the Deerfield crossing, investigators found charred portions of a wallet belonging to Robert Domer. They also found his Playboy Club key. Scorched credit cards crumbled in the fingers of the investigators, and a plain gold wedding ring, size twelve and one-half, contributed to the picture of a man who during life had enjoyed a certain degree of status and affluence.

This, roughly, was the information available to the investigators and to Dr. Adelson as he began his autopsy on the shrunken seventy-seven pounds of charred bone, skin, muscle, and cartilage that was identified as the physical body of Robert K. Domer.

Who was Robert K. Domer? A team of skilled investigators fanned out around the Canton area and soon had some of the answers.

Physically, Domer was a huge, puffy man, forty-four years of age, married to a charming woman named Evelyn, and the father of two daughters. Several people interviewed estimated his weight at three hundred pounds, although this was something of an exaggeration.

He was described by such adjectives as "congenial," "extroverted," "brilliant," "a wonderful guy," "a fine man." He was a leader in civic and church affairs in his community, a "pillar of the community," and "above challenge."

The investigators discovered that Robert Domer graduated from the law school of Western Reserve University in 1949, but the prospects of building a lucrative law practice that might pay off financially twenty years in the future held no appeal.

"I'm going to make my money now," a classmate of Domer quoted him as saying soon after they graduated from law school. "I can't wait until I'm an old man, too old to enjoy what I might accumulate from a law practice."

Four years later Domer deserted the law, in more ways than one, really before he was seriously wed to it. The mortgage brokerage business held out the greatest financial opportunity for immediate, tangible success. He plunged into it with a consuming drive and zeal, with an aggressiveness characteristic of all his undertakings.

He formed his own mortgage loan and mortgage servicing companies, which at the beginning of 1963 were purported to have assets of $93,000,000. There was considerable water in these figures, a fact that was discovered by auditors of the Federal National Mortgage Association (commonly called "Fannie Mae"), a home finance agency of the United States Government; but at one time Domer was netting $100,000 a year.

Almost one year earlier, Domer knew that his precariously inverted pyramid of mortgage assets was tottering. It would come down with a resounding crash if he could not shore it up by substantially improving his cash position. After many unsuccessful attempts to raise $25,000 from friends and members of his family, Robert Domer became a clever, crafty embezzler.

The spidery line between a legitimate business operation and a fraudulent one is surprisingly easy to cross over once the embezzler adopts the classic mental attitude. It involves acceptance of only two subtle premises. The first is that there is nothing morally wrong in making a few simple bookkeeping entries to temporarily divert funds, since the diversion is only *temporary*. Thus, this differs in no real way from a legitimate loan from either a bank or a personal friend, because some fortuitous event is going to transpire in the near future that will permit the embezzler to make good his "borrowing." The embezzler, therefore, does not run any dangerous risk of getting caught, which in the final analysis is the only real deterrent against this particular crime, or any other.

The second premise is that even though this fortunate event should be delayed so that the embezzler cannot cover his shortages in time to prevent their discovery, no actual *person* will be hurt by the diversion of funds. An impersonal, artificial, legal entity, such as a corporation or a bank or an agency of the Federal Government, does not suffer a personal loss; and even if the embezzler's target is a person, the embezzler reasons that this other person is in a much better position to accept and deal with the loss than the embezzler himself whose needs have become overwhelming.

Who knows how many fortunate events have occurred to save the millions of undetected embezzlers? Robert Domer was not one of the lucky ones.

In the late afternoon of Saturday, March 30, 1963, the FNMA auditors confronted Domer with the statement that the Government custodial account was $38,150.27 short. They had also discovered that over the preceding several months, Domer had illegally diverted approximately $85,700.00. Domer's reaction was characteristic of his personality.

"There must be some mistake," he replied with outward calm. "There has to be an explanation. I will have it for you the first thing Monday morning."

Robert Domer then drove thoughtfully home.

For a great many years he had been an enthusiastic advocate of tape recorders. Alone in his house, in the secret confines of his own bedroom, he dictated a one-hour personal message to his wife. Speaking in carefully chosen phrases, he did not mention either suicide or death. He spoke of their *separation,* which would become inevitable once the facts were known.

He would rather live with her than apart from her . . . many of *their* problems could be solved by the simple writing of a check if they only had the funds . . . he was going to take steps to cause these funds to come into being. . . .

"If I don't do what I am about to do, I'm going to be separated from you anyway because you know very well when the circumstances and facts are known, this will be the only result possible." He wished to "work things out on a safe, routine basis."

In this circuitous manner, Domer said good-bye to his wife, admonishing her never to let anyone else hear the tape recording; for over three weeks, she meticulously followed his instructions, even though Robert Domer had walked out of her life.

Evelyn Domer surrendered this tape to the investigators who called at her home late in the morning of that memorable Tuesday, April 23rd. She also confirmed the fact that Robert Domer's life was heavily insured. It was subsequently discovered that the aggregate amount of life benefits was $288,000.

The investigators were satisfied that the jigsaw pieces had fallen neatly into place. They had a "suicide note" in the form of a bizarre tape-recorded message. The suicide motive was clear. Robert Domer, the man "above challenge," who was always confident and in complete command, had worked things out on a "safe, routine basis." There were a few loose ends yet remaining, but these could be tidied up without great difficulty. Any legal ramifications would be between the insurance companies and Robert Domer's estate and heirs or beneficiaries.

Dr. Adelson's meticulous autopsy at the Cuyahoga County morgue did produce two findings which needed routine clarification. The gums of this badly decomposed, brutally charred body were bare. There were no signs of recent extractions. This person's teeth had obviously all been removed some time earlier. Further, there was an old infarct in the wall of the heart, an area of scar tissue caused by a severe heart attack which had taken place at least weeks or months earlier. The area of scar tissue was sufficiently large so that the person would probably have been hospitalized as a result of the heart attack.

These two findings suddenly loomed as serious complications rather than easy clarifications. Evelyn Domer said that her husband had never suffered a heart attack. Furthermore, he had a full set of strong teeth, and as recently as the preceding March 1, he consulted his regular dentist to have a tooth filled. As it developed, Domer's dentist at that time had taken a full set of dental X-rays.

It was now disturbingly obvious that the body which Dr. Adelson had autopsied was not that of Robert Domer. The investigators faced two new questions: Who was the victim of the flaming automobile? Where was Robert Domer?

Methodically and painstakingly, they soon uncovered their answers.

The victim was Howard F. Riddle, a fifty-five-year-old itinerant fruit peddler from Akron, who was known as a skid row wino. Domer's apprehension was effected some five days later, after he returned home to seek treatment from his wife for painful burns about his hands, wrist, neck, and face.

He was immediately charged with two counts of first degree murder.

Domer's nonsensical wanderings between the night of his disappearance, March 30, and the time of his reappearance on April 28th are characterized by one perverted, well-planned thread: he desperately wanted his whereabouts and activities to be discovered. Except for one occasion, he used his correct name as he registered in one motel after another, also writing down the number of his own car license, M-491-R. He selected motels that would accept credit cards, and paid for his rooms by using his own cards. He cashed a series of bad checks—ten dollars, twenty dollars, thirty dollars—which were returned marked "Insufficient funds." At one point, he had a woman call a motel to make a specific reservation for a man who needed a king-sized bed. At one motel, he took elaborate pains to see that a typewriter which he had rented in the name of one of his mortgage companies was left in the room and subsequently called to the attention of the motel manager. He purchased airline tickets on his air travel card, for flights to Newark and Philadelphia. The airlines were also victims of his bad checks.

During the day, he restlessly drove his automobile—11.3 gallons of gasoline purchased in Cleveland, 12 gallons of gasoline in Canton, 15 gallons of gasoline in Cuyahoga Falls.

His automobile was seen in the area of the Deerfield crossing. A farmer plowing his field wrote down the license number of Domer's car on his tractor about three weeks before the fire, because Domer's activities around the Deerfield crossing were so unusual. At one time, he encountered a lady to whom he had made a mortgage loan on her house, and she thanked him for his kindness. On April 17th, while sitting in his parked car near the Erie Railroad terminal in Akron, he was approached by a man who asked him whether he had seen four high-school girls who had disappeared. Domer had seen the girls, and pointed out the road they had taken.

The "big fellow" was seen and remembered in the bars in several skid rows in Akron, Canton, and Cleveland. He was seen lounging aimlessly in bowling alleys, in cheap cafés and restaurants.

At one time he picked up a skid row habitué known only as "George," who spent a night with him in one of the many motels he frequented.

No one will ever know the exact thoughts, plans, schemes, or concerts that passed through Robert Domer's mind during this period of his wanderings, because Robert Domer cannot explain them himself. The investigators and the prosecutor, Norman Putman, drew the reasonable and logical conclusion that he was looking for a skid row bum whom he could kill in such a manner that it would appear that Domer himself had met either an accidental or a suicidal death.

Prosecutor Putman may be entirely correct when he says that Domer found his intended victim in the form of Howard F. Riddle. Domer has never convincingly denied it.

Whoever or whatever directs the destinies of man brought Robert Domer and Howard Riddle together in a cheap Akron bar. On a misty Friday night, April 19th, Riddle approached Domer and asked him to buy him a beer. Domer agreed, but the bartender refused to serve it, explaining that he had already "cut Howie off." This initial meeting was no more complicated than a ten cent glass of beer.

Had Robert Domer fortuitously been presented with the solution to his financial problems? Perhaps he thought so, for the two men walked together out of the bar and up the street to a place that would serve Riddle a beer.

Domer then took Riddle to Murphy's Quality Motel in Strongsville, where the two of them spent the night. The strange tryst continued for about three full days. A great portion of the time, Riddle was sick and vomiting violently. At one point, Domer bought him a bottle of Bufferin, and it is interesting that at the time of the autopsy, six milligrams percent of salicylate were recovered in the urine, which indicated that Riddle probably took aspirin or Bufferin within at least a few hours of the time of his death. The two men, the "big fellow" and the lumbering wino with his bottle, were seen together in several bars and restaurants during this interlude of their companionship. Domer bought his newfound friend a meager amount of food and supplied him with beer, wine, and whiskey.

We are limited to Domer's description of the events during the final hours of Riddle's life, because there are no other witnesses. And Domer does not inspire confidence. Not only was he an embezzler, he lied stupidly to the arresting officers about his burns and "stolen" car when he was first interrogated.

It was now Monday, April 22nd. After a meaningless drive to Youngstown, Domer and Riddle returned to the Top-O-The-Mark, where they had been staying, and "just watched television and watched the sun go down."

Domer fell asleep in a chair, while Riddle was relaxing on the bed. When he awoke, Riddle was asleep and there was an old movie in progress. Domer was hungry, so he left to get food to bring back to the room.

He drove around "a couple of hours" and decided that he would drive by his home, but he could not compel himself to guide the car down his own street. He did drive down the street in back of his house and saw the lights were on, and he drove by and looked helplessly at "Mother and Dad's house."

When he returned, perhaps two hours later, to the Top-O-

The-Mark, he saw that "obviously, something was very much wrong." Riddle's motionless body sprawled across the bed, the pillows lying on the floor. There was vomit on the headboard of the bed and on the wall.

"I just stood in the door looking," Domer testified later. "I panicked. He wasn't moving. I didn't know what to do. I thought 'My God, what a mess I've made of this now.' "

Domer closed the door and went outside and walked around. "But," he testified, "I knew I had to go back in there."

He edged his way through the door and said, "Howard, are you all right. . . . I shook his foot, and there was no response at all. I shook the other foot, and he didn't do anything. He just lay there. The odor made me ill to the stomach."

Domer says that he carried the dead body of his skid row friend out of the room and laid it on the back seat of his car, covering it with his topcoat and newspapers. He then made a desperate effort to clean up the room, and left the Top-O-The-Mark just as the dawn was breaking.

His compulsive, aimless driving was now considerably complicated. A dead body lay in the back seat of his automobile, with Domer not knowing how, when, or where to dispose of it. He drove toward Youngstown and rented a room in the Congress Inn Motel; he "just sat in the motel all day. I knew Mr. Riddle's body was in the car, and I went out repeatedly but I couldn't look at it, and I went back and just sat, and sat, and sat."

"Sometime that afternoon," Domer testified, "I decided to have an accident and leave his body in the car for me."

The indecisive Domer of the preceding three weeks now reverted to the aggressive, energetic, outwardly calm individual who "worked things out on a safe, routine basis."

Late in the night of Monday, April 22nd, Robert Domer drove back to the now familiar Deerfield crossing, just west of Massillon, on County Line Road 103, where he parked and waited. The air that swept down off Lake Erie was crisp and cold, the night still and silent. An occasional cloud masked some of the stars that dotted the sky. Robert Domer waited, waited for the train to make its way to the Deerfield crossing.

Domer also realized that "if it was going to look like it was me, he was going to have to be in the front seat." There was also an additional major problem. Riddle weighed somewhere between 170 and 190 pounds, perhaps a hundred pounds less than Domer.

Patches of dirty snow crunched under his feet as he struggled to move Howard Riddle's odorous body from the back of the car to the right-hand front seat. Domer tried sitting beside it, but the odor was so offensive that it overwhelmed him. He then doused the body with a can of gasoline.

And still he waited for the train. He would maneuver the car so that it could be set afire just before the train struck it. Howard Riddle's body, which would subsequently be mistaken for the body of Robert Domer, would be consumed by the flames. In one grand collision of steel striking steel, and match contacting vapor, both Howard Riddle and Robert Domer would disappear from the face of the earth, except that Domer would remain to walk in the never-never land that lay somewhere between legal death and physical life.

When Domer heard the train approaching, he struck his match and threw it into the car, but he was unfamiliar with the physical properties of gasoline and fire. The body and car literally blew up in his face, causing second and third degree burns on his hands, wrists, face, and leg. He realized with horror that he also was on fire. His first concern was to extinguish the fire that was burning him, which he did by thrashing around on the ground; and then he saw that the approaching train was a passenger train instead of a freight train as he had anticipated. He was able to run back to the car, release the brakes, cramp the wheels, and let the car roll down off the track.

It was at this point that the engineer of train Number 50 made his observation and radioed the Orrville tower.

The discovery of this chain of events now drastically altered the conclusions demanded of Dr. Lester Adelson and his autopsy back at the Cuyahoga County morgue. An entirely new and different medico-legal problem was injected, one that Dr. Adelson had not faced at the time that he performed his autopsy. The question can be phrased simply: Was Howard Riddle alive at the time the fire in the automobile started? Unfortunately, the answer cannot be so simply given.

If Howard Riddle was alive at the time the fire started, then Robert Domer was a murderer and should be dealt with accordingly. If, on the other hand, Howard Riddle was dead before the fire began, Robert Domer was not a murderer, and was guilty only of the lesser offense of destroying a dead human body.

The distinction involves something far deeper than academic, legal technicalities. In the Anglo-American system of jurisprudence, a man is entitled to be charged and tried for a specific predefined crime. It is not sufficient to accuse him of having a bad reputation, of being a burden on the community, of thinking bad thoughts, or of holding ideas repugnant to the State.

Robert Domer was a confessed embezzler. He should eventually be tried for his shortages and defalcations. It did not follow at all, however, that because he was an embezzler he was also a murderer, nor did it follow that because he incinerated a dead human body, he killed his victim with cunning and premeditation.

It is certainly logical to conclude that Domer had contemplated someone's murder at some time; but plotting and planning are not enough in the eyes of the law to constitute a crime. There must be an act in furtherance of the scheme, since the law gives every man an opportunity to stop and repent his bad thoughts.

He obviously attempted an insurance company fraud. Who can possibly hold any real brief for these activities? But was he a murderer?

The legal problem of proving the fact of death is complicated by the absence of a uniform, medical definition of death.

Like poets and philosophers, doctors have pondered the imponderables of death, but their areas of agreement are relatively few.

Medicine uses the term "clinical death" to describe the condition that occurs when there are no observable or perceptible vital signs of life. These include heartbeat, pulse, and respiration; and in some rare cases where the patient is in the operating or examining room, also measurable brain wave activity on the electroencephalogram.

There is an interval of time after clinical death, usually said to be between three and five minutes or three and seven minutes, during which the failure of respiration or heartbeat can sometimes be reversed and restored through the use of artificial respiration, heart massage, or artificial stimulation. This is the period during which effective resuscitation can be accomplished, before irreversible brain damage takes place.

"Medical death" occurs when this interval of possible resuscitation following clinical death has passed. Medical death is final and irreversible.

In a great many situations, clinical death and medical death cannot be distinguished. The mechanism causing death may be so overwhelming that no effective interval of possible resuscitation exists. By way of example, President Kennedy was both clinically dead and medically dead the instant that Oswald's bullet coursed through his brain, even though unsuccessful resuscitation procedures were subsequently attempted at Parkland Memorial Hospital, and the official time of death was reported several minutes later.

Agreement ceases at this point, and medicine rides off in all directions in keeping with the interests of its many specialties.

The biologist asserts that the proper starting point toward a correct definition of death is an examination of the metabolic processes. He would base his definition on the "disintegration of the coordination of the different systems of the body." "Fixing the moment of death as the instant when the heart stops its spontaneous action is only a conventional and traditional habit. It is in no way scientific . . ."

Still other writers argue that the proper criteria for determining death include an evaluation of cell and tissue life of the various body structures. How can the body be considered dead when, as long as twenty-four hours after heartbeat and respiration have ceased, active, motile, living sperm cells have been found in the male which are still capable of fertilizing a female ovum?

Transplant surgeons are frantically crying out for a new medical and legal definition of death so they will know when they can remove a kidney from a "dead" donor and place it in the body of a live recipient.

The internist emphasizes a cessation in the vital signs of respiration and heartbeat; but a scientific debate still continues as to whether breathing fails before circulation, or circulation before breathing.

Dr. Alan Moritz* has written on the medical controversy over the definition of death:

> It cannot be said with certainty that death has occurred until it is established that the heart has ceased to beat for at least five minutes . . .
> After injury or collapse from natural causes, a protracted period of suspended animation may occur, during which time it may be difficult to determine whether or not the heart is beating. Cessation of respiration is not conclusive evidence of death. The heart may continue to beat for many minutes after breathing has stopped.

In most cases, the courts have successfully evaded the necessity of evolving a precise legal definition of death. They have been satisfied to say that "death is the opposite of life," or "death is the cessation of life." A few have used the dictionary definition that death is "a total stoppage of the circulation of the blood and a cessation of the animal and vital functions thereof, such as respiration, pulsation, etc."

Proving death also involves a metaphysical problem. Death is a negative, and proving a negative challenges the ingenuity of the keenest minds.

Still, in spite of the mist and haze that surrounds the definition of death, the only issue to be settled by the three judges in Robert Domer's murder trial that began in the Canton courtroom early in November 1963, was whether Howard Riddle was dead before Robert Domer threw the lighted match into his automobile at the Deerfield crossing. It was a burden sufficient to stagger the judgment of three Solomons.

The onus fell first on Dr. Adelson. At the time he completed his factual, objective autopsy late in the afternoon of April 23rd, he presumed that he was working on the putrified dead

* A recognized authority in the field of forensic medicine, former Director of the Institute of Pathology at Western Reserve University, and for twelve years a professor of legal medicine at Harvard University.

body of Robert Domer. He committed himself to a cause of death: "Incineration of head, trunk, and extremities"; although he would testify at the trial in response to questioning by Prosecutor Putman, as follows:

Q. As the result of your examination, your autopsy, the things that you did after you saw what you saw in connection with this case, did you arrive at a conclusion about the cause of death?
A. I did.
Q. Would you state that to the court?
A. Mr. Riddle died as the result of being exposed to intense heat and flame or extremely hot gas, and went on to die.

The investigative notes of Richard Kauffman, an assistant Wayne County prosecutor, supply a clue to Dr. Adelson's line of reasoning after the true identity of the body was established. The pertinent entry reads:

4/24/63

5:15 . . .
Met Dr. Adelson at Morgue. Summarized for him. Showed him pictures. He said found .21 alk in blood .22 in urine No CO in blood. Unable to type blood—cells destroyed. Found fat globules in lungs. Says this indicates there was circulation of blood at the time of application of extreme heat. Speculated that fire was immediately intense—perhaps causing a spasm of larynx & therefore no intake of air or smoke into lungs and thus no CO in blood.

Dr. Adelson was properly concerned over an absence of "CO," carbon monoxide, in the blood. It has long been a well-accepted premise in forensic medicine that persons who are alive at the beginning and who die as a result of a fire breathe in carbon monoxide, generated by the fire, in sufficient quantities so that the CO levels in the blood will be in excess of 10 percent.

Further, Dr. Adelson had not found any soot or black carbon particles in the alveoli, the little air sacs deep in the lungs where carbon dioxide and oxygen are exchanged during life. It is also a well-accepted principle that a person living at the time of a fire inhales small carbon particles which reach these deep air sacs of the lungs before he dies. These premises are, in reality, rules of safety, efforts to eliminate mere speculation in an allegedly cloudy area of scientific fact.

Already committed to the cause of death by "incineration," Dr. Adelson now turned his efforts toward finding some plausible theory that would support his previous evaluation. He did not stop at this time to reexamine this initial conclusion, or to consider the possibility that the body on which he had performed the autopsy might have been dead before the fire started.

The first degree murder prosecution envisioned by those who represented the State of Ohio was now floundering badly.

In addition to the negative findings for carbon monoxide and soot, X-rays had shown gas bubbles in some of the body's soft tissues, notably those of the liver, to further disrupt the prosecutor's theory of life at the time the fire started. Dr. Adelson had reported: "Each pleural cavity contains a few drops of malodorous, syrupy, bloody fluid." The pancreas was in a badly disintegrated state, as was the brain; and the two adrenal glands which rest atop each kidney could not even be seen. What remained of the body besides the charred bones and tissue was in an advanced state of postmortem decomposition.

Dr. Adelson realized that he needed help and support, so he turned to Dr. Alan Moritz at Western Reserve, who described himself at the trial as a "courtesy-appointed consultant to the Coroner's office." Dr. Moritz agreed to buttress Dr. Adelson, and it was entirely upon the basis of these two expert medical opinions that the murder case against Robert Domer got as far as the Canton courtroom.

The State's medical witnesses faced three challenging hurdles which they had to get over to prove that Howard Riddle was alive at the time the fire started:

1. How do we account for the lack of soot in the deep air passages of the lungs, and a negative reading of carbon monoxide in the blood?

2. How do we show that Riddle took at least one breath after the fire started?

3. How do we account for the advanced state of decomposition that Riddle's body had reached at the time Dr. Adelson began his autopsy?

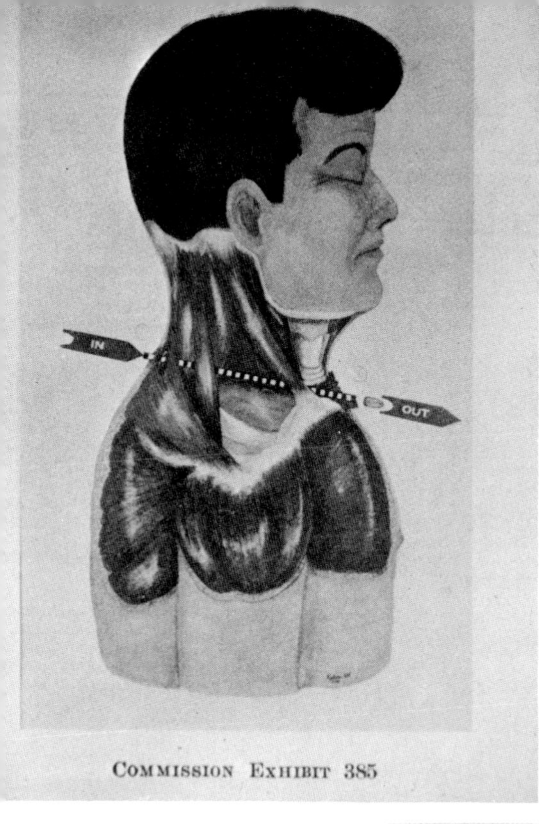

Commission Exhibit 385

This schematic illustration, along with Exhibits 386 and 388, was prepared two days before Commander Humes' testimony before the Warren Commission.

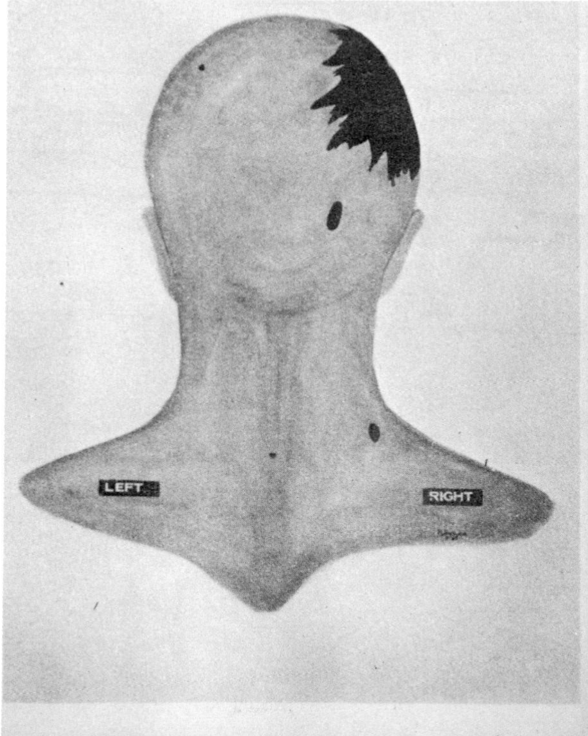

Commission Exhibit 386

These medical illustrations (Exhibits 385, 386 and 388) were prepared by a hospital corpsman from *second-hand* descriptions given him by the autopsy surgeons. The artist never saw the pictures of the President's wounds.

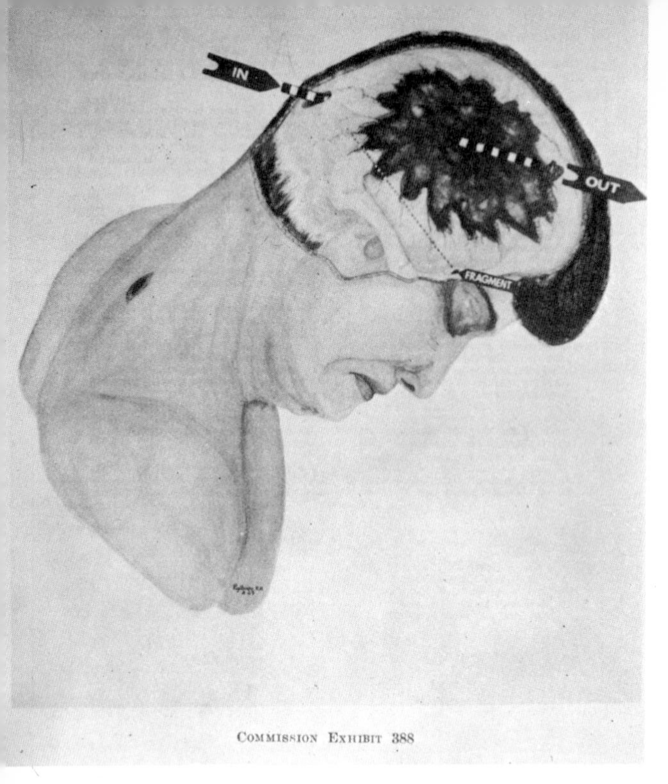

COMMISSION EXHIBIT 388

We *must* assume that this illustration is *not* drawn to scale. Otherwise, the wound in the back of the neck is either a wound of *exit,* or it was made by a bullet with a caliber larger than Oswald's rifle.

Front view of the President's coat. The clothing often furnishes valuable evidence as to the direction of a bullet as it passes through the body. The coat was cut off the body.

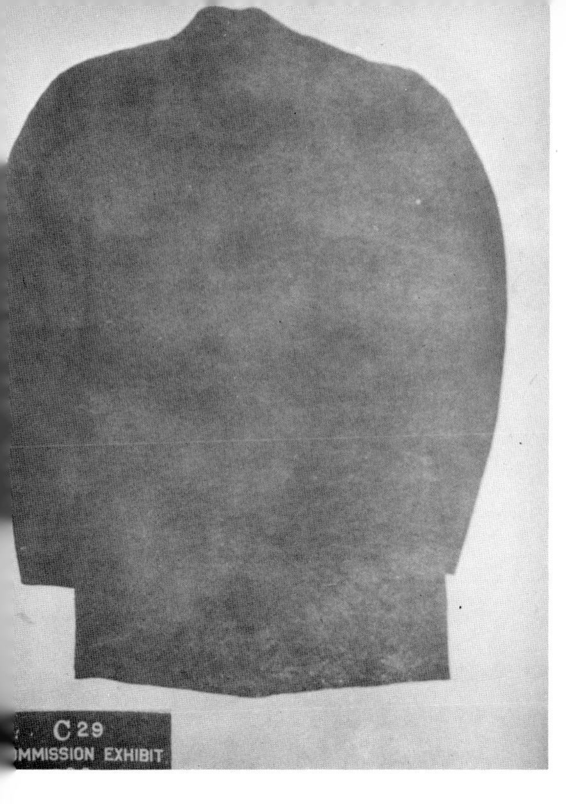

Back view of the President's coat. The reproduction of this picture in the Warren Commission Report is so poor that it is meaningless.

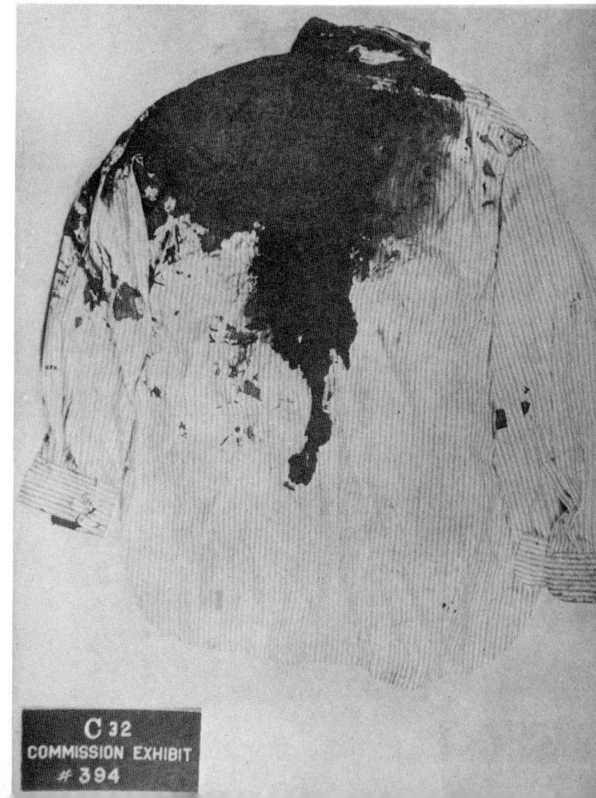

Back view of the President's shirt. The clothing of the victim of a bullet wound should always be examined in conjunction with the *medico-legal* autopsy.

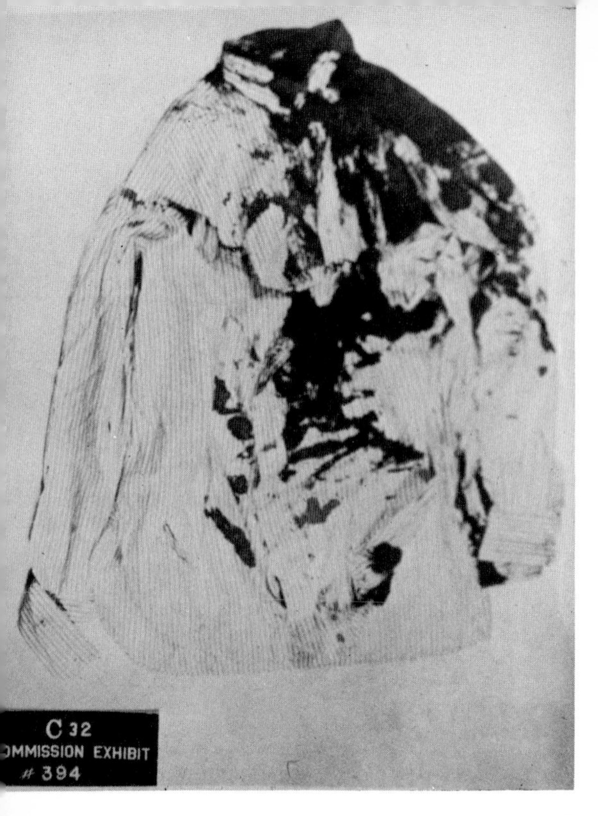

Front view of the President's shirt. The autopsy surgeons did *not* have access to the information contained in the President's clothing at the time of the autopsy.

The President's tie which was cut off of him at Parkland Hospital. Whether it has any clue to contribute has been the subject of some speculation among forensic scientists.

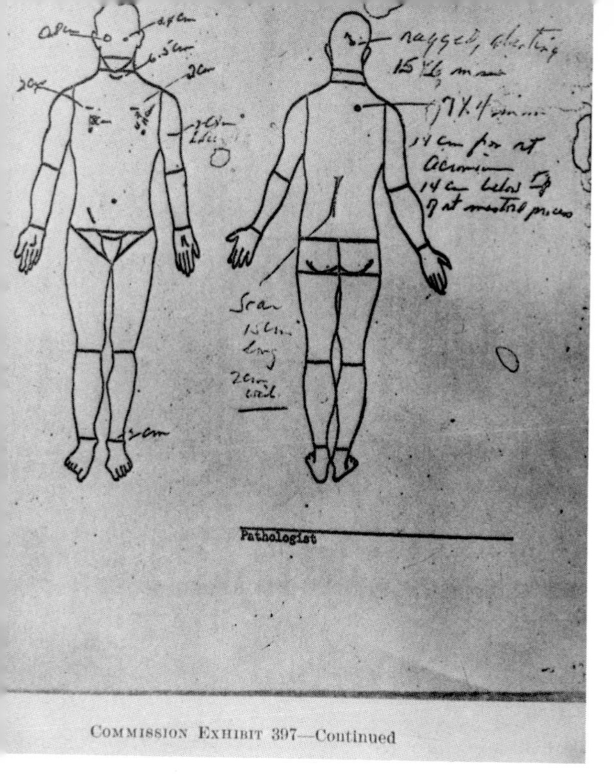

Commander Boswell's "shorthand" notes on the location of the President's bullet wounds. Charts of this nature are never intended to be drawn to scale. Otherwise, they would defeat their time-saving purpose.

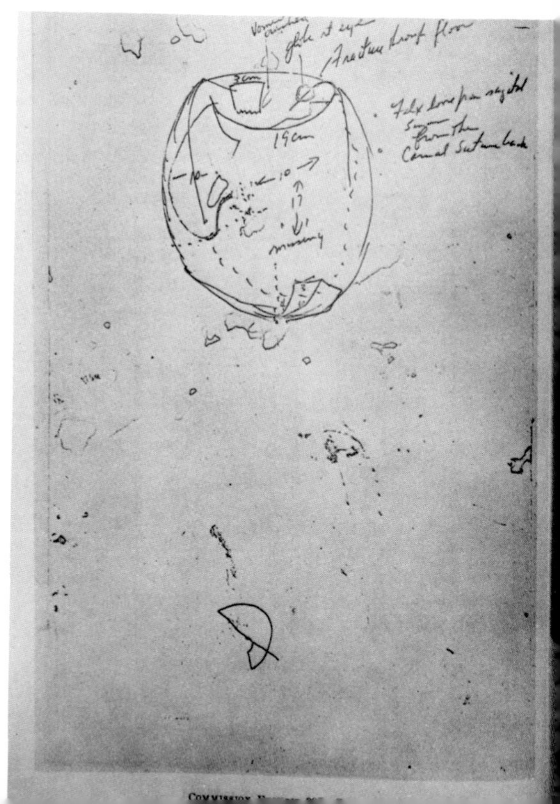

Additional "shorthand" notes of the autopsy surgeon on the size and position of the President's massive head wound.

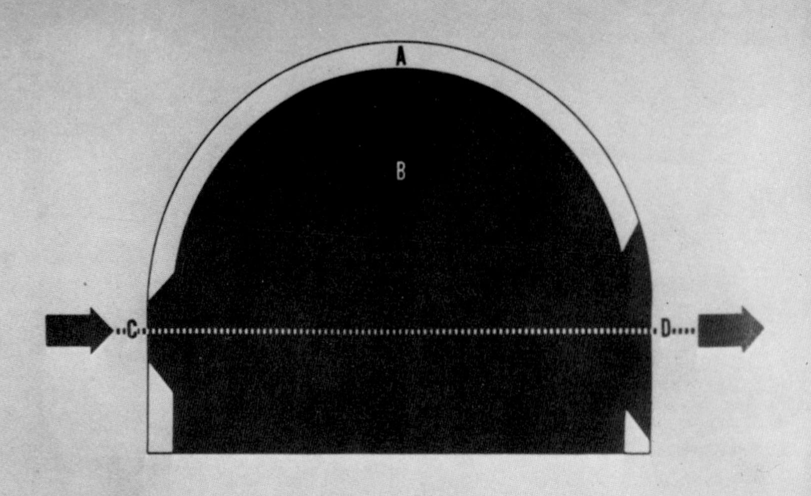
PERFORATING MISSILE WOUND OF THE SKULL
A
B
C
D
A = Cranial vault. B = Cranial cavity. C = Entrance. D = Exit.
Arrows indicate missile path.
Entrance is often smaller than exit because of bullet "mushrooming" or tumbling and/or secondary missiles.
Note "coning," "cratering," or "beveling" of the bone.
The diameter of the hole is smaller on the impact side. (The same differences of diameter apply to a glass pane.)
(Scheme by Scientific Illustration Division, AFIP,
from data provided by Lt Col Pierre A. Finck, MC, USA. AFIP Neg. 63-4825.)
COMMISSION EXHIBIT 400

Colonel Finck's teaching scheme to illustrate the characteristics of wounds of entrance and wounds of exit in the head. Of the three pathologists who performed the autopsy, Colonel Finck was the only one with any experience with bullet wounds in the body; and he was relegated to a "back seat" role.

According to the Warren Commission, this *incredible* "single bullet" passed through *seven* layers of human skin, and shattered bones in Governor Connally's body, and lost only 1.4 to 2.4 grains of its original weight. Next to bone, skin offers the greatest resistance to a bullet as it passes through the body. Dr. Helpern cannot accept the Commission's "single bullet" theory.

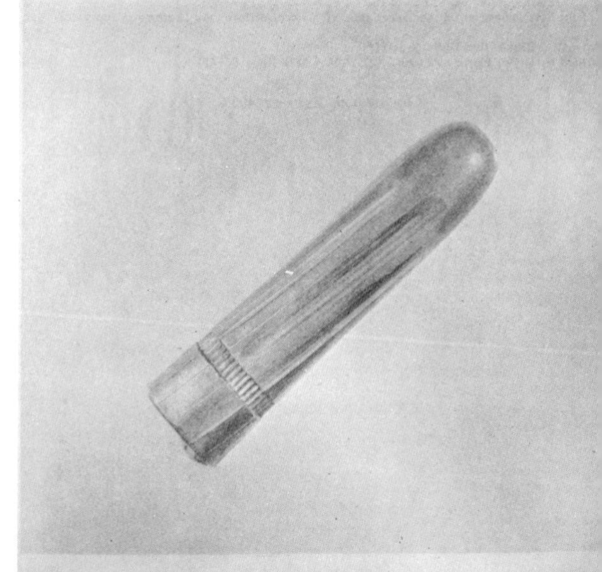
COMMISSION EXHIBIT 399

Commander Humes' certificate which covers his destroyed "draft notes." This should be interpreted only as evidence of Commander Humes' lack of experience with *medico-legal* autopsy situations.

U. S. NAVAL MEDICAL SCHOOL
NATIONAL NAVAL MEDICAL CENTER
BETHESDA, MARYLAND 20014

In reply refer to

24 November 1963

C-E-R-T-I-F-I-C-A-T-E

I, James J. Humes, certify that I have destroyed by burning certain preliminary draft notes relating to Naval Medical School Autopsy Report A63-272 and have officially transmitted all other papers related to this report to higher authority.

J. J. HUMES
CDR, MC, USN

COMMISSION EXHIBIT 397—Continued

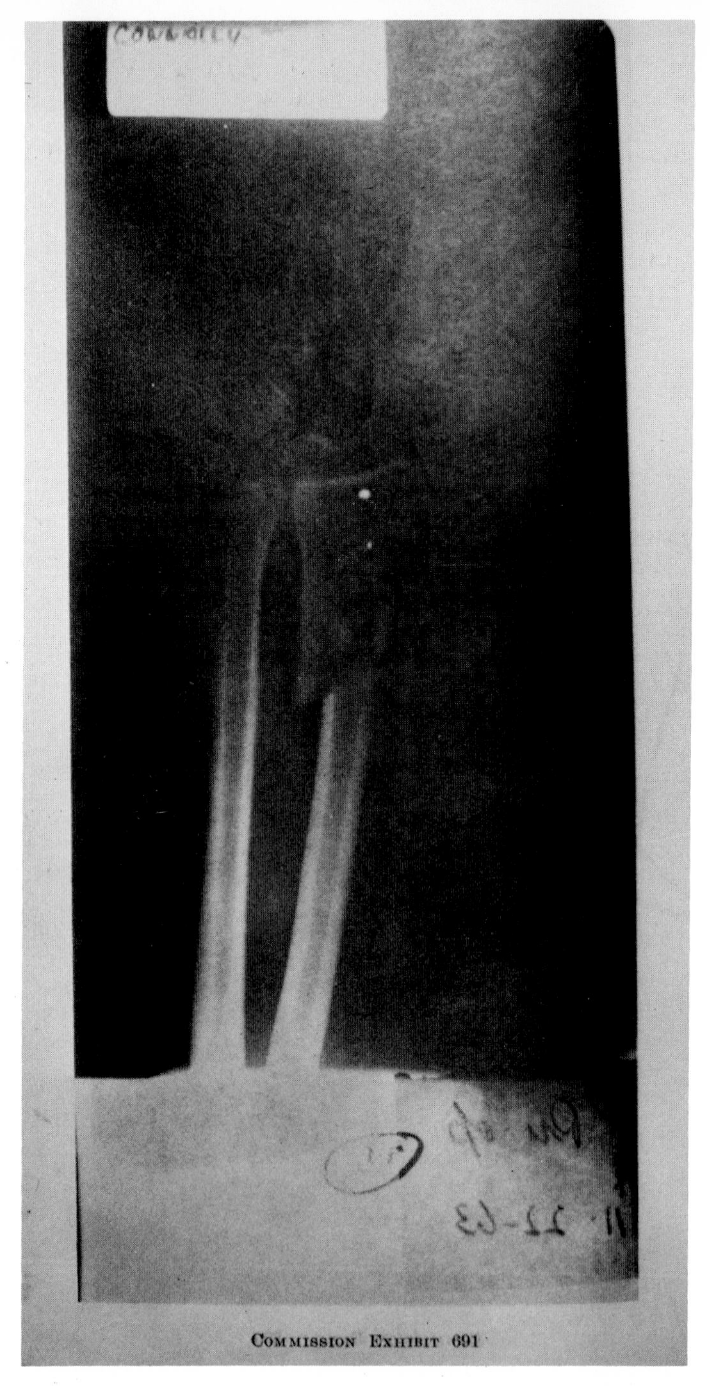

Preoperative X-ray view of Governor Connally's wrist. This is one of nine X-rays of the Governor's body which were obviously not considered offensive in the Commission's Report. The X-rays of the President, on the other hand, were deemed to offend good taste, and therefore, not printable in the Report.

The transcript of the State's medical evidence attests to their admirable ingenuity. Under cross-examination, Dr. Adelson handled the first problem conservatively and conventionally.

Q. You say there was no soot in the lung—correct?
A. Yes, that's correct.
Q. You believe and it is your best opinion that this man did breathe after the fire had started?
A. Yes.
Q. If he did breathe after the fire started, strike that. You did find soot or burned material on the larynx?
A. On the epiglottis and the back of the tongue.
Q. If this person had breathed, there would be soot or black particles in the lung too, would there not?
A. If at the time he breathed the fire was producing soot and smoke, I would have expected to find it.
Q. You don't know when the fire produced the soot and smoke in order to breathe smoke and soot into the larynx, it would go into the lungs?
A. No, because it tends to get caught.
Q. You found no soot below the larynx?
A. I found a little bit in the trachea, but I found none in the lungs.

On the question of carbon monoxide in the blood, the record continues:

Q. Excluding this case, did you ever have a case where a person died of burns in a fire, that you have an independent recollection of, where there was no carbon monoxide in the body?
A. I have no recollection of such a specific case.

The stage was set for the final lift by Dr. Moritz:

Q. Now, I believe you said this morning that it was your opinion that this person who was in this fire had breathed while the fire was in progress?
A. That was my opinion, that this person inhaled the atmosphere of the conflagration.
Q. And if he inhaled the atmosphere of the conflagration he would have inhaled some of the smoke?
A. I would think so, yes.
Q. And if he would have inhaled the smoke, it is probable that he would have carbon monoxide in the blood?

A. I think that I explained in my answer this morning that if he breathed very much of this atmosphere I certainly would have expected carbon monoxide in the blood. I don't believe he breathed very long. If he did breathe very long there was very little carbon monoxide in the smoke.

Q. Isn't it true that the absence of specific elevations of carbon monoxide in the blood of a burned body, wouldn't that indicate that death probably occurred prior to and not during the fire?

A. If I'm being asked this unrelated to the general proposition, I would say the finding of no carbon monoxide in the blood of a burned body would indicate they breathed very little of the hot ash smoke of the conflagration.

Q. You wrote a book about this, didn't you?

A. Yes, I guess I did.

Q. You didn't say anything about that in your book?

A. I don't really know whether I did or not.

Q. Let me see if I can refresh your recollection. "Some form of association evidence relating to the time of death can be derived by the medical examiner. Thus, the absence of significant elevation of carbon monoxide in the blood of a burned body found on the premises of a recently burned building would indicate that death had probably occurred before and not during and because of the conflagration?"

A. Yes, this is a statement of which I am the author.

Q. You and Dr. Adelson. He collaborated with you on that?

A. No, on this particular section I don't believe he did.

Q. I'll ask you to look at the front of the book and see who you give credits for collaboration?

A. Dr. Adelson, Mechanical Injuries of the Cardio-Vascular System.

Q. Let me continue. "Victims of conflagrations whose dead bodies are removed from the place of the fire are almost invariably found to have an excessive amount (more than 10 percent) of carbon monoxide in the blood?"

A. We are still discussing this in relationship to burned buildings.

Q. Of course there is a difference in a burned building and a burned automobile? [Attorney Schmuck says that this question was asked in a sarcastic tone.]

A. Ordinarily, yes.

Q. In this statement you made no such exception?

A. No exception.

Q. Let me ask you this, how many autopsies have you personally performed on persons who have died in conflagrations, approximately?

A. Oh, probably forty or fifty.

Q. And in that forty or fifty that you have performed have you ever found any—you did not do it on this case—have you ever found any that had no carbon monoxide in the blood?

A. Yes.

Q. How many?

A. That I don't know. I can remember very clearly of two boys who got trapped with a gasoline can in a cave, that cave was lighted and they were burned to death or died as a part of the conflagration. Neither had carbon monoxide in the blood.

Q. Any other cause of death from that autopsy?

A. Not that I know of, except suffocation.

Q. Now, Doctor, just one other question, one other phase. That person, you said this morning, breathed, in your opinion, at least several times before he died. Was that your statement?

A. One or more times I think I said.

Q. After the fire started?

A. I believe so, yes.

By referring to a vague case of two boys burned in a cave, Dr. Moritz deftly converted the death of Howard Riddle into an exception to the general rule that a person who dies in a fire will have soot deep in his lungs, not just in the air passageways to the lungs, and will also have carbon monoxide in his blood.

Next came hurdle number two, to show that Riddle took at least one breath after the fire started. Without this step, the State's murder case against Robert Domer would fly out the window. They would not be able to transform embezzler Robert Domer into murderer Robert Domer.

Dr. Moritz, who had written earlier that "It cannot be said with certainty that death has occurred . . ." and ". . . during which time it may be difficult to tell whether or not the heart is beating . . ." rose to the demands made on him by Prosecutor Putman.

Dr. Adelson had removed thin layers of tissue from the area of Riddle's throat during the autopsy. These were mounted on glass slides so that they could be preserved and studied; and they were built into a large composite photograph which was used at the trial.

The slides of prime interest involved the epithelium covering the vocal chords and the false vocal chords. Epithelium is the "cemented" structure of cells that lines and covers the internal and external surfaces of the body and its organs.

Dr. Moritz' testimony at this point refers to these epithelial surfaces:

Q. What conclusion do you come to then with respect to the direction the heat came from that burned off the epithelium?

A. The conclusion I came to was that one or more breaths of very hot air or flame passed over this surface in order to make these heat changes so much more pronounced at that surface than they are a fraction of an inch below it.

Q. Your word "flame" includes burning vapor?

A. It would.

Q. All right, you may continue. Please excuse the interruption.

A. I think I have concluded.

Q. Will you illustrate now on the blackboard, if I can find some chalk, just where the voice box is located?

A. If the circle represents a section right straight through the neck with the spinal column back here (*indicating*) and the voice box here (*indicating*), with the vocal chords in that kind of a position.

Q. What is that?

A. The false vocal chord. The false vocal chord is the upper fold and the true vocal chord is the lower chord. If you see, those in the false vocal chord come down, stick out into the passageway like that (*indicating*) and air passes along here (*indicating*) and induces a vibration of part of this fold. We are looking at a section cutting down through the fold.

Q. You described in detail the heat changes that you observed on this photograph. Did you observe changes of that quality or characteristic at a point below the voice box?

A. Yes.

Q. How far below would you say, approximately?

A. I don't know precisely how far below. It was less than six inches below. About how much below I don't know because at six inches below I couldn't tell. At that place the burning was so severe that I couldn't tell which way the heat was moving. Whether it was moving from outside in or from inside out. Here in the larynx there is no doubt but that heat was moving from outside in because of the burning of the skin of the neck and muscles of the neck.

Q. To be precise, now, you mean from outside the tissue, but inside the windpipe?

A. No, this particular moment the heat was from outside of the body through the skin and in the tissues of the neck. This produced burns of the tissues of the neck there, but there was another movement of heat and that was from this air passage (*indicating*) outside the air passage and into the surrounding soft tissues of the neck, and that is the reason that can be identified, because of the severity of the changes in the lining of the covering of the vocal chord as compared to the less severe changes that one gets a fraction of an inch away.

Q. Do you feel I have given you a fair opportunity to explain the evidence that you have testified concerning [sic]?

A. Yes, I am satisfied.

Now to hurdle number three. No one even remotely connected with the case denied that Howard Riddle's body was in a foul state of decomposition, and this requires the passage of a considerable amount of time after death.

The State's medical witnesses disposed of this problem without any great difficulty. The tissues, they said, which were exposed to the intense heat were roasted "fresh," "fresh" in this sense being used to mean that no postmortem decomposition had begun before the fire. Further, body tissues that have already begun to decompose after death cannot be restored to their pre-death condition by heat.

According to doctors Moritz and Adelson, the decomposition of the body, therefore, occurred during the interval between 2:20 A.M. Tuesday, and 2 or 3 P.M. the same afternoon, when Dr. Adelson began his autopsy. The normal decaying processes were hastened by the heat of the fire, plus the fact that the body was wrapped in both the plastic and rubber sheets.

Dr. Adelson first evaded a direct question by Prosecutor Putman as to how long the body had been dead:

Q. This body had been dead for thirty-six hours before you saw it?

A. Under ordinary circumstances, one of the sites of postmortem change of the intestines is accumulation of a large amount of gas in the bowel formed by organisms multiplying and the bowel becomes ballooned out.

Later he testified:

Q. Did you claim the man died within eight hours from the time you made the examination?
A. Twelve to fourteen hours.

Dr. Moritz also fixed the time at the proper point for the State:

Q. You are not able, are you, to say with reasonable certainty as to the period of time necessary for this condition [putrefaction] to take place?
A. No, beyond that it took more than a few hours.
Q. Would you be able to say twelve hours to fifteen hours?
A. Well, twelve hours would be a fair estimate.

This was the state of the medical evidence when Dr. Helpern took the witness stand as the defendant's prime medical witness.

"Now, Dr. Helpern, based upon your study and examination of the autopsy report prepared by Dr. Adelson, based upon these pictures, and based further upon reasonable medical certainty, do you have an opinion as to whether the body found in the car at the Deerfield crossing was alive at the time the fire started?" Attorney Schmuck continued.

"I have an opinion."

"What is your opinion?"

"In my opinion, the deceased in this case was not alive when the fire started."

"Can you explain the reasons for your opinion?"

"Two important considerations are certainly the findings of no carbon monoxide in the blood and no soot in the deep air passages of the lungs. I would say that over the years I have autopsied or supervised the autopsies of the bodies of at least two thousand persons who have died in fires or conflagrations. I have not encountered a single case of a person who was alive at the time these fires started who did not have carbon monoxide in the blood and soot in the lungs."

"Pardon me, Doctor, are you talking only about fires in buildings, or also about fires in automobiles, or in airplanes?"

"I'm talking about all types of fires. Let me give you a specific example, if I may. In February 1957, an airplane crashed on Riker's Island in New York, carrying 101 passengers. Eighty-one were fortunate enough to escape and be rescued. Twenty, however, were trapped in a section of the plane and were asphyxiated and burned to death. The bodies looked very much like this one. In fact, many of them were more incinerated than this body. Yet, in every one of the airplane cases, we found a considerable amount of carbon monoxide in the blood and we found abundant amounts of soot in the deep air passages of the lungs. I don't mean soot just in the throat area, or the windpipe, but a lining of soot that went all the way down to the alveoli of the lungs. The immediate cause of death was fire and asphyxia, not some other mechanical or physical injury."

"Now, sir, do you have other reasons for expressing the opinion that Howard Riddle was dead at the time the fire started?"

"Yes. The autopsy protocol contains certain findings which compel me to conclude that this person was not only dead at the time the conflagration took place, but had been dead for some time before. I refer to the descriptions of various organs of the body which show that advanced postmortem decomposition had already taken place before the body was incinerated."

"I think, Dr. Helpern, that you should explain to us just what you mean by decomposition and how it takes place."

Attorney Schmuck was asking for a description of the age-old process, perhaps described first in the Book of Genesis, of ". . . for dust thou art, and unto dust shalt thou return."

"I will do so as briefly as possible and omit many of the details. The human body lives by way of its oxygen cycle. As long as this cycle is maintained, the cells remain healthy, food and water are ingested and absorbed, metabolism is normal, healing and repair take place, excretion continues, and locomotion is possible. The body's chemical processes are maintained in balance so that its own self-destructive enzymes are neutralized by antagonistic ferments. All self-destructive processes are held in check. Once, however, the oxygen cycle is interrupted by a cessation of breathing and circulation, there is nothing left to hold these self-destructive enzymes in check. A process which we call autolysis begins."

"Pardon me, Doctor, there has been some other testimony about autolysis. Is this also called 'self-digestion'?"

"Yes. This is all a part of the natural cycle of man's existence."

"Will you please continue?"

"Another process known as putrefaction also begins. This is an invasion of the various organs and body structures by certain types of bacteria which are present in the intestinal tract, or which may be introduced into the body from the outside. The bacteria thrive in a culture medium that no longer offers any resistance to their growth. They produce odorous gases. The organs and soft tissues of the body liquefy as the decaying process continues. So, instead of being reduced to dust, as the process has been graphically and poetically described, the body is turned into liquid and gas by its own enzymes and the invading bacteria."

Attorney Schmuck then carefully led Dr. Helpern, step by step and item by item, through the autopsy report as it described the condition of each organ or body system.

"The microscopic and gross anatomical findings here, I think," Dr. Helpern concluded, "clearly show evidence of moderately advanced postmortem decomposition. In my opinion, there isn't any question."

"Burned bodies simply do not decompose in this manner," Dr. Helpern said emphatically. "This is the most important fact in the entire case."

The transcript continues:

JUDGE WEBER. How many hours would be involved, would you say?

A. I would say from reading this autopsy, if you didn't tell me anything else about this case, that this suggests a process of about forty-eight hours, at least forty-eight hours.

JUDGE WEBER. Prior to what, the postmortem or fire?

A. Prior to the time of the autopsy.

JUDGE ROSSETTI. So that I understand you, are you saying that he was dead forty-eight hours before the fire?

A. Before the autopsy. The observations were made at the autopsy. I would say that a body like this is suggestive of . . . when I say forty-eight hours I mean that it is more than a few hours. I can't fix the exact time. I can't say from reading this autopsy record and the description here precisely how long this person was dead before the autopsy, but I can say that it was more than twenty-four hours and more in the area or region in the point of time of forty-eight hours. It could be less, somewhere between twenty-four and forty-eight, or it could be longer.

Dr. Helpern was then asked to leave the witness stand to point out on the X-rays the gas bubbles in the liver, which had been described in the autopsy protocol. He testified later that:

"In my opinion, the putrefactive change observed in this body occurred prior to the fire, and that following the fire any additional putrefaction was minimal or absent. In other words, the extent of the decomposition in this burned body indicates that it was there before the fire took place."

As to the singed vocal chords on which the State relied so heavily, Dr. Helpern explained:

JUDGE ROSSETTI. Do you know that the vocal chords were burned in this man?

A. They could have burned.

Q. Is this what the protocol says?

A. No, sir.

Q. Doesn't that indicate that he breathed some hot gas?

A. No, it means there was a lot of heat around the mouth, and the mouth being a large place, and the nose being a fairly large place, that material dropped back in there. That is not infrequently seen.

JUDGE ROSSETTI. It can also mean that he breathed some hot gas.

A. No, I don't think so. If he breathed in hot gas he would have had to breathe in soot, and he doesn't have any soot in the air passages. He would also have to have carbon. It just doesn't add up any other way.

Q. In this kind of fire, based on this kind of opinion that you have, that heat damage would be applied all the way through the neck and throat area, is that right?

A. Yes, I would say from the extent of the charring of this man's face and neck that the heat penetrated into the tissues; so, merely finding a heat effect in the presence of all this burning does not establish that this individual was alive. I have seen cases where individuals were burned to death in conflagrations where they were trapped in a car, where they were trapped and burned to death, and we found smoke and carbon monoxide in those cases even though the death may occur fairly rapidly. It doesn't take very long to accumulate carbon monoxide in the blood so that you can detect it chemically, and it doesn't take very long for the soot to get down.

What of Dr. Moritz' one case of the two boys burned in the cave, who had no carbon monoxide in their blood or soot in their lungs?

JUDGE ROSSETTI. If another pathologist testified that he knows of two cases of two boys burned to death and in both of these cases they found no carbon monoxide in the blood, does that attach any particular medical significance to you?

A. I would say that has not been my experience, and my experience has not been entirely limited. I have seen several thousand cases of burned bodies and I would be very suspicious about that case. I would want to have that case checked over, have the chemical tests checked. It would be an extremely unusual thing. I frankly would not accept it as the basis for the conclusion that those boys were burned to death. I would have to know all the conditions.

There were other medical witnesses called by the defense. Dr. Frank Cleveland, Professor of Pathology at the University of Cincinnati and Chief Coroner's Pathologist at Cincinnati, forcefully supported Dr. Helpern's position.

Now, however, an underlying, intangible, sickening theme which experienced trial lawyers feel but cannot describe or reverse began to haunt the trial. It signaled the introduction of a false issue, but one which, as is often the case, might prove decisive.

JUDGE ROSSETTI. Doctor, is it your opinion that this man, Riddell [sic], had a heart attack twenty-four hours before the fire?

A. I wouldn't know whether he did or not. I have no opinion when he had a heart attack.

JUDGE ROSSETTI. You have no opinion as to his cause of death?

A. No, I do not.

JUDGE ROSSETTI. You don't know what caused his death, as I understand it, is that right?

A. That's right.

JUDGE ROSSETTI. Is there anything in the postmortem examination to indicate that this man, Riddell, had a heart attack before he died?

A. Yes, he had a heart attack in September of 1962.
JUDGE ROSSETTI. I mean April 23, 1963, did you find evidence of any heart attack in that report?
A. I did not.

In effect, the judges were saying: "Mr. Defense Attorney, unless you can give us some other cause of death, we are going to find that this man, Riddell, or whatever his name is, died as a result of the fire. If something else did not cause this death, ergo, the fire did."

Attorney Schmuck called Dr. Leo Underwood, an internist, who described Howard Riddle's heart attack in September 1962, when he was hospitalized in Akron. He was admitted in January 1963, suffering from congestive heart failure, and again on March 22, 1963 with evidence of severe heart failure and pneumonia of the right lung. "He was living a rather day-to-day existence as far as prognosis for any length of life."

At autopsy, in addition to an old scar area in the heart wall, Dr. Adelson had reported a heart that was almost two times normal size.

"This is the usual picture of severe and approaching terminal heart disease," Dr. Underwood summarized. If ever a man was a candidate for death by heart attack, Howard Riddle appeared to be that man. Still, no doctor who testified, prosecution or defense witness, could stay within the bounds of reasonable medical certainty and say that Howard Riddle did die from a heart attack. The autopsy would not permit so fine an interpretation.

The defense attorney could not meet this new thrust which the judges themselves rejected; relying on the testimony of Dr. Adelson and Dr. Moritz, and disregarding entirely the testimony of the defendant's witnesses, the three jurists decreed embezzler Robert Domer to be murderer Robert Domer, without recommendation of mercy.

There was no separate debate on the question of penalty. Ohio law specified death in the electric chair.

Robert Domer was led silently to his cell, to await his own death by burning, a different kind of burning where it mattered not a shred whether his larynx went into spasm or whether "one or more breaths of very hot air or flame passed over" the surface of his vocal chords.

So the case went up on appeal, that worn-out horse of legal maneuver, thought many of those who followed the Domer trial. An appeal! That expensive legal subterfuge that only buys the convicted murderer an ounce more time.

The Court of Appeals for the Fifth District of Ohio thought otherwise, as is evidenced by a testily worded opinion handed down December 8, 1964, almost one full year later:

Before considering these two questions [venue and due process], there is the other matter that requires attention. After the Court's decision of guilty on the first count on the indictment without recommendation of mercy had been pronounced on November 29, 1963, and the overruling of defendant's motion for new trial entered on December 30, 1963, the Court said, upon calling the defendant before the bench for sentence:

THE COURT. Have you anything to say why sentence should not be pronounced?

DEFENDANT. I would like to say, I believe the evidence in this case and the decision of the Court does not prove me guilty. As God is my witness, I am innocent of this charge, now and always.

MR. SCHMUCK. If the Court please, before the trial ever started, I went to see the Court. I offered Mr. Putman and Mr. Dowd to submit the defendant for polygraph test or sodium Pentothal test, if administered by an unbiased person, provided that it be introduced in evidence and that was refused. As far as I am concerned this man is innocent. He is being sentenced for something he did not do.

THE COURT. You say he is being sentenced for something he did not do? I was informed that counsel approached the prosecutor and asked if he wouldn't accept a plea of second degree murder in this case.

MR. EVANS. This is the first time I ever heard of it and I certainly did not do it.

MR. SCHMUCK. I did, and I don't mind telling you I did it, without the consent of my client. I am well aware that he would have to spend many years in prison and if I could save the family from the embarrassment they would have to undergo I did suggest it.

MR. EVANS. I also discussed the question with this defendant and was advised by the defendant that he would not make such a plea.

MR. DOMER. I never did.

JUDGE WEBER. This Court had no knowledge of it until after the trial. The three of us never gave any consideration to it.

MR. EVANS. I am surprised that that had to come to the attention of this Court. I'm glad it's in the record.

JUDGE ROSSETTI. That hasn't anything to do with our decision. I knew nothing about it until weeks after the decision was rendered.

THE COURT. That's what I meant to say. I knew nothing of this until after the trial and verdict. Anything further? It will be the sentence of the Court, therefore, that the defendant, Robert Domer, be put to death in the electric chair. If there is any question about it, the execution will take place on . . .

JUDGE WEBER. That is the duty of the warden and not the Court.

MR. EVANS. There will be an appeal and probably a stay.

THE COURT. I don't think we do either. I have had them before and I have never fixed the date, but if there is any question about it, the Court will fix the time as of April 20, 1964.

MR. DOWD. State of Ohio has nothing further.

THE COURT. That's all.

The opinion of the Fifth District Court of Appeals continues:

The foregoing statements of the Court . . . must be interpreted in the light of the date of the decision which was only thirty-one days before the day of sentence. Whether this could be said to be "until weeks after the decision" or not, is doubtful. The disturbing factor of the statement of the Court is the fact that it was said in an attempt to counter defendant's claim of innocence and to strengthen the Court's judgment of guilty. Any conversation on the subject of offers to plead, if there be such between counsel, until there is an agreement to submit the question to the Court in open session, should never have been related to the Court and since it was used by the Court in a sense as refuting defendant's claim of innocence at the time of sentence and ruling on the motion for new trial, error prejudicial to the defendant is shown on the record.

The Fifth District Court of Appeals warmed to the subject of the prime issue of the case. The opinion continues:

We come finally to the question of whether or not the defendant maliciously and with deliberate and premeditated malice killed Howard Franklin Riddle. The question is dependent upon the question of whether or not Riddle was alive when he was covered with gasoline by the defendant and set on fire in defendant's automobile at about 2:10 A.M. on April 23, 1963. The State relies on the testimony of two pathologists who testified that by microscopic examination of sections of flesh taken from the fleshy part of the body of the deceased as a part of a postmortem examination, they determined that the sections were taken from live flesh, thereby determining that the body of Riddle was alive when the fire was started. It should be stated that the body had been reduced by incineration from an estimated one hundred seventy to one hundred ninety pounds to seventy pounds.

On the other hand, the pathologists who testified on behalf of the State and for the defendant agreed that the postmortem examination of the deceased's blood showed no trace of carbon monoxide. It is the positive conclusion of the pathologists who were called by the defense that this is positive proof that the body that was burned in defendant's automobile was dead when the fire was started. The State's witnesses, for the most part, agreed with this conclusion but say that they have heard of two or three cases where death was caused by fire where no carbon monoxide was found in the blood of the victims. Here again it should be noted that one of the pathologists called by the State said that he observed no carbon monoxide in the blood of the deceased and that this is one of the principal tests for the determination of death by fire but he forgot to mention this finding in his report.

Certainly when considering the state of the record on the question of whether or not Riddle was alive when the fire was started, as claimed by the State, with the many other facts developed in the record challenging such conclusion, it cannot be said the State has shown that the defendant caused the death of Riddle by incineration beyond a reasonable doubt. For this and the other reasons stated above, the judgment is, therefore, reversed and the case remanded for further proceedings according to law.

Back came the case to Prosecutor Putman's office for further proceedings according to law, and he proceeded.

There is a saying among lawyers that old prosecutors either die or fade away long before they give up; so in March 1966, Robert Domer was once more on trial for his life in a Canton courtroom. The cast of characters was altered slightly; but the basic script remained the same. The production was staged before a new audience. The case had received so much publicity that it was impossible to obtain an impartial and disinterested jury; so once more, Attorney Schmuck and his client were placed upon the graces of three trial judges, but "newer, more alert" ones, as one observer described them.

It proved to be Robert Domer's inning. The new judges bought the testimony of Dr. Helpern and the other defense witnesses, rejecting the entreaties of the prosecution.

The judgment was "not guilty" of murder; and the following day an ambivalent Robert Domer stood before the bench of the court to receive substantial consecutive sentences on his guilty pleas to numerous counts of fraud and embezzlement. His great circle had been long and chastening. He would be an old man when, if ever, his apogee came round again.

Dr. Helpern considers the Domer Case a perfect teaching tool for his classes in forensic medicine at Cornell and New York University.

"If I had hypothesized this set of facts," he says, "no one would believe it. My students would think that the old man was popping his buttons, really smoking the opium pipe. But, hell, this case happened; and it didn't happen way back at the turn of the century, or during World War II, or five years ago. The second trial just wound up last March. I feel sorry for Domer; but I can't hold any brief for his actions. I am completely convinced, though, that he did not kill Howard Riddle by burning him to death the way the State claimed he did."

Why is the Domer Case the perfect teaching vehicle?

"Because it illustrates so beautifully so many of the basic fundamentals," Dr. Helpern continues, "and it's dangerously easy to let the fundamentals get buried under a lot of fancy frills and decorations.

"In the first place, the case illustrates that in many situations, the law demands more from medicine than medicine can honestly give. The law wants a positive answer, down to the split second, of a man's death. While medicine has made some rapid advances during my lifetime, it is still far from being an exact science. It's pretty frightening when the law can put a man, any man, on trial for his life two times, and let the whole thing rest on whether the prosecutor can get some doctor to say that the victim sucked in one or two breaths of hot vapors that changed the microscopic appearance of the lining of his vocal chords. Medicine simply isn't that good. We can't cut it that fine in many areas.

"In the second place, the case shows how the findings of a well-performed autopsy can be exploited as the basis of a distorted and erroneous conclusion that defeats the ends of justice. Too many people wring their hands and say, 'Oh, if we had only had an autopsy, we would be all right.'

"An autopsy is not a mathematical audit procedure where an accountant totals up all the organs, multiplies them by the square root of six, then feeds the result into a computer, and automatically comes out with the right answers. The findings at autopsy must be evaluated carefully and studied, and then interpreted in the light of all the other known facts. Sure, the beginning point of these cases is an autopsy; but it needs to be an autopsy performed by a man who knows what to look for, and then how to interpret what he finds.

"Next, the case shows how easy it is to get sidetracked away from the basic issues, and on to tangents that really do not control. In my opinion, the main issue in the Domer Case was the putrefaction of Riddle's body. It wasn't all this hocus-pocus of the singed vocal chords, or what he actually died from. Neither I nor anyone else can say with certainty what the real cause of death was. The odds were overwhelming that it was a heart attack; but you could see this collateral issue developing in the minds of those judges during the trial. If the doctors could not give them some other cause of death, it had to be the fire. This does not follow at all. It is about as logical as saying that if a man doesn't like redheads, he hates all women, and had rather be with the boys."

All facts of the case of *Ohio v. Domer* will be arduously debated in lecture halls and forensic medicine groups for years to come. Who can say but that Robert Domer may have made a substantial contribution to this subject, a result totally foreign to his mind the night he dictated the "suicide note" to his wife and wandered off on his mad exile from reality.

CHAPTER 3

"I Refuse to Play God"

"I learned an early lesson about testifying in court that I have always been thankful for," Dr. Helpern says, his eyes sparkling as he reflects back to his second year as Assistant Medical Examiner.

It was a few months after Franklin Delano Roosevelt's first inaugural, when the words "fear" and "panic" dominated the nation's vocabulary, perhaps more so than ever before. It was the time of soup kitchens and street-corner apple sellers, the NRA and the WPA, script and bank holidays, when $100,000 loomed far larger than $100,000,000 in the days before the Crash.

In his own personal way, Dr. Helpern felt the pinch. His beginning salary of $4100, when policemen were making $2500 and school teachers $2000, was now slashed to $3820; but the cutback in basic salaries did not stop there. All New York City employees were also given a payless furlough of one full month. They continued to work full-time; but through the ruse of a tricky accounting procedure, they were paid for only eleven months of the year instead of the normal twelve.

The John Quincy Adams International Correspondence School was one of the first victims of this Great Depression. It was the oldest and most venerable operation of its kind in the

United States, dating back almost to Civil War days, and now had branches in twenty-odd principal cities. It grossed several million dollars annually, but people struggling to buy bread were not easy candidates for self-improvement courses in business management and accounting, law and typing. There were precious few opportunities for even the most gifted and experienced job applicant.

Franklin Scott Preston, the company's dapper, sixty-year-old president, was one of the first to go down in the collapsing row of dominoes. Although he had given the company over thirty years of devoted service, he remained nothing more than a high-salaried employee. Ownership participation by corporate officers had not yet become an accepted method of rewarding top executives.

The board of directors arbitrarily dismissed Preston, without even a week's notice; and it rankled and embittered him and his entire family.

Preston's gloom was increased when he learned that his best friend had died in Detroit. He went out to attend the funeral, and two days later, he boarded the New York Central's "Wolverine" to return to New York and brood over what to do with the balance of his life.

He retired to his lower berth at 9 P.M., leaving a call with the porter for six o'clock the next morning, so that he could eat a leisurely breakfast before the train reached Grand Central at eight o'clock.

When Preston failed to respond to the porter's routine "It's six o'clock, sir," the porter reached his hand through the curtains in an effort to arouse his passenger. The helpful black hand encircled a cold, rigid white arm; and the porter immediately drew the correct conclusion that the occupant in Lower 5 was dead.

The conductor telegraphed ahead that he was coming in with a dead body, and sent along all the identifying information. Following established operating procedures, the train was met by an ambulance crew, an assistant medical examiner, and Spencer Trotter, Preston's brother-in-law who would identify the body.

By this time, the body was so stiff that it had to be removed through the window of the Pullman car before it was placed on a stretcher. Trotter identified it as his brother-in-law, and the medical examiner gave it a careful external inspection. Because all aspects of the death made it appear to be from natural causes, no autopsy was ordered.

Trotter stood inconspicuously in the background while the medical examiner completed his report.

"I'm releasing the body to you for burial," he said to Trotter. "There are no other formalities."

"Thank you," Trotter said as he stepped forward. "What date did you put down?"

"You mean the date of death?"

"Yes."

"Why, April 29. In a case like this, we always put down the date on which we see the body."

"May I see your report, just to be sure," Trotter persisted.

"Sure. It's right here on this line," the examiner answered, pointing to the entry for "Date of Death" on the printed form.

"Thank you. That's all I want to know," Trotter said, a smile breaking across his face, accompanied by an audible sigh of relief.

The examiner thought at the time that Trotter's questions and attitude were somewhat unusual; but in periods of bereavement, bizarre conduct is not unusual.

Hardly a week passed after Preston's funeral before Trotter's interest in the exact date of death became clear.

Two insurance policies on the life of Franklin Scott Preston, totaling $100,000 in benefits, and running on the grace period, expired at midnight on April 28.

"I only hope that I live until one minute past midnight, April 28," Preston had forcefully told Trotter the day he was fired by the John Quincy Adams International Correspondence School. "I don't want those bastards to benefit from my death."

The company had taken out the policies on Preston's life, with his consent, and had paid the premiums; but the company, not Preston's family, was the sole beneficiary.

A major medico-legal battle was forming between the Adams

School and the insurance carrier, with the Preston family sitting on the sidelines as embittered, legally disinterested, but at the same time interested observers.

There was but a single point of controversy: Did Franklin Scott Preston die before the hour of midnight on April 28? If he did, the Adams School might be bailed out of its dire financial difficulties by the $100,000 due and owing on the two insurance policies. If he lived for as much as a minute into the next day, April 29, the date of death recorded perfunctorily on the death certificate by the medical examiner, there was no valid claim against the insurance carrier. The Adams School would probably go under, leaving the Preston family to reap a sort of vengeful pleasure at the demise.

The Adams School filed its proof of death and claim for benefits; but the insurance carrier backed off, finally making an offer of settlement of $33,000. It was based on an interesting formula. There was an interval of nine hours in doubt, the period between 9 P.M. April 28 and 6 A.M. April 29. The policies were in effect during the first third of this time; therefore, the carrier would pay one-third of their face value. The Adams School turned it down. Thirty-three thousand dollars would help, but it would not save them.

So the case went to trial, the Adams School as plaintiff against the insurance carrier as defendant, with $100,000 resting on the exact time of Franklin Scott Preston's death.

Scientific methods of fixing the precise time of death were then extremely crude. Regrettably, they still are. Forensic medicine has been such a neglected stepchild that practically no money is available for research in even such basic areas as determining the time of death.

The principal medical tool available was rigor mortis, that often joked-about phenomenon that follows the cessation of circulation. What aspect of death has not served as the butt of the comedian's jest, death with its trauma so overwhelming that it must be laughed at.

Rigor mortis, the stiffness that envelops the muscles of the body after death, is another timeless pattern in the grand scheme of man's existence. When death interrupts the life-sustaining oxygen cycle, the muscle cells react by developing a slightly alkaline condition. The muscles are completely relaxed. The jaw often sags. The head can be turned with ease, and the arms and legs moved to any position without the slightest resistance; but the body refuses to remain static even after death.

In two to six hours, the alkaline condition begins to convert into acid, and a gradual rigidity flows through the muscles of the face, jaw, arms, trunk, and legs—in that exact order. The process is completed in an additional two to six hours, when the entire body literally becomes as stiff as a board. The feet and legs can be lifted so that nothing but the head touches the table or floor on which it rests. The muscles not only become stiffened but also shortened by the intensity of the process.

The rigidity endures for twelve to forty-eight hours, until the muscle protoplasm converts back to alkaline as the result of additional chemical changes. The rigor then leaves the body in the order of its appearance. The face relaxes first, then the jaw, arms, trunk, and legs.

Even in death, the philosopher's dictum holds that "change is the only thing unchanging on the earth."

These time intervals apply to the "average" body; but is there ever an average human body?

Different conditions may cause a variance in the onset, persistence, and departure of the rigor mortis. It comes early to those with thin muscles, infants, and emaciated persons; late to those who are powerfully built. Franklin Scott Preston was of medium build. High temperatures may advance the onset of rigor mortis, while cold retards it.

Its arrival may be hastened in those who die during periods of intense emotional or physical excitement and activity. There have been cases of instant rigor mortis—a soldier killed on the battlefield who falls in a classic, picturesque pose of a rifleman executing a bayonet thrust.

Because of these many variables, rigor mortis should be used only as a gross method of estimating the interval between the time the body is discovered and the actual time of death. One authority, for example, asserts that if rigidity is observed in the torso and arms but not in the legs, death has probably occurred less than twelve hours earlier; and if the legs are stiff but not the torso and arms, the body has probably been dead for three days.

Since rigor mortis was the only medical tool available to the John Quincy Adams International Correspondence School and the insurance carrier at the time they began their $100,000 battle, each decided to make the most of it.

The basic facts were admitted by both sides. At 6 A.M., Preston's right arm was stiff. Since the Pullman porter did not feel any other part of the body, his information stopped there. By a few minutes after 8 A.M., the entire body was so stiff it had to be removed through the train window, and the medical examiner described rigor mortis as being fully developed.

The Adams School called a pathologist whose qualifications were tremendously impressive. He was a laboratory director of one of the large New York hospitals and head of the department of pathology at one of the leading medical schools. He had written and published one hundred scientific papers in the medical literature. Modestly, he admitted that he was considered one of the leading authorities in pathology.

"Doctor," the plaintiff's attorney asked, "do you have an opinion based upon reasonable medical certainty as to the time of Franklin Scott Preston's death?"

"I do," the doctor replied confidently.

"What is that opinion?"

"He died some time between 9 P.M., April 28, shortly after he retired, and 11 P.M. that same night."

"On what do you base your opinion?"

"On the rate of the development of rigor mortis."

The doctor then proceeded to describe a convincing formula, tailor-made to support the $100,000 need of the Adams School, that death had occurred before midnight. There could be no doubt about it. It could not have occurred one minute past midnight.

The insurance carrier countered with an equally well-qualified pathologist, who was also a laboratory director in another hospital, and head of his own department of pathology in a rival, crosstown medical school.

"Doctor," the defendant's attorney asked, "do you have an

opinion based upon reasonable medical certainty as to the time of Franklin Scott Preston's death?"

"I do," the doctor replied with an even greater amount of confidence.

"What is that opinion?"

"He died between the hours of 2 A.M. and 4 A.M. on the morning of April 29."

"On what do you base your opinion?"

"On the rate of the development of rigor mortis."

Now came this doctor's own tailor-made formula to support the need of the insurance carrier; and he was also without any doubt. The death occurred between 2 and 4 A.M., well after the fatal hour of midnight when the policies lapsed.

The expert medical evidence was at a direct standoff; but the attorney for the Adams School was resourceful and fought hard for his client. He called Preston's personal physician as a rebuttal witness.

"Doctor," he asked, after completing his preliminary questions, "at the time of Franklin Scott Preston's death, and for approximately two years before, were you treating him for any disease or medical condition?"

"Yes, I was treating him for an enlarged prostate gland, and for prostatitis."

The witness then went on to describe this condition that has been labeled "the old man's burden."

"What are some of the manifestations of an enlarged prostate gland?" the plaintiff's attorney continued.

"Perhaps the most serious is that it causes difficult and frequent urination."

"You say frequency in urination, Doctor?" the plaintiff's attorney almost shouted ecstatically.

"Yes. My records on this patient show that during his last several visits to my office, he complained that he was having difficulty getting a good night's sleep. Almost every hour, or at least every two hours, he would have to get up and go to the bathroom."

This, the Adams School attorney would argue, was controlling evidence. Neither the porter nor any of the passengers in the Pullman car had seen Preston after he retired to his berth at

9 P.M. If he had been alive, his annoying prostate condition would have compelled him to get up and go to the men's room at least once before the hour of midnight. It was a logical conclusion.

Preston's widow, however, was to have her opportunity to land a blow against the Adams School which she now hated so bitterly. She did not appear in the usual role of the poor widow claiming her widow's mite from the greedy and wealthy insurance company. She was joined as the company's chief ally.

"Yes," she testified when the attorney for the defendant insurance carrier called her to the stand, "it is true, that my husband suffered from this prostate gland condition. It caused him great discomfort. Many nights he did have to get up almost every hour to go to the bathroom; but he didn't have to do this every night. Franklin thoroughly enjoyed traveling by train. He always said that he could sleep better in a Pullman car than any place else, even in his own bed at home. I remember very distinctly taking trips to Florida and Chicago with him not over six months before he died. We had a drawing room on both of these trips, and he never once had to get up to go to the bathroom, from the time he went to bed until it was daylight in the morning. He said there was something about the motion of the train that completely relaxed him. We used to joke about living on the train for a few weeks, it did so much for Franklin. He slept so well that I really did begin to wonder if spending several nights on the train might not be the best treatment he could take for this prostate gland thing, really. I will always regret that we did not try it."

By this time, the jury sat in total confusion and amazement. As many juries do, they had decided to discount completely the expert testimony of the two pathologists, content to call it a medical draw. The injection of the evidence of Preston's prostate gland condition was equally perplexing.

In desperation, the attorney for the insurance carrier telephoned Dr. Helpern, to see if he would agree to appear as a witness.

"Sure, I'll come down," Dr. Helpern responded, "but I don't know that my testimony will help you. I'll call the case just as I see it; and that will be as far as I'll go."

Dr. Helpern took the stand and was qualified on voir dire. Then came one of those happenstances which frequently occur in a trial, when both attorneys are under such stifling pressures to advance the cause of their clients that they grow careless of the rudimentary mechanics.

The defense attorney should have phrased his question: "Doctor, do *you* have an opinion, based upon reasonable medical certainty, as to when Franklin Scott Preston died?" The proper answer would be: "Yes, I have an opinion." The attorney would then continue: "What is that opinion?" and the witness would give his answer, and go on to explain the reasons that support his opinion. This technical rule of the law of evidence and procedure attempts to confine the testimony of an expert witness to the basic medical issues and to prevent irrelevant testimony that has no bearing on the real questions to be decided from creeping in to confuse the jury.

The attorney asked: "Dr. Helpern, based upon the evidence we are limited to in this case, is it possible for *anyone* to have an opinion that is based upon reasonable medical certainty as to whether Franklin Scott Preston died before or after midnight April 28?"

If the attorney for the Adams School had objected to the question, it undoubtedly would have been sustained, because the question did not ask for Dr. Helpern's *own* opinion on the time of death, but rather for Dr. Helpern's *comment* on the opinions of the other doctors.

"No," Dr. Helpern replied, "it simply is not possible for anyone to say with certainty exactly when he died. You can argue either way, as obviously both of you gentlemen have been doing; but no one can say with anything approaching reasonable medical certainty whether he died before or after midnight."

Judge Ferdinand Pecora, one of the great trial judges of the century, was presiding. He said later that Dr. Helpern's answer was one of the most refreshing statements that he ever heard in the courtroom. Since he had been called by the defendants, Justice Pecora expected just another medical opinion which would attempt to buttress the insurance carrier's theory of the case.

The attorney for the Adams School soon recognized the irreparable damage this answer had dealt to his case. Since the medical examiner had entered April 29 on the death certificate, the Adams School had the burden of proving that the death had occurred before midnight April 28. If he could not meet this burden, if the evidence was equally balanced, his case would be gone forever. He launched a desperate attempt on cross-examination to salvage something that would get him past a defense motion to dismiss for want of evidence.

"Now, Dr. Helpern," he began, "you've just made this pontifical statement that no one can tell exactly when Franklin Scott Preston died?"

"I did not mean it to sound pontifical," Dr. Helpern responded evenly.

"Well, you made some sort of a statement?" Sarcasm seemed to be the proper vehicle in view of Dr. Helpern's age at the time. The other two pathologists who had testified were at least thirty years Dr. Helpern's senior.

"Yes, I made a statement. I gave my best opinion."

"Then, obviously, you don't agree with either of your eminent colleagues who have preceded you to the witness stand?"

"I do not know who has preceded me or what they have testified to."

"You didn't have any faith in a world-recognized authority in the field of pathology who has told us that, in his opinion, Mr. Preston died between 9 P.M. and 11 P.M. on the night of April 28?"

"On the basis of this evidence as it has been explained to me," Dr. Helpern explained courteously, "I repeat that I do not believe a certain answer is possible. I refuse to play God. If your doctor wants to assume that role, he is perfectly entitled to attempt it."

The jury was finally given the case. After debating it for the better part of three days, they advised Justice Pecora that they were hopelessly deadlocked at six for the plaintiff and six for the defendant. The judge thanked and dismissed them. Rather than go through another trial, the insurance carrier paid the Adams School $66,000 on the policies in full settlement, which increased the bitterness of Franklin Scott Preston's widow and family.

Dr. Helpern was quite badly shaken by this trial; a few weeks later at a medical meeting, he ran into the two pathologists who had testified.

"Would you have told your students in class the same thing that you testified to in that courtroom?" he asked one of the doctors.

"Tut! Tut! Tut!, my boy," the graying, venerable pathologist replied in a condescending manner. "You've got a lot to learn. Don't ever confuse the courtroom with the classroom."

"Would you have testified that same way," Dr. Helpern asked the other man, "if this had been a murder case and the defendant's alibi hinged on the exact time of death?"

"That's the trouble with you young fellows," the doctor replied evasively. "You're always speculating and worrying about things that do not really happen. Come on! Let me buy you a drink."

But Dr. Helpern did worry about it; and he has continued to worry about it ever since.

He refers to this case frequently in his forensic medicine lectures.

"The main problem," he tells his students, "is that for some reason I have never been able to explain, getting a subpeona to come into court brings out a Jekyll-Hyde facet of character that seems to lie dormant in a great many doctors as long as they stay out of the courtroom. They are complete gentlemen in every respect, they are impartial, scientific observers with total professional integrity; but something that I simply cannot understand happens when you put them under oath and seat them in the witness-box.

"They lose their scientific objectivity and throw professional caution to the winds, and get all involved in playing the game of 'Win With This Witness,' or 'This Witness Wants to Win.' Some of them become even more partisan than the lawyers who are paid to be partisan. They get so engrossed in the outcome of the case and playing the game that they forget they are doctors. They spew forth a bunch of garbage in the most convincing scientific prose that is pure, unadulterated medical horse manure.

"Regrettably, some of the worst offenders are my own colleagues in pathology. They seem to feel that since they have the final look, this gives them a biblical right to the final word; so they make the most of it.

"Another paradox is that the worst offenders are the hospital pathologists. Colorful old Charles Norris, the first Medical Examiner of New York City, used to call them "pissologists." These fellows do a bang-up job on running urinalyses, but they have had absolutely no experience with the problems of forensic medicine. Still, they will come into court and be completely positive and dogmatic on matters that are completely outside the area of reasonable medical certainty.

"They are doubly dangerous because they express their opinions in such polished, sonorous tones of complete confidence that the jury sits back and says: 'Now here's a man we can believe. That other fellow who said he couldn't be sure sounded pretty wishy-washy; so I guess we can safely forget all about his opinion.' Hell, the guy who says he can't be sure is the one who is staying within the bounds of recognized medical knowledge, while the 'pissologist' is the charlatan.

"We still come back to a basic fundamental," Dr. Helpern concludes. "The law demands more than medicine can honestly give. It doesn't move the lawyer's case along very fast to have a witness who says: 'I can't be sure'; so the lawyer shops around for one who will be sure. If a lawyer wants to go philandering with the medical truth, he can usually find a doctor to go right along with him."

Dr. Helpern's refusal to play God in the courtroom may well be the key reason why all those who are active in the field of forensic medicine say with one voice that they have never heard of him getting way off base or out on a limb in any case in which he has participated. He has also made it a tenet of faith to never say anything in the courtroom that he would not say in the classroom.

CHAPTER 4

"The Human Body Attests Man's Individuality"

"This is the body of a well-developed, well-nourished, white male, measuring six feet in height, and weighing an estimated 180 pounds," the autopsy protocol began.

The human body has received a special tribute in every culture we know anything about.

To the Eastern mind of orthodox Hinduism, the cosmos itself was spun out of the divine sacrifice of some vague primeval body, from whose mouth, arms, thighs, and feet poured the four orders or castes.

In the Western mind, perhaps more than 4000 years ago, the ancient Hebrews began to verbalize the concept: "And God said, Let us make man in Our image, after Our likeness. . . . So God created man in His *own* image, in the image of God created He him; male and female created He them." This body housed the spirit that communed with Yahveh (Jehovah), a name so sacred that the orthodox Jew will not pronounce it directly, although it is mentioned over 7000 times in the Bible.

"This is the body of our Lord Jesus Christ . . ." the Christian sacrament of Holy Communion begins.

It is hardly surprising that every formal autopsy protocol opens with a ritualistic tribute: "This is the body. . . ."

The body under consideration at the Fordham morgue the spring night of May 11, 1933, was that of "Mike Molloy, interred as Nicholas Millory." The death certificate had been signed three months earlier, on Washington's Birthday, by a private physician who entered the cause of death as "lobar pneumonia" with a contributory cause of "bronchitis and La Grippe."

Almost immediately after the unembalmed body had been buried in the cheap pine coffin, dressed only in "undershirt, pants, drawers, shoes, and stockings," the police began to receive rumors and rumblings. Now, the district attorney had ordered an official exhumation by the medical examiner.

Although the office of medical examiner was created by law in 1915 following the exposé of a shocking scandal in the old coroner's office, it was not implemented until 1918 when Charles Norris was appointed first Chief Medical Examiner. The physical facilities of the medical examiner were housed in that sprawling twenty-seven acre, 1800-bed medical prominence known as Bellevue Hospital, whose blackened brick buildings still mar the East River landscape. There were a few dusty cubicles that served as offices; and the medical examiner was given access to four autopsy tables in an upstairs room that was shared with the hospital's own pathology department. There was no separate space for the badly decomposed bodies whose offensive odors overwhelmed the entire autopsy area, or for the newly dead who were brought down from the floors above. Relatives and friends were properly revolted when compelled to appear at the Bellevue morgue to identify a loved one so that the legal requirements could be complied with. This condition was to continue until 1961, well into Dr. Helpern's term as the third Chief Medical Examiner for the City of New York.

The autopsy on the body of Mike Molloy was performed in a remote private mortuary in the Bronx because there was no other place available, but the saga of Mike Molloy's rather difficult death had its immediate beginning in a Bronx speakeasy owned and operated by Tough Tony Marino. By almost any standard, this first-floor room was grim and dirty, and it smelled of human sweat, stale food, rancid grease, and raw Prohibition whiskey. Toward the front, the long wooden bar, its caked layers of varnish scarred and gouged, was presided over by a jovial Irishman named Red Murphy. From time to time, on holidays and Saturday nights, the standing customers overflowed the bar to occupy a few stained tables with their unmatched chairs. Even on these more prosperous occasions, there was no waiter. It was every man for himself. The rear quarter of the room was curtained off by long strands of multicolored glass beads. A makeshift kitchen, with gas hotplate but without any semblance of refrigeration, took up half of this space. It was the era of the free lunch; and here certain souring and molding delicacies scrounged from nearby delicatessens were welded together for service to the paying customers up front.

In the other dimly lit corner of the room, Tough Tony sat behind a round, partially broken, poker table where he held court and observed the operations up front.

Tough Tony's speakeasy served a useful social purpose. It was the neighborhood bar, the gathering spa where the habitués could socialize, regardless of economic status.

Bartender Red Murphy was a faithful and conscientious employee. When an unsuspecting stranger wandered in off the street from time to time, Murphy would glance through the beads. If he received the barely perceptible signal from Tough Tony, he would seed the victim's drink with just enough chloral hydrate to temporarily anesthetize him. When he crashed to the floor, Murphy would assume his helpful attitude, walk around to the front of the bar, lift the man by his armpits, and drag him back through the strands of beads.

"Poor guy," Murphy would lament sympathetically. "I didn't realize he'd had so much to drink before he came in."

Tough Tony would help Murphy roll the victim, who would then be dragged out through the back door, hopefully to regain consciousness in the alley. Murphy's expertise in the field of anesthesiology became so adept that, as far as is known, no untoward anesthetic deaths occurred.

Tough Tony's closest confidant was a Bronx undertaker named Frank Pasqua, an alcoholic of such grand proportions that when he received the down payment for his infrequent funerals, he would end up stiffer than the corpse he was hired to bury. Even though Pasqua was sometimes paid to embalm, he never carried out the assignment. Embalming fluid cost money, which reduced the net profit Pasqua desperately required to keep himself embalmed with whiskey.

Both Tough Tony Marino and Frank Pasqua approached the Christmas season in a funk. A speakeasy price war raged unchecked in the Bronx, reducing Tony's revenue schedule to fifteen cents a shot, two for a quarter, with every fourth one on the house. Frank Pasqua had not been paid to pass out before a funeral for two months, and his casket suppliers were pressing him for payment of long overdue bills.

As the two men sat around Tony's broken poker table, brooding over their dismal prospects, they looked through the beaded curtain to see Mike Molloy enter the front door. With one mind, they saw an instantaneous solution to their difficulties.

The estimate of Mike's age on the autopsy protocol was "40?". Those who had been regaled with his tremendous repertoire of stories, told in a genuine brogue direct from the Emerald Isle, thought that he was closer to his mid-sixties. He was suave, gracious to the point of courtliness, in complete command of a broad and expressive vocabulary, so that he appeared every inch the retired Shakespearean actor that he claimed to be. He was one of that rare breed who automatically elevate the quality of their clothes simply by putting them on. If he could have afforded so much as a secondhand Foreman & Clark suit, he would have far outclassed the Prince of Wales.

He made his living by caging drinks from those who enjoyed his conversation enough to pay for it. Most of the speakeasies in the area had cut him off from the free lunch counter, but, somehow, he continued to be well nourished.

His great appeal for Tony Marino and Frank Pasqua was his lack of known relatives or intimate friends. They launched phase one of their program the following day.

Pasqua and Marino called on a life insurance agent whose need for money equaled their own. He readily agreed to waive the formalities of a physical examination and personal signature by the applicant; so while Mike Molloy stood drinking and talking at Tough Tony's bar, he also became the insured on a

$1200 policy that named Marino as the beneficiary. Pasqua was promised the funeral at his usual price, just as soon as his services were required.

The team now moved to phase two, which brought Red Murphy into the plot—Murphy the skilled anesthesiologist. For a $100 right of participation in the proceeds of the policy, he agreed to guarantee that a properly filed claim would be due and payable.

He abandoned the chloral hydrate with which he was familiar, and decided to use automobile antifreeze. As he explained later, he was out of chloral hydrate but did have a can of antifreeze behind the bar that he had used in his 1927 Model-T Ford the night before.

Molloy probably thought that he was only reaping the benefits of the Yuletide season when Murphy served him three drinks of the house's finest on the night the plotters decided to execute their plan. The fourth round was antifreeze—chemically wood alcohol and solvents—cut with a little water. Five more shots of antifreeze, spread over a two-hour period, were required before Molloy collapsed on the floor. Since Tough Tony's was not Delmonico's, the appearance of a passed-out customer on the floor did not disturb the regular patrons. When Red Murphy locked the doors at 3 A.M., he joined Pasqua and Tony at the poker table behind the beaded curtains, in a sort of pre-death wake, to wait for Molloy to die.

By virtue of his profession, Pasqua was deemed to be knowledgeable on the subject of death. Periodically, between ceremonial drinks furnished by Tough Tony, Pasqua would stagger out front to check Molloy's pulse and respiration.

"He's going fast. It won't be long," Pasqua reported at first. "Just time for one more round."

Tough Tony became highly suspicious when the bottle they were using at the poker table ran dry. He thought that Pasqua was taking advantage of his good graces to attain the customary state of pre-funeral anesthesia which was his rite; so Marino staggered up to the front of the room to make his own unprofessional observations as to whether the moment of death had arrived.

"Aye, and a good morning to you, mine host," Mike Molloy said in a firm voice just as Tough Tony bent over him. "Nothing like a good night's sleep to put a man in fine condition for the new day."

Tough Tony jumped back at this voice from the dead, tripped over a chair and fell to the floor beside Molloy. He was so stunned that he offered no resistance when Molloy walked to the free-lunch table and cleaned up the scraps and remnants of the previous day's offerings.

All three of the plotters agreed that Murphy simply had not given Molloy a sufficient quantity of antifreeze to accomplish the purpose. For the next six days and nights during Christmas week, Murphy poured three gallons of antifreeze into Molloy out of a bottle especially reserved for the number one customer of the house. It was enough to blind and kill several "average" men.

The invariable result developed into a ritual. Molloy would pass out. Murphy, Pasqua, and Marino would retire to the poker table to wait for him to die; but he always awoke bright and smiling, thanking Tony for his hospitality, and ready for the new day.

The day after Christmas, Red Murphy decided to alter the routine. He opened a can of sardines, on the correct assumption that they would soon putrefy in the unwholesome air of the speakeasy.

"We'll make him a ptomaine sandwich just as soon as the fishes get ripe enough," he told Marino and Pasqua.

It took only three days for the fish to become so pungent that they overpowered all the other odors of the speakeasy. During this interval, Molloy continued to thrive on a liquid diet of pure antifreeze.

"Wait a minute," Marino interjected when Murphy suggested that it was time to prepare the sandwich. "Give me the can."

He returned in a few minutes with a paper sack filled with curling shreds of tin. Someplace he had been able to get the sardine tin sliced into ugly, thin uniform strips.

"Now, mix this with the fish," he ordered Murphy. "It'll rip the guy from gullet to anus." It must be added, parenthetically, that the word "anus" was not a part of Tough Tony's vocabulary.

If Molloy ever became suspicious of the solicitous care shown him by the bartender, he did not disclose it. Gratefully, he accepted the sandwich, which he washed down with several shots from his own special bottle; and for two additional days and nights, the three plotters maintained their unrewarding vigil.

Further action was demanded. At some time during his career, Pasqua remembered vaguely, through his alcoholic haze, of hearing of a death that resulted from either oysters or clams marinated overnight in whiskey. The whiskey turned the shellfish into rocks which lay in the victim's stomach, causing him a painful death. Since he could not be sure whether it was oysters or clams, Red Murphy prepared an antifreeze marinade into which he poured one pint each of oysters and clams. Molloy ate this delicacy with relish; but still nothing happened.

It was well into the new year when the original three conspirators added a fourth member to their group. He was Hershey Green, a Bronx cabdriver, who was also an habitué of Marino's speakeasy.

Shortly after closing time, Marino and Pasqua carried the passed-out body of Mike Molloy and shoved it into the back seat of Green's cab, who then drove to a deserted area out around Claremont Park. While Green maintained a careful lookout, Marino and Pasqua dragged the limp body off the road and laid it face up behind a row of shrubbery. The temperature was well below zero, and the ground covered with a sheet of frozen sleet which had fallen earlier. Molloy did not own a topcoat, so they stripped him of his jacket, opened his shirt, and lifted his undershirt to expose as much bare flesh to the raw elements as possible. Learning from their experiences of the past several weeks, Marino returned to the cab and brought out a three-gallon tin can filled with water, which he carefully poured over Molloy's body, saturating him from head to foot. This, they thought, would insure a rapid death from pneumonia, "a legitimate death from natural causes," Pasqua pronounced it, while gleefully rubbing his chilled hands.

In the late afternoon, Marino and Pasqua were treating

themselves with medicinal alcohol for chills and fever they had contracted earlier that morning from exposure to the elements at Claremont Park. Hershey Green had checked the row of shrubbery around noon and reported that Molloy's body was gone. He was undoubtedly either in a morgue or seriously ill in some hospital. They were attempting to plan their next move when the front door opened and a smiling Mike Molloy bounced in.

"Can you give me a clue, Red my boy," Molloy said to Murphy, who more or less automatically shoved a glass of antifreeze across the bar, "how I could possibly have got over to Claremont Park during the night? It will be hard for you to believe it, but that's where I woke up this morning."

These untoward developments convinced the quartet that they needed still a fifth member to help them collect the $1200 that rode on Mike Molloy's life, before the next quarterly premium fell due. Anthony Bastone, another Marino habitué, was hastily recruited.

Tony Bastone's suggestion appeared to be the route they should have adopted in the beginning. It was not only simple and direct; it was foolproof. They would load Molloy into Green's cab in the early morning hours, after he passed out, and drive him to some remote area. Bastone would then hold him by the side of the road. When Green came by in the cab at the proper speed, Bastone would push Molloy in front of the car. Molloy's death would be attributed to a hit-and-run accident and written off by the police as just another traffic statistic. To guarantee faithful performance, Bastone and Green were each to receive $100 when the insurance benefits were settled.

Around two o'clock the next morning, Marino, Bastone, Pasqua, and Green, with Molloy sprawled on the floor in the back seat, drove away from the speakeasy, in search of the appropriate place for the hit-and-run accident. They thought they had found it on a street called Gun Hill Road. Marino and Bastone got out with the limp body. Green and Pasqua drove farther down the street and turned around. They had worked out a signal whereby Green would blow the horn twice, just in case another car happened by, so that Bastone and Marino would not push Molloy in front of the wrong vehicle.

Green's taxi raced down the street at about fifty miles an hour. He blew the horn twice and Marino and Bastone executed their assignment, only to see the cab swerve and avoid Molloy's body at the last minute. Unknown to the madly cursing Marino and Bastone, a light had flashed on in the only house in the entire area, causing Green to get cold feet.

They found the proper location, without any flashing lights, half an hour later on Baychester Avenue. Each member of the team executed his assignment perfectly, and Molloy's upright body was struck with the front of the cab as it traveled at an estimated speed of sixty miles an hour.

The relief felt by the conspirators changed to uncertainty and then to despair when they searched all the afternoon papers without finding a single story about a hit-and-run accident in the entire Bronx. Red Murphy was relieved of his duties behind the bar and sent on a mission to check all the morgues and hospitals for his "missing brother." His search was futile.

A week went by and the conspirators decided that their only way out was to find a substitute for Molloy. This, Bastone provided in the person of James Patrick McCarthy, another Irishman who followed Molloy's pattern of living, but who lacked Molloy's polish and class. McCarthy jumped at the opportunity to sweep out Marino's speakeasy for a dollar a day, plus all his food and drink, plus that even more important intangible of being welcomed as an important member of Tony Marino's staff.

The following morning, after he had properly passed out, McCarthy was given the hit-and-run treatment by Green's taxi on a narrow street in the Claremont Park area. Bastone had added the practical twist to insure the proper legal identification. He had the foresight to have some business cards printed which bore the name of Michael Molloy. These were carefully placed in McCarthy's hip pocket before the accident took place.

Murphy located James Patrick McCarthy in Fordham Hospital under the name of Michael Molloy, still alive, but gravely injured with fractures of the skull, arms, legs, and ribs, and suffering from multiple internal injuries. McCarthy hung on in a comatose state for almost two weeks; but then it appeared that he would recover.

The morale of the conspirators hit an all-time low. It was almost imperative that they seek a substitute for McCarthy, the original substitute for Molloy. McCarthy appeared due for a long hospital confinement. As though guided by some premonition, Bastone had kept a supply of the business cards which bore the name of Michael Molloy.

Their debate over strategy ended abruptly the next day. Mike Molloy breezed into Tough Tony's speakeasy to announce that he had been laid up in Fordham Hospital for bruises suffered at the hands of some unknown motorist who had not even stopped to lend him aid after striking him. Apparently, some administrative oversight in the hospital records, or carelessness on the part of a hospital clerk, had prevented Red Murphy from locating the real Mike Molloy when he was searching for him the day after the first hit-and-run accident staged with Green's cab.

An even more direct and positive method of collecting the insurance benefits was now agreed upon, once the conspirators added a sixth man to their team. He was Daniel Kreisberg, another habitué of Tough Tony's.

Kreisberg inveigled Mike Molloy to his room in a flophouse on Fulton Avenue, where he got him thoroughly drunk. He called Tough Tony to report that the preliminaries were taken care of. Tough Tony dispatched Red Murphy, who arrived with a coil of rubber hose. He attached one end of the hose to the illuminating gas outlet, shoved the other end down Molloy's throat, and opened the turn-on valve.

This was an unfair advantage that even Mike Molloy, "interred as Nicholas Millory," could not overcome.

Even though Molloy's body in death developed the characteristic cherry-red color of carbon monoxide poisoning, the obliging private physician signed the death certificate as "lobar pneumonia"; Frank Pasqua presided over Molloy's burial.

The $1200 in death benefits were paid over to Marino without any question, and the saga of Mike Molloy might never have been known, except that the conspirators fell out over the division of the proceeds. Twelve hundred dollars was not a great amount when split into six shares. Hershey Green began to seek the opinion of complete strangers as to what they thought his share should be, particularly in view of the dent in his radiator that was then beginning to leak. Kreisberg and Bastone talked openly of their part in the murder.

When the district attorney launched his official inquiry, all six men fell over themselves in an effort to be the first to turn State's evidence in the vain hope of leniency. Green and Bastone did escape with prison sentences; but Marino, Pasqua, Murphy, and Kreisberg died at Sing Sing in the electric chair.

The determination of the cause of death at the autopsy as carbon monoxide poisoning, ". . . present (32.6 percent)," was not impeded by embalming fluid. It was another case where Frank Pasqua had been paid to embalm, but quietly omitted this formality.

Dr. Helpern uses the Mike Molloy case in his lectures to illustrate the two basic questions that must be solved in any death case. The first is the *cause* of death; the second, the *manner* of death.

"The cause of death," he points out, "is always a medical question. In the Molloy case, it was fairly simple: carbon monoxide poisoning with a concentration of 32.6 percent. This we found at autopsy without any difficulty, even though the body had been buried for almost three months.

"The manner of death," he continues, "is a horse of an entirely different color. The manner of death is the means that brings about the cause of death. In this case, what was the instrumentality that was responsible for putting the carbon monoxide concentration into Mike Molloy's body? It could have been accidental from a leak in the gas pipe. It could have been suicidal. In this case, it was clearly homicidal.

"The important thing to remember is that the manner of death is usually not a purely medical determination. The manner of death has to be proved by evidence that is not medical. It's all right with me when people refer to us in the medical examiner's office as 'medical detectives,' provided they know what they mean by that term. Our job is to detect the cause of death; but it usually stops there. We may be able to assist the police and other detectives who have to uncover the *manner* in which the *cause* of death was brought about. We can say, 'Yes, that stab wound could have been made by that bloody knife you found near the body'; or, 'No, that knife isn't long enough to make this kind of stab wound.' But it isn't our job to say, or to attempt to say, who wielded the knife that made the stab wound, or why. It's our job to say '*What* Done It,' not '*Who* Done It.'

"The determination that Mike Molloy's death was murder instead of suicide or accident could only be made by evidence which we could not develop at the autopsy. Our medical look would not furnish any clue whatsoever to all those shenanigans that those characters were pulling in their efforts to kill Molloy. This information is in the district attorney's files.

"Now, it is right here that a lot of 'specialists' get into trouble. They draw all kinds of conclusions from the autopsy about the manner of death, when all they should be worrying about is the cause of death. They want to play the game of 'Medical Detective' and 'Win With This Witness' all the way across the board. They want to be 'Rover Boys At The Morgue.' They want to help hang the manner of death on some particular individual, when all they should be concerned about is finding the exact cause of death. And once they get involved in playing the game, they become stubborn, biased; they develop blind spots when they have to justify their preconceived and prestated opinions; and they become downright dangerous."

In private conversations, Dr. Helpern says that the Molloy case has a deeper meaning.

"You know," he says pensively, his Ben Franklin glasses arched over the top of his head, "the human body attests man's total individuality. We are all different, no two of us are the same. Mike Molloy is a classic example. I wish we knew how old he was when he died. At autopsy, he looked like a healthy forty; but some of his acquaintances would place him a full generation ahead.

"Look at this autopsy report," Dr. Helpern continues. " 'Stomach: Empty. Mucosa normal.' Except for the changes attributable to carbon monoxide, the heart is normal; the kidneys are normal; the lungs are natural; the brain is normal; the coronaries are 'clear and natural throughout. There are no scars. The valves are natural.' Yet, the evidence is that Mike Molloy was not only badly abused during the last several weeks of his life, but he had been abusing himself for years before that, probably all his adult life.

"On the other hand, take a practicing Mormon, for example. You know he has never had a drink of coffee, much less alcohol, or smoked a cigarette in his life. He has taken the best possible care of his body. Still, at autopsy, you see him with a fatty liver, and great white plaques in his coronary arteries, and the lining of his stomach is fiery red. He looks for all the world like an old alcoholic.

"Contrast Mike Molloy with the man who imbibes one ounce of whiskey and goes into a condition called pathological alcoholic intoxication. He may become a raving maniac, or he may die. Somewhere in between these extremes, all of us handle alcohol in our own individual way.

"Two men may walk down the same street and get stung on their right thumbs by two bees. The first man barely gets a welt out of it and in two hours, the second man is dead. People shake their heads and say: 'Oh, it just does not make any sense.' Well, it does make sense, once you understand that every human body is different.

"One thing that makes medicine so difficult is that there is no such thing as the *average* man. I always have disliked that word. When we talk about a laboratory procedure like a white blood count, about all we can say is that the reading is 'within the range of normal.' We don't even try to use the word *average*.

"We used to measure whether a man was overweight by a set of tables, worked out by the insurance companies, that were based on age and height. Now, it is thought better to measure such an 'uncomplicated' concept as whether you are overweight strictly on an individual basis. The tables can be used as guides, but they aren't controlling. The same thing may be true with cholesterol, which made such a splash a few years ago in the heart disease picture. Now, some doctors are saying that it may be necessary to establish normal cholesterol values for each individual, and that the group averages of what is normal and what is elevated cannot be applied across the board to all patients. Man is so distinctive and individual that he defies classification.

"No man is just one mass statistic that is called average. He is individual. He is something special. I used to be continually amazed at how different each body appeared at autopsy. The hearts are shaped just a little bit differently, or the pattern of the arteries is different, the contours of the livers are not the same, the kidneys are never suspended in just the same way. And these differences are all within this so-called range of normal. I'm no longer surprised. I expect to find these differences. And if man is individually different in death, he is different in life.

"There are no two human bodies that are identical. You know, it's kind of a thrilling thing when you stop to think about it. Because every man is different, this means that he is special—each man occupies a special position on this earth."

CHAPTER 5

"The Mind Is a Product of the Body"

It was a Wednesday night in early January and Dr. Helpern was lying in bed in his pajamas, attempting to relax with the current issue of *The New Yorker.* His interest was piqued by a clever murder story.

The world's greatest criminologists, pathologists, and detectives were holding an international meeting in London. This meeting presented an irresistible challenge to the villain of the piece. He would commit the perfect crime right under the noses of the most famous investigative minds ever assembled, and they would be utterly baffled. The intended victim, whose physical and psychological dimensions Dr. Helpern does not remember other than her compulsion for chocolate candy, suddenly and without provocation, received something like twenty-five pounds of tempting chocolates from an anonymous admirer.

According to the villain's perfectly conceived scheme, she would not be able to resist the temptation of the chocolates. This would trigger her emotional system so that an oversupply of insulin would be discharged into her bloodstream to combat the glucose produced by the excess intake of sugar. This insulin, in turn, would cause a condition of hypoglycemia, an abnormally low concentration of sugar in the bloodstream. Her insulin supply would finally be totally exhausted. Her blood sugar would climb so high that she would quickly die.

The medical possibilities were intriguing, but Dr. Helpern was not permitted an opportunity to check them out. The phone on the night table beside his bed brought him back to reality.

"Dr. Helpern," the apologetic voice said, "I'm sorry to call you at this time of the night, but this is Captain Hannigan over at the Twenty-fourth Precinct. We think we've got a murder case, except that we haven't got any body; and it doesn't look like we're going to have a body. We wondered if you could come over here and help us interrogate these two characters so that we don't foul it up some way."

"What happened to the body?" Dr. Helpern asked.

"Well, that's the problem," Captain Hannigan replied uncertainly. "We'd like to know if what these guys tell us they did is medically possible. Can you make a murder case without a body?"

"Sure you can," Dr. Helpern replied, "provided you remember the two basic problems involved. Send over a car and I'll come see what you've got."

Dr. Helpern reluctantly closed his *New Yorker,* threw it on a chair, and prepared to walk into a case far more engrossing than the fictional lady with her twenty-five pounds of chocolates.

When Dr. Helpern arrived at the 24th Precinct station, the police and an assistant district attorney were questioning Thomas George Daniel and Leobaldo Pijuan.

"Here's what we've got," Captain Hannigan began after Dr. Helpern shook hands with a dozen or so detectives, uniformed officers, and representatives of the district attorney's office. "It looks like it's about all we're going to get, and we don't know whether it's enough, or particularly whether it makes any sense from a medical point of view."

The beginning point was the cast of characters.

Thomas George Daniel, whose parents were of Greek origin, was twenty-five years old, a native of Weirton, West Virginia. A clue to his volatile heritage developed at the subsequent trial when his widowed mother had to be barred from the courtroom because her anguished shouts in a combination of Greek and broken English completely paralyzed the proceedings. After testifying in Greek through an interpreter, she refused to leave the witness stand and was carried bodily from the room.

Tom Daniel's impoverished parents had scrimped and saved their pennies, nickels, dimes, and quarters, as only the foreign-born can, so that their only son could have every reasonable opportunity to create a name and niche for himself in this land of opportunity.

The family moved to Warren, Ohio, but the public schools were not deemed adequate. He graduated from Riverside Military Academy in 1948, and then enrolled at Kent State University. The Korean War intervened, but Daniel went back to Kent State, honorably discharged, after a two-year hitch in the Army in Germany.

As is the case of millions of other men, the Army had made Tom Daniel restless. He found it difficult to study, although he was in his senior year; and the hovering presence of his solicitous mother was a final inhibition that triggered his rebellion.

Tom Daniel wanted to be a writer of great books. He attempted to explain his goals and ambitions from the witness stand:

Q. I want you to tell us what you were planning to write about?
A. It would take some time to explain.
Q. Well, what was the subject? Was it history, was it fiction, short stories, or biography, or detective stories?
A. No, it does not fall into any of those categories.
Q. Well, tell us what it falls into?
A. You can't categorize it.
Q. What was the subject?
A. Well, the theme of what I was intending to write and which I was working on was. . . . See, if I may properly explain it to you. . . . The struggle that man, the only struggle that man should pursue, that struggle being one to acquire a higher self-consciousness and to be able to understand the universality of the place in which he lives.
Q. Well, within the scope of my limited education and awareness, would that fall into the category of philosophy—in a broad way?
A. Yes, definitely.

In the middle of 1954, Tom Daniel moved to New York City. To support himself while struggling with his first book, he became a salesman for the Miller Harness Company on East 24th Street and began to meet the "horsey" set, selling them saddles, bridles, boots, crops, and riding habits.

Next came forty-seven-year-old Leobaldo Pijuan, who had other driving ambitions in his youthful days in Puerto Rico. He dreamed of being a great surgeon, but the poverty of his large family denied him the opportunity to attend medical school. He took the second-best route open to him, and became a licensed nurse in San Juan in 1946.

He, too, was lured to New York City by the dream of professional and financial opportunity. He became a "scrub nurse," first at Adelphi Hospital in Brooklyn, and then at Lincoln Hospital in the Bronx. He was contented and happy, as happy as anyone in a "next-best" situation in life could be. He scrubbed in along with the real surgeons, handed them their instruments, sometimes in Puerto Rico, closing and suturing the surgical incision following the entire gamut of operations—appendectomies, gallbladders, hemorrhoidectomies, hysterectomies, colostomies, and other delicate procedures.

His peers and superiors alike considered him highly competent and professional. By Christmas Eve 1955, his active participation in upward of a thousand major surgical procedures had clothed him with a confident and professional demeanor.

Pijuan and Daniel chanced to meet each other in early 1955 at a party in the apartment of a mutual friend. Pijuan had also brought a special guest of his own, Ramiro Mireles. Dr. Helpern immediately recognized him as the sine qua non ("without which not") to the successful murder prosecution that the police officers at the 24th Precinct station house envisioned.

Twenty-seven-year-old Dr. Mireles was a graduate of the Medical School of the University of Nuevo Leon in Monterrey, Mexico. After completing a one-year rotating internship at St. Mary's Hospital in Tucson, Arizona, Mireles returned to his native Mexico, where he was licensed to practice medicine. In 1952 he, too, felt the magnetic pull of New York City, and obtained a residency in surgery at Adelphi Hospital.

Mireles' chance meeting with Leo Pijuan was in Adelphi's

operating room, where both men were assisting a senior surgeon in a tricky gastrectomy, the surgical removal of a part of the stomach. After Mireles moved from Adelphi Hospital to Lincoln Hospital, Pijuan followed him there.

Mireles was a lonely stranger to the big city when he first arrived. As he testified later on: "We both speak Spanish. Leo introduced me to the city, getting me to know the highways and all that, how to get around, and to his family also."

Pijuan was continually doing favors for his friend. For almost two months, he moved out of his apartment on the upper West Side of Manhattan, so that Mireles' mother and sister could occupy it when they visited the doctor in New York.

Mireles felt an obligation to Pijuan, "like a brother." Their friendship was founded on mutuality of language, nurtured by their common loneliness in the impassive city, and buttressed by their common professional interests.

Mireles provided the proper tranquilizing balm and succor to Pijuan's frustrated surgical aspirations. Wherever they went, he always introduced his friend as *Doctor* Pijuan, after which "scrub nurse" Leobaldo Pijuan gratefully bowed and beamed contentedly.

The missing character in this otherwise perfect script, missing in every possible connotation of the word, was Jacquelyn Louise Smith, a pert, "petite," talented but grossly introverted twenty-year-old native of Lebanon, Pennsylvania. She, too, had been pulled to the city by the dream of artistic accomplishment.

Although carefully honed, her facial features lacked that one certain, intangible ingredient to permit the stamp of beautiful to apply. Perhaps if her thick brown hair had been more carefully groomed, the term "pretty" might have been appropriate. People who met her for the first time, however, did not give her face a second look. Her perfect size-nine figure had entrancing proportions—from the delicate curve of her rounded hips, rising above dainty legs, to her pointed breasts. Although she was not a model she might well have been.

With her parents' consent, in October 1953, Jackie left Lebanon and enrolled in the Traphagen School of Fashion on upper Broadway; she soon became an employee of H. Dworkin, a silk broker who marketed his merchandise under the name of Dwortex Designs. There she sharpened her skills as a pattern designer for silk scarves. She lived at a girls' residence club overlooking Central Park West, until she moved into an apartment of her own on West 95th Street, which she shared with two other girls.

Tom Daniel had casually met one of the girls with whom Jackie shared the new apartment, and he helped them with the moving chores. Something clicked when he and Jackie were introduced. The magic worked fast, so fast that Jackie only slept one night in the new apartment. The next day, she moved in with Tom Daniel in his fifth-floor walk-up flat on East 27th Street, literally only a stone's throw from the Bellevue Hospital morgue where Milton Helpern was still performing his medical examiner's autopsies.

Daniel's apartment was a sparsely furnished unit, with a grubby kitchen, small dining room, living room, and bedroom. Leo Pijuan had been one of Daniel's first visitors when he moved to the apartment several months earlier. He brought Tom some secondhand dishes and a tool kit which Daniel planned to use to completely redecorate the quarters. At the same time, Pijuan loaned Daniel twenty-five dollars to cover the deposit required by the telephone company, even though Pijuan had only met Daniel once before.

We know little of the true relationship between Daniel and Jackie. He was an accomplished chef who enjoyed preparing exotic food. She performed the cleaning and other housekeeping duties and was seen from time to time at the incinerator and garbage can by other residents in the apartment building.

Every Saturday, Jackie dutifully made her way back to the apartment on West 95th Street, where she still maintained her legal residence for the sake of appearances. She picked up her mail and left $9.58 as her share of the weekly rent. In November, her parents came to visit her on West 95th Street, at which time she introduced them to her "guy," Tom Daniel, who casually and coincidentally dropped by.

Perhaps some clue to their pretended husband-and-wife idyll is furnished in this exchange, which took place at the trial, between Assistant District Attorney Alexander Herman* and Daniel, when Daniel was on the witness stand:

Q. You mean you weren't even on talking terms, of talking conversation with Jackie?

A. Yes, we conversed but not—most of the time not directly. We talked through someone else.

Q. You mean there was a third party who transmitted messages between you and Jackie?

A. A party? Not a party.

Q. Well, did you write notes to her, did she write notes to you?

A. No. No.

THE COURT. Well, tell us.

Q. Tell us what you mean by "indirectly?"

A. Well, you see, there was Tom Morgan.

MR. HERMAN. I don't see anything funny, and please refrain from laughing at me.

THE WITNESS. You see, Tom Morgan, we talked through Tom Morgan.

THE COURT. Well, who is Tom Morgan?

THE WITNESS. Tom Morgan is a dog, a play dog that when you squeeze he barks.

Q. Have you ever been in a mental institution?

A. No. Would you like me to explain it to you, sir?

THE COURT. I just want to clear up one point, Mr. Daniel. There were times when you and Jackie were alone in the apartment?

THE WITNESS. Yes, sir; yes, sir.

THE COURT. And when you wanted to talk with her or ask her something, what would you do, how would you convey your thoughts?

THE WITNESS. When we had a discussion that was in the nature of argumentative, we both resorted to this little play dog. That's the way we got around each other.

Q. Well, that was play, was it not, or was that—

A. We tried to humor each other—in other words, not to get angry. And, through this little dog we were able to do it.

Q. When you woke up in the morning—

A. (*continuing*) Perfectly normal. . . . When we had an argument or serious discussion, when Jackie did not want to tell me any-

* Mr. Herman was Chief of the Homicide Bureau, New York County District Attorney's Office, which is still presided over by Frank Hogan, dean of district attorneys in this country.

thing or when I didn't want to tell her anything, we would resort to Tom Morgan, and through the humorous part of it we would agree on certain points and come around.

Q. This was all good humor—you were not arguing in the sense that you were quarreling?

A. No, no, not exactly. You see, the dog was her, it belonged to her.

Q. It was a pet—it was a toy animal?

A. Yes, yes.

THE COURT. Well, weren't there times when you spoke to her directly also?

THE WITNESS. Yes, definitely.

THE COURT. When you say you drifted apart spiritually—

THE WITNESS. Yes.

THE COURT. Can you tell the Court and jury just what you mean by that, sir?

THE WITNESS. Well, if there is a spiritual attachment, there is a sort of oneness between people, you see. Not only is there a physical intimacy, but there is spiritual intimacy, they understand each other's needs . . . you see, not their physical needs but their spiritual needs . . .

Q. So you drifted apart?

A. In that sense, yes.

Q. Well, did you remain friendly otherwise?

A. Oh, definitely.

Q. But not friendly enough to sleep in the same bed with her?

A. Well, now (*witness laughs*).

Q. What's funny about this?

A. I am not sure that I know what you are talking about.

THE COURT. Well, were you sleeping with her during this period of time that she stayed over?

THE WITNESS. In the same bed, yes, yes.

THE COURT. Every night that she stayed over, you would sleep with her?

THE WITNESS. Yes.

THE COURT. Had your physical interest in her diminished also?

THE WITNESS. Entirely.

During September and October, Jackie developed vaginitis, an infectious process known to most women from time to time, and consulted a Dr. Michel. At the time of the trial, Daniel's attorneys were to commit an unpardonable tactical blunder, an attempt to imply that this vaginitis was some form of loathesome venereal disease. All they accomplished was to thoroughly antagonize the jury.

On November 30th, Jackie's doctor told her that the infection had cleared up; but then he shocked her by telling her that she had a "new condition."

"What is my new condition?" she asked plaintively, fearing but undoubtedly expecting the answer he gave her.

"To the best of my estimation, you are five and one-half weeks pregnant," Dr. Michel advised her.

Jackie asked Dr. Michel if he would be willing to deliver her; he answered in the affirmative, and he called and made a reservation for her admission to the Madison Avenue Hospital for the following July.

She asked for and received a certificate of health, which was a prerequisite to obtaining a marriage license in the State of New York.

Marriage, however, was not Tom Daniel's ideal solution for their mutual problem.

We can get some clue to their anguish from the testimony of Jackie's superior at the H. Dworkin Company:

Q. Did you notice anything unusual about Jackie's manner, beginning after this visit to the doctor?
A. Beginning after Thanksgiving?
Q. More or less?
A. Well, yes, I did in a sense. She seemed to be quite a bit paler than usual and she looked kind of pale and flushed occasionally, and it was not only I who noticed it—
Q. Don't tell us what anyone else noticed, tell us what you noticed.
A. She seemed more depressed and much more uncommunicative; she didn't seem to want to talk to anybody.
Q. Quiet?
A. Yes. She did her work as usual, except that her output was slower. On lunch hour, occasionally, she would be sitting in the room and looking out of the window, which was very unlike her. She seemed to be staring out at the water, and it went on for half an hour and she wouldn't move; she just stayed there.
Q. At any time do you recall whether or not something specific happened, which was to your knowledge?
A. Yes. I recall on one occasion she was sitting at the desk in the morning—she had been working all morning and she hadn't said

anything, she was very quiet; and suddenly she burst out crying and ran from the room.

Tom Daniel began searching for his own solution to their problem, first with his fellow employees at the Miller Harness Company. He asked four or five if they knew where he could get any "pills" for Jackie, and finally if they knew anyone who could perform an abortion.

He then remembered meeting Dr. Ramiro Mireles at the party some months earlier. Using the telephone which was still in his apartment by virtue of Leo Pijuan's twenty-five-dollar loan, still unpaid, he requested help from Dr. Mireles. He called him on three different occasions, and each time Mireles replied that he, personally, could do nothing; but he would "see what I can do." There is no evidence that Mireles actually ever did anything. He testified at the trial that he was merely stringing Daniel along.

Daniel apparently gave up on Mireles, but then turned to Leo Pijuan, the perpetual granter of favors and doer of good deeds for other people.

Pijuan agreed to perform the abortion on Christmas Eve, when the spirit of Christmas would be permeating most of the city; he arrived at Daniel's apartment shortly after 10 P.M. He was dressed in a three-quarter-length topcoat, with belt and green fur collar. He carried two packages, one a mustard-colored, tightly tied Army duffel bag which contained his surgical instruments and medications. The second package contained a simple enamel vegetable tray out of a refrigerator.

Daniel ushered him into the kitchen and handed him five ten-dollar bills, and promised to pay him an additional fifty dollars the following month.

Jackie now made her appearance from the bedroom, wearing black pedal-pushers, pink slippers, and a black and white striped sweater.

Scrub nurse Leobaldo Pijuan's surgical instinct rebelled at this attire. It was not conducive to sterile operating room requirements. He knew that the greatest hazard of any abortion, therapeutic or otherwise, was infection; so he sent Jackie into the bedroom to change clothes. She now looked through the kitchen door and saw the refrigerator pan filled with surgical instruments submerged in boiling water on one of the gas burners of the small stove. The seriousness of the procedure to which she had finally agreed to submit, after days of urging and coaxing by Daniel, staggered her. Pijuan's bedside manner, however, was reassuring. He told her that she must go to sleep for no more than fifteen minutes, and when she woke up, everything would be all right.

While Jackie was removing all her clothes and putting on the tops to a pair of Daniel's pajamas, Pijuan and Daniel were busy in the living room. They unfolded the hideaway bed and covered the floor with newspapers. Daniel had a narrow slab of wood from a packing crate, which they jammed into one corner of the couch. To this, Pijuan taped a one-liter,* 1000 cc. bottle of sodium pentothal which he had taken the preceding day from the operating room at Lincoln Hospital.

Jackie sat slowly on the couch and reluctantly agreed to lie down at Pijuan's urging. He attached a plastic tube to the neck of the inverted sodium pentothal bottle, and inserted the needle on the other end of the tube into a vein in Jackie's left forearm. Tom Daniel lay down beside her on the couch, to comfort her and also to be certain that the needle did not slip out of her vein.

Pijuan now decided that her hips had to be elevated, so he folded two blankets and placed them underneath the lower part of her tense and taut body. He brought in two folding bridge chairs from the dining room, elevated Jackie's knees, and draped and tied them across the backs of the two chairs.

He opened the regulator clip on the plastic tube so that the anesthetic would begin to flow into her body. Within minutes, Jackie was unconscious.

Pijuan then retired to the kitchen, where he scrubbed his hands carefully for fifteen minutes, to be certain that he would induce no infectious bacteria into Jackie's genitourinary tract. This was the first surgical procedure that Pijuan had undertaken on his own. It must be done competently. Infection had to be prevented.

* A liter is a little more than a quart.

Pijuan's testimony at the trial, given in heavily accented English, describes what happened next:

Q. What instruments did you take? What do you call them, if you know?
A. Oh, I took a speculum.
Q. A speculum—a what?
A. A weight speculum, an instrument.
Q. What is a weight speculum?
A. An instrument with a heavy weight. I took another vaginal speculum, and I took a couple of curettes, a sponge stick; some antiseptic, we call Zephiran; we call the antiseptic Zephiran. I took a couple of stimulants, adrenalin; and I took Coramine, and a bottle of sodium pentothal, with a set, a complete set to give the injection.
Q. Now, you have referred to a weight speculum. What does that look like?
A. Well, it's an instrument, a vaginal instrument that is used to give some visualization. It has a weight down at the bottom.
Q. And what is the shape of that weight?
A. It's like a ball, like a ball; and at the top of the instrument is like an angle, a right-angle blade.
Q. And you put that in the vulva?
A. Yes, that helps to see inside.
Q. And, what is a speculum?
A. A vaginal speculum, another instrument that has two parts, that when you press a little handle and open . . .
Q. And how is that used?
A. To open the vagina.
Q. And you used the word curette?
A. Yes, I did.
Q. And what is that used for?
A. That's used to scrape.
Q. Scrape what?
A. To scrape the uterine contents, the material inside the uterine.
Q. And how many of these did you say you had?
A. I used a couple of them.
Q. Then what?
A. I scrubbed pretty well, fifteen minutes, and I come out with my hands up, they were raising down, and I told him "Pour some alcohol." He poured me some alcohol, and then I took a sponge and I wiped my hands.

Q. Go ahead.
A. And I told him "Don't touch nothing here, because this is sterile," so I proceeded and I painted her sides in the vagina. Then I put in the weight speculum, and then I put the valve, the vaginal speculum, the other one. Then I proceeded and I saw she had, it was red inside, red so I painted with Zephiran.
Q. Is that red stuff?
A. A red solution, a red antiseptic.
Q. Go ahead.
A. And then I dilate, dilated the cervix a little bit.
Q. With what?
A. With an instrument I brought.
Q. What instrument?
A. A sponge stick.
Q. Go ahead.
A. And there was another instrument I had, that we call it a sponge-packing forceps. I introduced the forceps and I open it a little bit to open the cervix. When there was a half a inch or a inch open, then I scrape inside.
Q. You scraped with what?
A. With a curette, I scrape inside.
Q. How far into the privates of Jacquelyn did you go with the curette, how far?
A. Well, I scrape. When I felt by . . . I felt that it was the soft material that was inside at the beginning. It disappeared, there was no more soft material inside.
Q. What happened to the soft material?
A. I used to sponge it out, sponge it out with the same curette, scrape and scoop it out. I used to scoop it out, and clean; and that together with some blood used to come, run down the weight speculum, run down. I clean her as best I could, and I told Daniel, "Hold the bottle of the sponge." He held the bottle upside down, and I told him, "Everything is finished."
Q. How long had you been doing what you describe when the time came when you said to Daniel, "It's finished?"
A. About ten minutes.
Q. At that time, during that time, could you see whether or not Jackie was breathing?
A. At the same time I was working, I was watching her stomach, the respiration.
Q. And did you see respiration?
A. She was all right that time. Then when I—this time I told Daniel,

"Everything is finished," Daniel said, "But she's very pale, very pale." I looked close too, I looked at her face. In the meantime I had been kneeling in the front, you know. So I look at her face. In fact, she was very pale. I told him—I got a fright right away. I ripped the needle from the vein, and then I lower her legs from the chair. I told him, "She's in shock, get me some towels. Let's keep her warm." So Daniel brought me some towels. I remember one of them was a pink towel, and some white towels, bath towels. I went to the kitchen. I dipped them in the water that was still there. I left there some water there. I squeezed a little bit the towels. I came and I covered Jacquelyn's body, to keep her warm. At the same time I started giving her respiration because I noticed that her respiration was bad now. I took her pulse and she was very thin, very thready, thin.

Q. What does thready mean?

A. Almost imperceptible.

Q. Go ahead.

A. At the same time I prepare an injection of Coramine and I give it to her in the muscle (*indicating*).

Q. You are pointing to your left arm, is that what you did?

A. I gave her an injection in the arm, Coramine. That's a heart stimulant. And I kept feeling the pulse, and the pulse was bad, very bad. So I kept keeping, trying to keep her warm, and giving her, helping her to have some mechanical respiration; and Daniel said, "Is she bad?" I say, "Yes, she's in shock, she's in shock." So I—then he—at last I found out that I couldn't feel the pulse no more. Then I told him, "I told you this was very dangerous—you never wanted to believe me. You thought I was just scaring you. Now do you believe it? It's here now." And he says, "Now, what can I do?" I thought she was dead at this time. I didn't want to tell Daniel. I didn't want to scare him. So I told him—he said, "Can I get a doctor?" I said, "Well, Daniel, no doctor is going to come here at this time for no money in the world." And he said, "Can I call Dr. Mireles?" and I said, "Yes, call Dr. Mireles, but don't tell him on the phone; call Lincoln Hospital, and when he is on the line, let me talk to him; don't say nothing." When Dr. Mireles was on the phone, that Daniel called him, he said he is Dr. Mireles. I said, "Dr. Mireles, I am in Daniel's apartment. I am in a very bad spot. Will you please come over here and bring a couple of stimulants with you." I gave him—I gave Jacquelyn the second injection I had, adrenalin. In the meantime about twenty or twenty-five minutes later Dr. Mireles arrived, and I said, "How quick did you come?" He said, "Yeah, I took a taxi." So he came and took her pulse. Right away he gave, he tried to give her an injection in the vein. He couldn't find the vein, and he used the same injection he had in the syringe, he gave it in the arm. In the meantime I was trying to keep going with the respiration. Then Dr. Mireles said, "There's nobody in the world who can bring her back, she's dead." Then he called Dr.—he called Daniel and he said, "Daniel, you put Pijuan in this mess. Think about how you're going to get him out of this." Daniel kept saying, "Oh I'm so young, I'm only twenty-five years old," and he said, "I'm thinking about my mother." I told him, "Yes, that what I'm thinking also. I have a mother."

Q. Go ahead.

A. Then I took my—I took the money from my pocket. I gave it back to Daniel in front of Dr. Mireles, and I told him, "Daniel, here is your money. I don't want it." I gave him the fifty dollars. Then he told me, "Anyway, I owe you twenty-five dollars. Here they are." He gave me two tens and one five, my twenty-five dollars.

Q. You gave him five tens back?

A. That's right. The money he gave at the beginning.

Q. And what did he give you back?

A. Twenty-five.

Q. And what bills did he give you?

A. Two brand-new tens, and one five from his pocket. I took the twenty-five because he owed me the money. Then Daniel said, "Well, only if this is a confession, or a body, they can make an indictment. Otherwise, why, they can't prove nothing in this case. I will report her missing."

Q. Did Daniel say that?

A. Daniel said that. Then I told him, "Well, if you promise that you are not going to say nothing, I'll help you to get rid of the body. Promise that you are not going to make no confession." I told him, "Remember, when you report her missing, the police station, they are going to come and get you; and then they are going to interrogate you for a long time."

Q. To do what?

A. To interrogate.

Q. Oh, to interrogate?

A. Yes. He said, "I won't confess. I will say that she go out of the apartment. That's all." And I say "Well, if that's the case, I'll help you. Let's bring her to my apartment. Let's bring the body to my apartment. Do you know somebody with a car, a friend's car?"

Dr. Mireles told Pijuan and Daniel that they should call the police to report Jackie's death. He then left the apartment to return to his dormitory at Lincoln Hospital, wearing the long, dark topcoat over his white hospital uniform which had attracted the attention of two ladies on the floor below Daniel's apartment when he rushed past them in response to Pijuan's emergency summons.

Pijuan and Daniel now faced the same classic problem that has haunted killers through the centuries. How do you dispose of a dead human body to avoid detection, so that the exact means of death can never be discovered? The volatile, cocksure Daniel was himself in a state of shock, and the onus of planning and direction fell entirely upon Pijuan.

He told Daniel that they must have a car, and Daniel made five desperate telephone calls to friends in an effort to borrow one. The only glimmer of hope came from one of Daniel's fellow employees who lived in Brooklyn; so he and Pijuan, after covering Jackie's body with a blanket and newspapers, went down to the street to call a cab. The ride was wasted, so they returned to Manhattan.

Pijuan left Daniel in a coffeehouse on East 14th Street and took a subway to his own apartment at 187 West End Avenue. In approximately one hour, he returned to Daniel's apartment, carrying two suit boxes, together with several large pieces and rolls of gaily colored paper.

The trial transcript relates Pijuan's own description of what happened next:

Q. What happened to Jackie's body?
A. We had decided to transfer the body to my apartment, Daniel and me; so I told him—Daniel said, "But the body is very heavy." I said, "Well, the only way we can transfer the body is to take it apart."
Q. Who said that?
A. I did.
Q. To whom did you say that?
A. To Daniel.

Q. Go ahead.

A. Then I told him, "Give me something, give me a knife." He went to the kitchen and he brought me a kitchen knife with a wooden handle; and I told Daniel to go back to the bathroom. He was pale. I told him to go to the bathroom. "I will call you if I need you." When he was there I dismembered the two arms.

Q. At that time, when you asked Daniel for the knife, was the girl dead? Was Jackie dead?

A. She was dead. I wrapped the two arms in some clothes, like a little box, like Macy's, and they sell dresses; and I wrapped the box in a Christmas paper bag.

Q. Where did you get the Christmas paper?

A. From the apartment. There were papers all over the place, and some—I found this box. I told him I used this box. I put the two arms in the box and I wrapped them in some Christmas wrapping paper, and I tied that with a string I found. I had a little string I found there. We went to my apartment. The other part of the body I wrapped in a plastic bag that's used to put clothes in, with a zipper. I put the body there first; and I put some old clothes and rags to absorb some of the blood. I folded the plastic bag. Then I took a piece of cardboard that had been used for the floors. It was cardboard, a black thing.

Q. Black cardboard?

A. Like a carton.

Q. A carton?

A. That material that you put under the linoleum to protect the linoleum.

Q. Go ahead.

A. I used a piece of that thing, a yard and a half or two yards, and I wrapped the torso there; and then I wrapped some Christmas papers; and Daniel took this big bundle to the car; and I took a small bundle with me.

Q. How many packages or bundles did you make altogether?

A. I guess there were three or four. The two packages were with part of the body; and another package was with the towels that I used; and all these newspapers that were all over the place that I wrapped in, and made in a package and took with me. I didn't leave them there.

Q. Where did you get the wrappings of Christmas, the cord or anything else?

A. They were—some few wrappers I got them from Daniel's apartment from gifts that he had received.

Q. And where was Daniel when you cut up the body, as you described?
A. I told him to go to the bathroom.
Q. And did he come out later?
A. He came out later when I was wrapping this bundle.
Q. And when he came out, did he say anything?
A. No. He sat at a distance, like from here to that chair, in the dining room, looking at me. I was kneeling on the floor making this big bundle; and he was leaning his elbow against the bridge table in the dining room sitting in the chair.

But Pijuan was ahead of his story. After the arms and legs were disjointed and wrapped in two neat Christmas packages, Daniel and Pijuan, each carrying a package, took separate cabs to Pijuan's apartment.

The apartment was somewhat unusual in design. It consisted of a living room and bedroom, and a small combination kitchen and dining room. It did not include a toilet. This facility was down the hall and was shared by Pijuan with the other tenants on the same floor. There was, however, a bathtub in the kitchen, which was covered with an enameled top. When the bathtub was not in use for personal bathing purposes, this enameled top served as a counter, storage and work area. The two Christmas packages were placed on it.

Pijuan and Daniel were now physically exhausted from their labors. The Christmas dawn was breaking, so they slept in Pijuan's apartment until around noon.

When they awoke, they still faced the frightening prospect of removing Jackie's head and torso from Daniel's apartment, where it had rested for what was now some eight hours. Access to a car still seemed to be their desperate need of the moment, a need that was not fulfilled until 1 A.M. the following day, when Pijuan arranged to borrow an ancient Oldsmobile from a fellow Puerto Rican who lived in the Bronx. He used the ruse of having to go to the airport to meet his sister who was arriving from San Juan.

After the loan of the car was arranged, a new hitch developed. Pijuan had never learned to drive an automobile. He set out in search of Daniel who could drive, and who, on Pijuan's specific instructions, had accepted invitations to two different Christmas parties during the evening.

Pijuan tracked Daniel down, and the two of them returned to the Bronx, but the car would not start. The battery was dead. They paid a cabdriver one dollar to push them to a service station, where they bought a new battery.

It was almost 3 A.M. Monday, December 26th, before they reached Daniel's apartment. It was a legal holiday since Christmas fell on Sunday. In less than five minutes time, the two men were headed uptown to Pijuan's apartment, Daniel driving, Jackie's torso wrapped in the linoleum felt padding on the passenger's seat beside him, Pijuan sitting in the rear seat with Jackie's head gaily wrapped in a separate package on the seat beside him.

These two additional packages were placed on the enameled cover of the bathtub in Pijuan's kitchen. The two men said a final good-bye, Pijuan assuring Daniel that he would take care of everything else, and that there was nothing to worry about. He also gave Daniel some specific instructions, which Daniel attempted to carry out. Daniel reassured Pijuan that Pijuan could count on him. Daniel would never under any circumstances admit to anyone what the two of them had done.

Since legal entanglements were foreign to their experience, neither Daniel nor Pijuan knew about or reckoned with that compulsive trait in all human beings to confess guilt of wrongdoing.

Daniel could not bring himself to return to his apartment. It was now a little after five in the morning. He called on Michael Bakaliaos, a native of Cyprus whom Daniel had met a year earlier in a restaurant where Bakaliaos worked as a counterman. Since they were both of Greek origin, they struck up a friendship and visited each other from time to time.

Bakaliaos got up and prepared coffee and toast. Later on they went out to a nearby restaurant and had a large breakfast.

They were now within two blocks of Jackie's legal residence on West 95th Street. Following Pijuan's instructions, Daniel stopped by the apartment and talked to one of Jackie's legal roommates. He asked if she had heard from Jackie, and when she replied in the negative, Daniel said that he presumed that Jackie had gone home to Lebanon, Pennsylvania, for the Christmas holidays. Daniel and Bakaliaos walked around town for two hours, looking at the Christmas decorations in the shop windows. They finally decided on a show at one of the many theaters near 42nd and Broadway.

At five o'clock the two men were in Daniel's apartment where Daniel prepared an exotic capon dinner. Just as Bakaliaos was leaving, Daniel, without any preliminary explanatory remarks, blurted out, "Jackie is dead."

Bakaliaos was immediately suspicious, but not wanting to become personally involved, did not ask any questions at all. He did agree to permit Daniel to take two suitcases of Jackie's clothes and personal effects to the storage room of his apartment house.

The following day, Tuesday, December 27th, Daniel put the rest of Jackie's possessions in two boxes and took them to the storage room at the Miller Harness Company. He placed a telephone call to the H. Dworkin Company to see if Jackie was there, and when told that she was not, he asked if she had reported in sick.

Two days later, he made a similar call. This time he talked to Jackie's immediate supervisor, and that evening he telephoned Jackie's father in Lebanon, Pennsylvania, to inquire of her whereabouts. Her parents had received a letter dated December 22nd, wishing them a Merry Christmas and a Happy New Year, and explaining that she would not be home for the holiday season.

The following evening, at approximately seven o'clock, Chester Smith, Jackie's father, arrived in New York by bus. He went immediately to Daniel's apartment, and the two of them went to report Jackie missing.

Daniel had a ready explanation. He had prepared Christmas Eve dinner for himself, a doctor friend, and Jackie. After the doctor left, he fell asleep on the couch in the living room. When he awoke at four the following morning, Christmas day, Jackie was gone. This was not surprising since she did this more often than not when she visited him, returning unescorted to her own apartment.

Detective Vincent Satriano of the 24th Precinct detective squad, took Jackie's father and Daniel to Jackie's apartment, where her two roommates were questioned. All of his detective instincts told Satriano that something was drastically wrong with Daniel's story.

Chester Smith and Tom Daniel returned to Tom's apartment. Just before Jackie's father left to board the bus for Lebanon, he said, "Tom, are you leveling with me?" He remembers that tears welled up in Daniel's eyes when he replied: "Yes, Mr. Smith, I am leveling with you."

Hindsight readily explains why the police made no progress in their search for the missing Jackie Smith; late at night on January 10th, Tom Daniel was picked up for additional questioning.

He first adopted the role of the irate citizen whose constitutional rights had been violated. This merged into a story that Jackie had stabbed herself to death with the knife from the kitchen after an argument about marriage. He could not rule out the possibility, he continued, that someone had sneaked into the living room while he was in the kitchen and stabbed her.

Regardless, he had wrapped her body in a large canvas bag and taken it by taxi to the area around 95th Street and Riverside Drive, where he threw it into the Hudson River. He led several detectives to the exact spot where he claimed the body had disappeared in the racing waters. He was so convincing in this description that the Harbor Squad was called to grapple for the body. Finally, after being confronted with the fact that the Harbor Squad could not come up with the body, Daniel buckled under. He told the police about the abortion, and involved Leo Pijuan.

Pijuan made no attempt to mislead the police and readily described his participation, with all its gruesome details.

After the four packages of Jackie's disjointed, dismembered body had reached the enameled bathtub cover in his kitchen, he had set out to fillet it into small pieces, employing all the manual dexterity and finesse of an accomplished surgeon.

As the larger members of the body were skillfully reduced to smaller pieces, each was wrapped in a gay and decorative piece of Christmas wrapping paper. Some were yellow, some red, some green, some silver. There were pastels and floral patterns. One piece was a reproduction of a manger scene, with the shepherds and the Wise Men kneeling in front of Mary, Joseph, and the baby Jesus.

There were some thirty packages in all.

Pijuan's neighbors in the apartment house were not startled to see him leave his apartment from time to time, carrying three, four, and as many as six Christmas packages. His generosity with his friends was a trademark to all who knew him.

The litter of post-Christmas debris saturated the city, so that the garbage trucks could never keep on top of it. Thousands of garbage cans were full and overflowing, their lids gaping open like the suit of a gluttonous man who had ingested a great turkey dinner. As Pijuan would pass a garbage can, he would casually drop in a single package, none within three blocks of his own apartment, and none more than eleven blocks away.

Jackie's head, wrapped in blue-green, shimmering foil, was the last package to be disposed of. This was three days after Christmas, on his way to work in the operating room of the Lincoln Hospital in Brooklyn.

Not even a tiny trace of Jacquelyn Louise Smith's body was ever recovered. It, like the physical remains of the aftermath of every Christmas, was consumed in fire and smoke at the city's great incinerators.

It should be added, parenthetically, that although experts from the New York Police Crime Laboratory meticulously combed both Daniel's and Pijuan's apartments, applying every known test for blood and for other human residues, none of the tests were positive. There was literally nothing left of Jackie Smith's body, nothing to attest to the fact that she had ever lived on this earth.

"Sure," Dr. Helpern explained to the detectives after hearing Captain Hannigan's negative report, "what Daniel and Pijuan describe is medically and physically possible."

"Then we can't make a homicide case," Captain Hannigan said plaintively, echoing the thoughts of all those involved in the investigation.

"Now wait a minute!" Dr. Helpern interrupted. "You can make this homicide case. Just don't get sidetracked by tangents and false issues."

"But we don't have a body," Captain Hannigan continued to protest.

"You don't need a body," Dr. Helpern replied again. "Let's analyze what it is that you have to prove in court. You only have to prove two things."

"But what about the corpus delicti?" one of the detectives insisted skeptically.

"That's a legal question for the D.A.," Dr. Helpern replied, "but my gratuitous advice is to go interview Dr. Mireles as quick as you can. I think you can prove the corpus delicti through him."

They did prove the corpus delicti at the trial through the testimony of Dr. Ramiro Mireles, together with that of Dr. Helpern.

The corpus delicti (the body of the offense; the essence of the crime) means nothing more or less than the elements of any predefined criminal offense, whether it be burglary, robbery, arson, or murder. It does *not* mean the body of the victim in a homicide case. In felonious homicide, the corpus delicti consists of two separate but necessary elements: first, the fact of death; and second, the criminal means or criminal agency that caused the death.

The applicable New York statute, Section 1041, spells out the quantum of proof necessary: "No person can be convicted of murder or manslaughter, unless the death of the person alleged to have been killed, and the fact of killing by the defendant as alleged, are each established as independent facts, the former by direct proof and the latter beyond a reasonable doubt."

The New York statute is nothing more than a legislative restatement of the common law which grew up through the centuries. In several early cases, an accused who confessed to murder was convicted and executed, only to have the supposed victim reappear alive and hearty sometime later. It was then too late to attempt to find out why the executed defendant had given the spurious confession. The rule evolved that the fact of death could not be established solely upon the confession of the accused; the New York statute does little more than restate this specific rule.

Proof of the fact of death is much simpler in the conventional case where a coroner, medical examiner, doctor, or law enforcement officer can view the dead body, but this was not the conventional case.

Without the testimony of Dr. Mireles, Asssitant District Attorney Herman would have been hard put to establish the corpus delicti; but Dr. Mireles had seen Jackie Smith on the couch in Tom Daniel's apartment on Christmas Eve, and he had pronounced her dead. He had also seen and heard enough to testify to the facts from which the ultimate conclusion could be drawn that an abortion had been attempted.

Dr. Mireles' testimony supplied a note of comic tragedy. When he rushed into the room and took Jackie's limp arm in his hands, he instilled a ray of hope in both Daniel and Pijuan.

"She will be all right," he said. "She have a good pulse."

Their joy, however, was short-lived. He explained his error from the witness stand:

Q. Tell us what happened after you saw this defendant Daniel in the doorway of his apartment?

A. The door was open and I walked in; and due to the fact that they told me on the telephone what was going on, the first thing I did, I went to feel the pulse of the girl, which at that time I thought she had a pulse; *but what I felt was my own pulse.*

But Dr. Mireles' testimony still fulfilled the requirement of the statute that *direct* proof be made of the fact that Jackie Smith was dead. The second element of the corpus delicti, the criminal agency of Tom Daniel and Leobaldo Pijuan, was supplied by Dr. Helpern.

Deputy District Attorney Herman asked Dr. Helpern a hypothetical question which ran for thirty-three minutes. In it he summarized all of the State's evidence that had been presented up to that point. At its conclusion, he continued:

Q. Can you, with reasonable certainty, give us the cause of death of the girl, Jacquelyn Smith, pursuant to and upon the basis of the hypothesis which I have given you?

A. In my opinion this girl died as the result of the abortion that was performed on her.
Q. Will you give us the basis for your opinion?
A. My opinion is based on all of the circumstances which you described in the hypothetical question, all the procedures that were carried out, and the fact that this girl was seen dead by a physician under circumstances that force me to conclude that the death resulted from the abortion that was performed. With regard to the precise medical cause of death, it is my opinion that the death occurred because of an overdose of sodium pentothal solution which she received.
Q. Please continue, Doctor.
A. I cannot rule out the actual procedure of the abortion itself, the curettage which was done, attended by hemorrhage, and all of the things that go along with that procedure. From the information which you supplied me in the hypothetical question, the injection of the sodium pentothal very well explains the death. I said originally that the death was caused by the abortion. In other words, within the area of that abortion, either the sodium pentothal alone, or the scraping of the uterus and the hemorrhage, something transpired that produced death.

Leobaldo Pijuan, the scrub nurse, had absorbed considerable knowledge of the actual techniques of surgery from his observations in the operating room. He was obsessed with the need to maintain sterile and aseptic surroundings. Unfortunately, however, as is often the case of a little knowledge being a dangerous thing, he knew absolutely nothing about the processes of anesthesia. He had injected a full liter, a little over a quart, of 9 percent sodium pentothal solution into Jackie Smith's vein, enough anesthetic for at least ten, and possibly fifteen operations. He had also gravely compounded his ignorance. Before beginning his procedure, he added a half-gram of pentothal powder to the solution he stole from Lincoln Hospital. This doubled its strength, so that Jackie received enough anesthetic for literally twenty to thirty operations. The fifteen-minute sleep that he promised her reassuringly before she agreed to take off her clothes and lie down on the couch in Daniel's living room was preordained to be her final sleep.

The drug totally paralyzed the vital respiratory and circulatory centers in the brain, irreversibly interrupting her oxygen cycle. In all probability, Jackie Smith died shortly after Pijuan announced to Daniel: "Everything is finished." The only practical result of including Dr. Mireles in the action was to simplify the district attorney's task of proving the corpus delicti.

Midway in the trial for first degree manslaughter, Leo Pijuan changed his original plea of not guilty to guilty, and testified for the State against his codefendant, Tom Daniel.

Daniel's performance on the witness stand was painful to watch. During his four-month confinement in the Tombs, his weight had dropped from 170 to 130 pounds. His deathly prison pallor had converted him to an eerie scarecrow, his bony Adam's apple jutting forward over a shirt collar a full two inches too large. At times he seemed demented, grimacing and laughing and making other inappropriate responses to serious questions.

To say that Daniel did not aid his own cause, if he ever had a cause, is a grave understatement. In response to a motion for a mistrial, presiding Judge Schweitzer showed clearly how Daniel affected him:

MR. DIANA (one of Daniel's attorneys). I regretfully move for the withdrawal of a juror in this trial, due to remarks made by the Honorable Mitchell Schweitzer, outside the presence of the jury, in reference to his personal feelings toward the defendant, showing great personal prejudice and bias. We have fears that in case there should be a conviction, the sentencing of the defendant will be prejudiced by the personal feelings as expressed by the judge's remarks.

THE COURT. That's correct, sir; I indicated that when you wanted to talk to me. I requested that the defendant be taken back to the pen, as he was sitting about two feet from me; and I couldn't stand his presence at that moment.

Both Pijuan and Daniel were sentenced to long prison terms. Pijuan would never realize his ambition to attend medical school eventually and become a great surgeon. Perhaps the greatest story that would ever come Daniel's way would involve his own personal episode with Jackie Smith, but great philosophic books are seldom cut from such cloth.

The Jacquelyn Smith case, which some reporters labeled the

"Christmas package" case, is another of Dr. Helpern's favorite teaching tools.

"It's incredible," he says, "the relatively small number of people who can cut right to the center of a problem without getting sidetracked by tangents and trivia. One of the wisest of the old aphorisms is the one that says: 'He can't see the forest for the trees.'

"Take the Jackie Smith case. When I got over to the 24th Precinct, the police were wringing their hands and cursing the law. They were mesmerized by the erroneous belief that you can't prove a murder case if you don't have the victim's body. It had developed into a kind of group hypnosis, and one officer would simply reinforce the other's mistaken idea by saying: 'What in heaven's name can we do? We don't have a body.' No one had stopped to cut through the trees and get around the trivia to analyze just exactly what corpus delicti meant, and what it took to prove it. This, of course, is primarily a legal question for the D.A. Still, the case illustrates the need for sufficient training of the police, coroners, and medical examiners so that they can gear their investigations to the law's needs. An awful lot of cases get all garbled up simply because the different people involved in the different steps and roles in this thing we call the administration of justice simply do not know what the law demands. It isn't the law that is at fault. It is the failure to understand the law and the exact, precautionary, procedural safeguards it correctly imposes."

The case also opens up the entire spectrum of philosophical discussion of abortion, therapeutic and otherwise.

"I have my own personal opinions on abortion," Dr. Helpern says, "but because of my official position, I do not think it is appropriate for me to volunteer them until they are officially asked for. There is quite a movement under way in various parts of the country to amend the abortion laws, and I am entirely familiar with all of the pros and cons that are being advanced.

"At one extreme, you have those who say that abortion should be treated just like any other elective surgical procedure on the part of the woman who is pregnant. If she doesn't want to bear the child, no matter what her reason, she should be able to go to a hospital and have the pregnancy terminated by standard, medically accepted techniques. It is more 'sinful' or 'morally wrong' to force a woman to bring a child that she doesn't want into this world, or that has an almost certain chance to be deformed or mentally retarded because the mother has been the victim of German measles or exposed to a toxic drug, or some other disease, than it is to terminate the pregnancy early in the game.

"Then you have those who hold to the traditional attitudes and assert with righteous indignation that any abortion, at any time, for any reason must be considered murder from all points of view, morally, religiously, and legally.

"Regardless of the philosophical opinion you hold, I don't think that anyone can dispute the practicalities of the situation. An unwanted pregnancy develops into quite a traumatic event. It has a certain urgency that causes panic, and action based on panic can be extremely irrational at times. What happens under the present laws is that you force the pregnant woman into an illegal abortion; and then you have all kinds of serious consequences. Take these people involved in this case. No matter what you think of them, I don't think that any of them was basically a criminal or social psychopath, or any other vile thing like that. Daniel's attorney argued that he was a 'victim of circumstances, caught up in a situation not of his own making.' Well, I can't exactly buy that right across the board; but there is a shred of truth in it. Neither of them started out to kill Jackie Smith; but both were ignorant of all the dangers and risks involved."

How many times does a tragedy like the Smith case happen each year?

"Nobody knows the answer to that question," Dr. Helpern continues. "You get all kinds of estimates that a minimum of one million criminal abortions are performed, but who knows. It may be two million, or three million, or five million. It isn't a subject that particularly lends itself to accurate statistical analysis. We only see the ones that result in death; but we see plenty of those. We have a standing rule in our office to make a careful examination of the uterus of every woman we autopsy who is of childbearing age.

"You see, what most people do not realize is that the human body is so constructed that anything capable of successfully terminating a pregnancy is also capable of causing a woman's death. There just isn't any easy way to terminate a pregnancy, although just about everything under the sun has been attempted at one time or another.

"Even curettage, the surgical scraping of the uterus, which is what Pijuan attempted, requires considerable surgical skill. While the uterus has great powers of stretching, the uterine wall offers little resistance to a curette or surgical instrument. It's easy to push the curette right through the upper end of the uterus, directly into the abdominal cavity. This causes hemorrhage and opens up a direct route of infection that leads to a generalized peritonitis, which moves very fast and causes an untold number of deaths. Still, abortionists have tried to scrape out the uterus with wires, coat hangers, hatpins, ice picks, lead pencils, forked sticks, plastic toys—anything that is long and rigid enough to be shoved up through the vagina to reach the uterus.

"Then they have tried to pack the uterus with all sorts of caustic and irritating products such as gauze saturated with iodine, slippery elm sticks that swell up when they get wet, and soapy pastes that contain potassium iodide and other chemicals. They have tried all kinds of douches such as potassium permanganate tablets dissolved in water. These may start serious bleeding in an hour or two, or the poison may be absorbed into the bloodstream to cause extreme kidney damage and a final collapse of the circulation, which results in shock and death.

"Even air is dangerous. We recently had a case of a woman who inserted the tip of an atomizer into the uterus and pumped a considerable quantity of air into the cavity. She died within a matter of minutes from a large air bubble that entered one of the veins and made its way to the heart and lungs. This is called air embolism. The bubble acts just like a plug or clot, and it can cause a very rapid death.

"Any woman contemplating an abortion should also realize that for some reason, many abortionists are impassive butchers. I remember a case where the abortionist perforated the young woman's uterus, and yanked four feet of intestine down into the vagina. He then cut off the projecting length of intestine so that it would not hang outside the body, inserted a handful of sulfadiazene tablets in the vagina, and sent his victim home where she was found dead in bed a few hours later.

"There simply aren't any 'pills' that have the magical powers of producing a safe and easy abortion. If there were, their inventor would be richer than J. Paul Getty. Anything that will cause an abortion can cause death; the pathetic thing is, a lot of these things that are tried will cause death long before they will produce an abortion. Women have tried all sorts of drugs—castor oil and quinine, ergot which causes muscle contractions, apiol, and other drugs that irritate the genital tract, such as cantharides or Spanish fly. Many of them die before they abort. It all makes for a terribly dangerous, pathetic, and nonsensical situation."

The Smith case invariably leads into a discussion of deeper significance. Dr. Helpern is frequently asked to explain Pijuan's reactions and motivations which permitted him to calmly and coldly dissect and dispose of Jackie's body.

"Well," he begins, "the point is that nobody knows just what Pijuan's experience was. No person can ever have or really share another person's reactions or experiences. What each person sees, or feels, or encounters, or interprets is his and his alone. We may try to speculate on what we think the other person is experiencing, but that is as far as we can go. We simply cannot participate in the other man's view. This is where an awful lot of mistakes in measuring human motivation take place.

"It's easy to say 'Oh, yes. That man is motivated by hate, or love, or jealousy, or greed, or fear. Pijuan got rid of that body out of terror. He did not want to get caught. He was completely stoic. He was a cold, calm S.O.B. without any feelings at all.' Or, 'Daniel was a much warmer human being and entitled to more sympathy and understanding because he almost got sick and had to go into the bathroom while Pijuan began his dissection.' The fact of the matter is that no one knows just what their individual reactions and motivations were, because no man can have another man's experiences. I remember asking Pijuan if he used the sink in his kitchen for his dissection. 'Oh, no,' he answered with great indignation. 'That would not have been sanitary. I used the bathtub.' Now, how do you interpret that?

"I once heard a professor of philosophy give this explanation of human motivation: 'This thing we call mind, or intellect, or personality, or reason, or spirit, or soul, has to be a product of the human body. You can view the brain as a great computer, the most elaborate and complex computer that has ever been contrived. The way it functions is the result of its physical construction—the 'hardware' as the computer people phrase it —coupled with what is put into it, what is stored, and what can be retrieved. What comes out is the result of the 'hardware,' the input, the storage, the retrieval. We can only look for the end results of these products, and we label them mind and personality.

" 'You can't see this thinking process take place. You can see only the tangible results. You can look at one man's brain at autopsy and find the most horrendous damage, and wonder how he could even live, much less think. But you get a history that he was mentally sharp and alert, and that he functioned well, right up to the time of his death. Then, you see another brain that appears to be in perfect physical condition. Its rich blood supply is unimpaired. There are no signs of atrophy or any other disease condition, but this man's history is that he spent the last twenty years of his life in a convalescent home, completely senile and unable to take care of his own physical needs.

" 'But, somewhere in this cycle of 'hardware,' input, storage and retrieval, processes take place that we have labeled motivation and reaction. Together, they produce intangibles which we have also labeled mind, intellect, spirit, soul, and personality. Unfortunately, centuries ago, we in the Western world attempted to separate the mind from the body, and it was probably a serious mistake. There is now a respectable body of medical opinion that is leading us back in the other direction, to treat the mind and the body as a unified, inseparable whole.'

"This is one man's philosophy that apparently satisfies him. There are, of course, other beliefs for other men.

"If the mind is the product of the body, and if each human body is separate, individual and special, then the separateness of each individual man is multiplied a thousand times when you realize that each and every one of his mental processes is his and his alone."

Dr. Helpern is still wondering what happened to the fictional lady in London and her twenty-five pounds of chocolates. During the pressures of the next few days after Captain Hannigan's call, his copy of *The New Yorker* disappeared, probably making its way to the garbage can and the city's great incinerators.

CHAPTER 6

"We All Know Periods of Frustration"

The final autopsy protocol on Jeanne Porter Bowens began: "This is the body of a well-developed, well-nourished, white male weighing 125 pounds and measuring 5′ 7″ in height."

There had been considerable confusion at the beginning of the procedures, and one of Dr. Helpern's young assistants had summoned him to the autopsy room for his opinion.

"Chief," he said excitedly, "we have a real weird case down here. You'd better come take a look at it."

When Dr. Helpern reached the autopsy table, he viewed the body of a shapely, brown-haired young lady. The facial features were delicate and symmetrical. The legs were pleasing, trim, and properly tapered. The breasts were full and well-rounded, perfect in every aspect except one; and Dr. Helpern's trained eye immediately picked up the inconsistency. Still, in life this body would have appeared as that of an unusually attractive and well-proportioned young woman.

"I see what you mean," Dr. Helpern said almost immediately, after his quick inspection of the external structures of the body.

"How did you pick it up so soon?" the young assistant asked him incredulously.

"You see," Dr. Helpern answered, "the nipple areas of those beautiful breasts are just a little too small to be for real."

Dr. Helpern stood by as the young assistant proceeded with his examination which produced the protocol:

The hair is dark brown, very long, and has a permanent wave. This permanent wave is in small ringlets, and the hair is worn in a female fashion. It contains hairpins. On the right ear, there is a pearl earring which goes through a perforation in the right ear. The left ear is also perforated for an earring. The eyebrows are plucked; and there is a cosmetic that is black which outlines the eyebrows in an arch fashion. There is also a cosmetic lining the lower edge of the upper eyelids; and there is a black cosmetic on the eyelashes. He is wearing lipstick and a powder on the face. It is very difficult when one sees the face or feels it to find any beard. Whether or not there has been depilation, or whether it is close-shaven with an electric razor is not known.
The breasts are of the female type, and this is secondary to plastic surgery. Beneath each breast is a thin-line transverse scar, and inserted beneath the breasts are conical foam rubber prostheses. On examining the breasts further, there is found to be fluid collected around the sponge rubber in the left breast; and this sponge rubber is inserted above the pectoralis major muscle and does not involve the muscle. It is lying within the subcutaneous fat.
The pubic hair is of the female type, but the hair up to the umbilicus has been shaved. The hair on the legs has also been shaved.
The external genitalia is of the female type, secondary to plastic surgery. The scrotum has been made into two labia majora, and these are loose fitting. The urethra is in the same place that one would find the female vulva, and there is a small vagina which is in the proper place. This vagina only measures 1 inch in depth. The penis has been removed and the testicles have been placed inside the body in each inguinal canal.
On the inner surface of the right thigh, there is a rectangular-shaped area of very faint scarring where skin has been removed to be used in plastic surgery. The exact reason for this is unknown.

"What history do you have?" Dr. Helpern asked after carefully examining the two fresh puncture marks above the veins in the area just inside the right elbow.

"This girl—person—I guess we'd better say," the assistant examiner answered, "was found dead in a hotel room up on West 77th Street, at about seven o'clock this morning. This hotel room was rented to a known narcotics addict, a woman about fifty years old, and this girl—person—"

"Just say Miss Bowens," Dr. Helpern interrupted.

"Okay, Miss Bowens knocked on the door about 3 A.M. Her older friend said that Miss Bowens was quite drunk. She let her in, where she passed out on the floor. When the older woman awoke around seven, Miss Bowens was dead. She called the police, and that's how we got the body."

"Anything in the police report yet?" Dr. Helpern asked.

"Just this little bit here," the assistant answered. "They went over to Miss Bowens' room and found a bottle of pink pills which had a label bearing the name 'Schering.' The pills could be anything; but they look a little bit like cortisone. They report that Miss Bowens had been quite a successful nightclub entertainer down in Greenwich Village. She had also done very well as a prostitute. They estimated her earnings at $300 to $400 a week."

Dr. Helpern stood at the table watching critically but approvingly as the assistant put the final sutures in the body so that it could be delivered to the mortician for burial preparations. He walked out to the reception desk of the medical examiner's office, which is presided over by Miss Cavanaugh, a registered nurse who has worked for Dr. Helpern in some capacity for the past twenty-five years. She is the first contact that members of the general public have with the medical examiner's office when they must perform the trying task of looking at a dead body to identify it as an acquaintance, friend, or relative. She performs her duties with great competence, developed over a quarter of a century of contact with thousands of persons in varying states of bereavement.

"Cavie," Dr. Helpern said, "I want to talk to whoever comes in to identify Miss Bowens. Don't release the body until I have had an opportunity to see them."

Promptly at nine o'clock the following morning, Dr. Helpern's intradepartmental pathological conference was interrupted by a telephone call from Miss Cavanaugh.

"Dr. Helpern," she said, "there are two people here to identify Miss Bowens. One is a man and the other is a young lady."

"Very good," Dr. Helpern responded. "Bring them in to my office, please."

Miss Cavanaugh introduced Dr. Helpern to Miss Frances Connally and Mr. Raymond Bowens, who said that he was the brother of Jeanne Porter Bowens.

"I'd like to know what you can tell me about the major operation that Miss Bowens obviously had," Dr. Helpern said sympathetically after a few strained preliminary remarks.

Miss Connally was neatly and modestly dressed in a gray tailored business suit. Her blond, shoulder-length hair had a rolling wave that gave it a fresh, casual, windblown effect. The pupils of her blue eyes were slightly constricted so that Dr. Helpern immediately suspected that she was on narcotics of some kind. The fitted suit, if anything, exaggerated a perfectly proportioned, trim figure. Her crossed knees, as she sat in the chair in front of Dr. Helpern's desk, revealed an attractive pair of legs. Dr. Helpern considered her quite a beautiful young lady, and estimated her age to be twenty-five or twenty-six.

"Well," Raymond Bowens began after some hesitation, "a Dr. Bell in California did the operation on my sister."

"How long ago?" Dr. Helpern asked.

"Oh, I guess about two years ago," Bowens answered. "She was really born a girl except for certain things, and Dr. Bell took care of those things so that she could lead a normal life."

Raymond Bowens was slender and of less than average height. His physical features, voice, and mannerisms were feminine in the extreme. The term "swishy," which the public often erroneously associates with the male homosexual, would accurately apply in his case.

"Well, I'd like to know some more about it," Dr. Helpern said.

"Well," Raymond Bowens answered, "that's about all I can tell you. Dr. Bell was good enough to help out my sister. That's all there is to it."

"How long have you referred to Miss Bowens as your sister?" Dr. Helpern asked.

"Well, for a long time," Bowens answered, "ever since we've been in New York."

"How long is that?" Dr. Helpern asked.

"Almost four years."

"Where did you live before you came to New York?"

"In Ohio. Jeanne and I both came to New York together about four years ago. Here, this proves that she is my sister."

Raymond Bowens handed Dr. Helpern a black and white photostatic copy of an amended birth certificate issued a year earlier. It officially described the birth of Jeanne Porter Bowens, a female child born some twenty-five years ago in the State of Ohio.

"That makes her legally my sister, doesn't it?" Bowens said in a semihostile tone.

"Well," Dr. Helpern said, smiling sympathetically, "I'm not really interested in that. I would like to know something more about the operation itself."

Bowens twisted in his chair, and there was a long pause in the conversation.

"Well," he said finally, waving his hand and gesturing toward his companion, "why don't you ask Miss Connally. She's had the same operation."

Yes, Miss Connally answered, she had indeed gone through the same operation as had her friend Jeanne Bowens. Both operations were performed by the illusory Dr. Bell in California, and at about the same time. She went on to explain the surgical and hospital procedures involved, perhaps protesting too much, Dr. Helpern thought, the great happiness which the operations had brought, both to her and to her friend Jeanne Bowens. The two girls had shared an attractive apartment in Greenwich Village. Miss Connally was employed, at a salary of $600 a month, as an executive secretary by an internationally known firm whose imposing building was located near Grand Central Station.

Dr. Helpern now observed her more closely. She had an air of efficient confidence. Her voice, although in the contralto range, was even and pleasant, almost musical. Her vocabulary appeared to be extensive, her grammar and syntax perfect. Dr. Helpern concluded that she could well be a highly competent executive secretary.

"How long had Jeanne Bowens been on heroin?" Dr. Helpern asked.

"Well . . . why?" Miss Connally responded with a question of her own.

"We haven't run all of the toxicological tests yet," Dr. Helpern answered, "but as of right now, it would appear that an overdose of heroin was the cause of death."

"Oh, how awful!" Miss Connally responded. "I don't really think too long; but she did start running around with some people over in that nightclub in the Village, where she worked. I didn't like that at all. So this is where it ended! I knew it all the time."

"There are no other formalities," Dr. Helpern said, ending the interview on a friendly note. "You may claim Miss Bowens' body and do whatever you wish with it."

Six months passed by. Dr. Helpern's energies were directed toward the curriculum committees of the Cornell Medical College and New York University Medical School. He has been lecturer in legal medicine and at present is Visiting Professor of Pathology at Cornell. Since 1933, the Chief Medical Examiner has been Professor and Chairman of the Department of Forensic Medicine at New York University, and Dr. Helpern has held this post since 1954. He asked for a formal course of instruction in forensic medicine at Cornell and an increase in hours of the lecture course at NYU from eight to twelve. To date, his requests have been pigeonholed.

The entire subject is treated on an electric basis. Nothing is mandatory. If a medical student is sufficiently interested, he may attend the lectures at his discretion. He receives, however, nothing in the way of credit or a grade in forensic medicine. If the student feels that his schedule is too crowded to permit him to attend the lectures, he ignores them entirely. Regrettably, the pressures of medical school are usually so great that the student does not voluntarily assume any obligations which are not absolutely demanded for his successful completion of the curriculum.

New York University is an exceptional school in that it does offer a formal program in forensic medicine. Most of the other ninety accredited medical schools in the United States ignore the subject entirely. Only the barest percentage of medical students who graduate in the United States today ever get sufficient exposure to forensic medicine to even know what the subject covers.

Yet these are the men who are called upon in communities all over the United States to determine whether a bullet wound is a wound of entrance or a wound of exit; whether bruises about a deceased's neck are consistent or inconsistent with some police officer's theory of manual strangulation; whether a burned body was dead or alive at the time of the fire; whether a newborn infant found in a garbage can ever breathed or was stillborn; whether a body found submerged in water drowned or was dead before it was thrown into the water; whether cuts and other marks on a body are consistent or inconsistent with a theory of suicide; whether death from a heart attack occurred before an automobile accident and caused the accident, or whether the accident occurred first and caused the heart attack; whether a stockbroker's anxieties over a falling stock market caused his death so that his widow and children are entitled to payment under Workmen's Compensation laws; whether a workman's heart attack was caused by carbon monoxide fumes produced by a motor in the room where he worked; or whether any one of a hundred other things took place in this whole great area of death that may control the happiness, liberty, peace, and financial security of the living who are left to deal with the trauma of death.

The profession of medicine is far more interested in diagnosing and treating the living than in worrying about how the living ultimately die. The healers are called upon to heal, so they must be taught healing. Death itself is an admission of failure of the healing art. How much simpler to "let the dead bury their dead," and be "forgotten as a dead man out of mind."

Dr. Helpern is weary and impatient at such a shortsighted, head-in-sand philosophical approach to the subject of death, for death is a vital subject because of the manner in which it affects the living. He works with death only in the present tense, never in the past; and if death is a subject that enters into the process of living, something about its whys and wherefores and hows should be included as a regular, required part of every medical school curriculum.

Dr. Helpern was fumbling with the keys for his office door early one morning when Miss Cavanaugh rushed up beside him.

"Dr. Helpern," she said excitedly, forgetting to say good morning, "Miss Connally is here."

"Miss Connally? Miss Connally?" Dr. Helpern responded absently. "What Miss Connally?"

"Don't you remember?" Miss Cavanaugh continued, "The friend of Miss Bowens. The one who came down to identify Miss Bowens a few months back."

"Oh, yes. I do remember," Dr. Helpern said, calling the Bowens' case to mind out of the thousands that he personally sees each year. "Miss Connally? What is she doing here? What on earth does she want?"

"You don't understand, Dr. Helpern," Miss Cavanaugh persisted. "Miss Connally is down on the table. She's dead."

Dr. Helpern deposited his heavy briefcase, took off his jacket, and slipped into his white surgery smock. He reached the autopsy room just as an assistant medical examiner was about to begin the postmortem examination. Instinctively, he looked inside the right forearm near the point of the elbow, and discovered fresh needle marks.

The autopsy on the body of Frances O'Neill Connally resulted in an autopsy protocol basically similar in almost all important aspects to the one on Jeanne Porter Bowens.

"Well," Dr. Helpern said to Miss Cavanaugh as he passed through the reception room on his return to his office, "let's do the same thing again. I'd like to talk to whoever comes down to identify Miss Connally. Don't release the body until you send this person in to me."

And at nine o'clock the following morning, Miss Cavanaugh called Dr. Helpern on the telephone.

"Dr. Helpern, a young lady is here to identify Miss Connally."

Dr. Helpern waited expectantly until Miss Cavanaugh arrived and presented an extremely attractive and expensively dressed young lady.

"We've already met, Dr. Helpern," the young lady said extending her hand. "I am Ramone Bowens."

"You are who?" Dr. Helpern asked.

"I am Ramone Bowens," the young lady responded with a trace of pique in her voice. "I met you first under the name of Raymond Bowens when I came down some time ago to identify my sister, Jeanne Porter Bowens."

"Oh, yes," Dr. Helpern replied, attempting not to look surprised. "I presume that you have also been to the Dr. Bell in California."

"Yes, that's right," Ramone Bowens answered. "Is there anything else that you want?"

"No, I guess not," Dr. Helpern answered. "You may claim the body. There are no other formalities."

Ramone Bowens turned to leave, and Dr. Helpern caught the sad, listless expression, built around the pinpointed pupils of the narcotics addict.

"There is something else," Dr. Helpern said firmly. "I'd just like you to know that I don't want to see you down here like your sister Jeanne or your friend, Miss Connally."

"Oh, you won't, Doctor!" Ramone Bowens said in a huff, before stalking out of the room.

Dr. Helpern is not so confident. He has placed a "hold" card on Miss Cavanaugh's desk. When the body of Ramone Bowens is received in the office of the Chief Medical Examiner, he wishes to be notified.

"We all know periods of frustration," Dr. Helpern says in discussing the Bowens and Connally cases. "They come upon us as the result of our work, our daily lives at home, our contacts with our spouses and children, our professional relationships and social contacts, and even at play. Fortunately, most of us are able to handle these frustrating episodes, and either do something about them or adjust to them.

"But look at these people. While none of us can actually share their experiences, their feelings, and their reactions, I think we can make the reasonable interpretation that their entire lives have been nothing but one great frustration. They attempted to cure it by one drastic, massive, dramatic operation, but it didn't actually work out. I say that because the clue here is the fact that they were all existing in the half-life, half-death, half-asleep, half-awake, halfway land of the narcotic addict. They took the irreversible gamble and it didn't pay off.

"When you get right down to bare fundamentals, you don't really cure frustration by the great dramatic plunge or break. Frustration is cured by a whole series of little things, an adjustment here, a shift there, a rearrangement in another direction. A great many people simply do not understand this. Instead of making their day-to-day adjustments so that they can roll with the punch, they look forward to the time somewhere out in the nebulous future when some unidentified dramatic event will fly down to them and magically wash away all their frustrations. It just doesn't happen that way.

"Too many people live out their entire life span waiting for this 'operation' to come along and rescue them. They do not realize that it is not coming, or that if it does come it will not be the magic transformation that they have dreamed about. These people tried to find their escape in narcotics. Others turn to alcohol. Many get trapped by a retreat into a genuine mental illness that takes them away from reality.

"Whatever the route, the result is still the same. They miss the opportunity to really live this one life that is given to them. A lot of people are afraid to die, but maybe even a lot more are afraid to live."

CHAPTER 7

"The Body Sometimes Defies the Logic of Our Senses"

"Milt," Dr. Thomas Morrissey began, "I've got a problem case."

Dr. Morrissey was a prominent internist in upper Manhattan, a longtime friend of the Helperns whom he had tracked down at one of their favorite restaurants on 56th Street. Dr. Helpern had just ordered one of his special preferences: thick, cold fillets of salmon, served in a wrapping of seasoned, jellied consommé.

Dr. Morrissey then went on to describe his patient, Randolph Hayes. Hayes was fifty-eight years old and chairman of the board of directors of an internationally known company which had offices throughout the world. He also served as chairman of the company's finance committee which held an emergency meeting Friday morning to finalize the details of a complicated stock issue, which was to go to the brokerage houses that afternoon for their approval and subsequent offering to the public. At the conclusion of the meeting, he walked a distance of three blocks to his favorite club where he was well known, and was shown to his usual table by the maître d'.

Hayes ordered a martini, which was his custom, and after the first two or three sips, began to act strangely. Although it was only about 12:15, the waiter concluded that he had been imbibing during the morning and that he was on the verge of getting drunk. Before even finishing his drink, Hayes left the table and went to the phone booth where he called Dr. Morrissey.

He told the doctor that he had a severe headache, that he had never had such a headache in his entire life. Dr. Morrissey suggested that he come right over to his office for an examination.

Hayes did not return to his table at the club, but went directly to the street, where he hailed a cab and gave the driver Dr. Morrissey's address. During the twenty-block ride, the driver believed that his passenger was drunk. He thrashed about in the back seat, mumbled in a loud unintelligible gibberish, and was unable to give the driver Dr. Morrissey's name when they arrived at the office address.

The cabdriver did not want to leave a man in Hayes' condition on the street, so he took him to the doorman of the building and asked if he recognized Hayes and knew where he might be going. Hayes had actually visited Dr. Morrissey perhaps one hundred times over the past several years and was well known to the regular doorman at the building. As the fates would have it, the regular doorman was off duty and it was a substitute doorman to whom the cabdriver presented his drunken passenger.

By this time, Hayes could barely walk. The substitute doorman and the cabdriver half-carried him to the elevator to see if the elevator operator could identify him. The regular elevator operator probably could have recognized Randolph Hayes, but it was also his day off and a substitute man was running the elevator.

The three good samaritans held the slumping Hayes against a corner of the elevator while they conferred on their next move. A psychiatrist had his office on the eighth floor of the building, so they decided they would take their problem up to him.

The three men half-dragged, half-carried the stuporous Hayes into the waiting room of the psychiatrist's office.

"Get that drunken bum out of here," the psychiatrist yelled at the two uniformed building attendants.

"But he's in bad shape," the doorman protested. "Don't you think he needs help? What should we do with him?"

"I don't care what you do with him," the psychiatrist pompously announced for the benefit of his patients. "Get him out of here and don't ever bring in anybody in that condition again. I'll certainly report your rudeness and poor judgment to the building manager."

The three good samaritans huddled again outside the psychiatrist's door. Hayes was now completely stuporous, unable to stand at all, and looking for all the world like a drunk who had just passed out. Two of the men held him up while the cabdriver looked in his pockets to see if he could find an address.

They deposited Hayes in the cab, and the driver drove him to his apartment house where he presented the superintendent of the apartment building with the pressing problem. The superintendent advanced the cabman his fare, thanked him for his courteous help, and with the aid of the doorman he carried Hayes up to his fifth-floor apartment, where they laid him on the floor in the bedroom. The superintendent assumed that he would sleep off his drunk, awake with the proper amount of guilt and embarrassment, and that Hayes would prefer never to hear of the episode again.

After the lapse of two hours, Dr. Morrissey started to worry because Randolph Hayes had not arrived at his office. He began his own investigation to see if anything serious had happened. His secretary placed several calls to the apartment where Hayes now lay passed out on the floor. She received no answer. Dr. Morrissey then talked to the elevator operator and the doorman of his own building. He became genuinely alarmed at the story they reported of the unknown drunk whom they had taken up to the psychiatrist on the eighth floor for emergency treatment. They described a man who could well be Randolph Hayes. Dr. Morrissey was finally able to contact the superintendent of Hayes' apartment building and asked him to reenter Hayes' apartment to check on him. Hayes had not moved off the bedroom floor and was in the same position in which they had left him earlier. The superintendent was worried and called in the physician who was on emergency call to the apartment house. By the time he arrived, Randolph Hayes was dead.

"What is his medical history?" Dr. Helpern asked after listening to Dr. Morrissey's story.

"Not remarkable," Dr. Morrissey replied. "He was considerably overweight, and I have treated him for high blood pressure for maybe three or four years. I know he was under terrific business pressure, and had been for the past six or eight months. In all probability he suffered a heart attack. Still, I don't think he was ever too much of a boozer. I'm puzzled by the fact that he would show up so drunk in the middle of the day, particularly after an important meeting at his office."

"Well, we'd better do a post," Dr. Helpern replied instinctively.

"That's the problem," Dr. Morrissey answered. "His wife and family are spending six weeks in Florida. I just talked to his wife. She is naturally still in a state of shock, but the one thing that she did not want was an autopsy. She says it's personally offensive to her."

"She'd rather let him go out under the cloud of dying in a drunken stupor than have an autopsy?" Dr. Helpern responded.

"I guess that's it," Dr. Morrissey said. "She might change her mind, but she won't be able to get back here until at least sometime tomorrow."

"Tom," Dr. Helpern said, "I'm going to do an autopsy. This man has been labeled a drunk. You and I can guess that he died of a heart attack, but it might have been something else."

"What about lack of consent from his wife?"

"We don't need anybody's consent. Under our law, I make the decision as to whether there will or will not be an autopsy. I'll do this one myself, and call you in the morning as soon as I'm finished."

Dr. Helpern did the autopsy. There was no alcohol in Randolph Hayes' bloodstream. The cause of death was a ruptured aneurysm in the circle of Willis.*

"A failure on the part of doctors and lawyers to understand the nature of these aneurysm cases," Dr. Helpern says, "undoubtedly causes more miscarriages of justice in both the criminal and civil courts than any other single factor. Even the

* The circle of Willis was first described by Thomas Willis (1622–1675) of Oxford in his book *Cerebri Anatome* (1664).

doctors who know what they are, do not understand what causes them or why they rupture; in some cases this can be even worse than not diagnosing them at all."

An aneurysm is nothing more than a sac or pouch or bulge in an artery. It may vary in dimension from the size of a match-head to the size of a grape, or a robin's egg in extreme cases. It may begin small and grow into sizable proportions.

To understand the exact nature of an aneurysm, it is necessary to know something of the anatomy of an artery. Any artery in the body is composed of three layers. It can be visualized as a garden hose made up of three separate layers or three separate tubes, one inside the other. The innermost layer is called the intima. The middle layer is known as the media, while the outer layer is called the adventitia. These three layers are each made up of fibers and muscles which are elastic. In the normal artery, as the blood is pumped through by the heart, the various layers of the artery expand and stretch, and their contractions help force the blood along its normal course.

The media, the second layer of the artery, is normally the strongest of the three layers. It may, however, be worn out or frayed, or a portion of it may be missing altogether. This defect in the arterial wall permits the intima and the adventitia, the other two artery walls, to bulge out and form the sac or pouch which is called an aneurysm.

As the blood courses through the artery, this sac or pouch is filled with blood, and because of its weakened condition, it is subject to rupture or to bursting. The thin arterial walls of the two other layers may simply blow out, just like an inner tube in a tire on which there is a bulge or a defective blister in the rubber. When this happens, blood escapes from the artery and causes a hemorrhage.

If the blowout results in a tiny hole, the leakage of blood may be quite slow. On the other hand, if the hole is large and substantial, the hemorrhage may develop rapidly and be catastrophic.

The circle of Willis is the anatomical name given to a group of arteries which lie underneath the base of the brain. It could just as well be called the "circuit" of Willis, since these arteries form the supply route of the blood which the brain must receive in generous quantities so that its millions of cells stay alive.

The most frequent site for blowouts of these aneurysms is in this circle of Willis, although a ruptured aneurysm can happen in any other part of the body. When they do blow out in the brain, there is no place for the seeping blood to drain. It remains in the tight, cramped quarters of the skull, building up pressure by occupying space. When this pressure becomes great enough, the vital brain centers that control respiration and circulation become paralyzed, and the person dies.

The person with the slow, leaking, seeping type of ruptured aneurysm in the brain may recover if the leak repairs itself quickly enough. If his condition can be properly diagnosed, there are surgical procedures by which the leak can be tied off and repaired. These, of course, are extremely hazardous because of the location of the aneurysm. On the other hand, if the leak is large, the blood pours out rapidly, and the patient dies before he can be prepared for surgery even in the fortuitous event that his condition is diagnosed immediately.

The premonitory signs of a ruptured, leaking aneurysm in the circle of Willis are severe headache, mental confusion, loss of ability to speak, and finally stupor and unconsciousness. They mimic exactly the symptoms of intoxication, so that the patient appears to be drunk and on his way toward passing out.

Unless these ruptured aneurysms are detected at autopsy, the death may be attributed to acute alcohol intoxication, and the reputation of the person maligned by the conclusion that he died in a drunken stupor.

Ruptured aneurysms in the circle of Willis, however, frequently produce an even more sinister result. They lead to prosecutions for murder and manslaughter which can result in the conviction of an innocent man.

An Oklahoma City case, in which Dr. Helpern and Dr. LeMoyne Snyder testified for the defense in 1961, illustrates the problem.

On December 6th, 1960, Robert Williams, George Cole, and Henry McIntyre, all students in their late teens at the University of Oklahoma in Norman, drove approximately sixteen miles from the campus to Oklahoma City, where they entered Fitzgerald's Bar. At the time, only 3.2 beer could be sold legally in the State of Oklahoma.

The three boys, relaxing from their study for final exams which they were to take the following week, ordered beer and began playing a pinball machine. John Wallace, twenty-four years of age, married, the father of two children, and a stranger to the students, was also at the bar drinking beer.

The four young men struck up a conversation, and Wallace joined the others at the pinball machine. They entered into a friendly wager of one dollar on the outcome of the pinball game. Wallace won the bet, but the three university students did not pay off immediately. There would be other games, and they were all on friendly terms. No dispute or recriminations occurred over the unpaid bet.

While the men were still playing the pinball machine, two women entered the bar, ordered beer, and were introduced to the students and Wallace by the bartender.

When the bar closed at midnight, Ed Fitzgerald, the proprietor and bartender, invited the four men and the two women to join him for a cup of coffee at a drive-in restaurant a few blocks down the street. Williams, Cole, and McIntyre got into Williams' car and drove to a parking lot adjacent to the drive-in. Wallace accompanied the two women in a car belonging to one of them, and arrived at the parking lot just before the boys got out of Williams' car. Fitzgerald drove his own car.

When Wallace emerged from the car, he was agitated and excited, cursing the three students and calling them "welshers." Without any provocation, he started swinging his fists at them and telling them that he would "show you what happens to sons of bitches that don't pay off their bets." The students did not want any part of a fight with Wallace, and continued walking toward the entrance to the restaurant. Wallace became even more abusive, and just before the group reached the door to the drive-in, he swung at Cole, hitting him in the face, breaking his nose, and knocking him down. He then jumped on Cole and continued to hit him about the upper part of his body with his fists.

At this point, Williams and McIntyre intervened, attempting

to pull Wallace off Cole. In the melee that followed, all of the men apparently exchanged blows.

Wallace and Williams finally got their arms locked together, attempting to wrestle each other to the ground, with Williams attempting to prevent Wallace from throwing any more blows. While locked together in this fashion, Wallace and Williams both fell over a metal stanchion, which was about one foot high.

Williams immediately got to his feet, but Wallace did not rise from the parking lot pavement.

The three students analyzed their situation. Ed Fitzgerald and the two women had gone directly inside the restaurant without seeing any part of the fight. The students decided that flight was their best move, so they got into Williams' car to return to their dormitory in Norman.

There was a slight drizzle falling at the time. After they left the parking lot, they worried about Wallace lying on the pavement in the rain. They circled the block, returned to the parking lot, and found Wallace in the position where they had left him. He was semiconscious, mumbling and groaning incoherently. The boys thought he was suffering from overindulgence in liquor or beer. They lifted him to his feet and more or less carried him over to the women's car in which he had arrived. They deposited him in the back seat in an upright position, closed the door, reentered Williams' car, and drove back to Norman.

Ten or fifteen minutes later, the two women emerged from the drive-in and found Wallace in the car. He was slumped down on the floor, apparently "passed out." The women returned to the drive-in to summon help, and an ambulance was called. It arrived twenty to thirty minutes later and took Wallace to a receiving hospital, where he was pronounced dead on arrival.

Shortly thereafter, the police apprehended Williams, Cole, and McIntyre, and all three were initially charged with first degree murder.

An autopsy had been performed on Wallace's body and showed no injury to the scalp or skull. It was the opinion of the examining physician, however, that death was due to a massive hemorrhage at the base of the brain. The only other injury of any consequence was a fracture of two ribs on Wallace's right side, evidently caused by the fall over the parking lot rail. There were a few minor bruises on the hand, the face, head, and side of the body.

The autopsy surgeon called in a professor in neuropathology at the University of Oklahoma Medical School. Together, they reexamined the area at the base of the brain involved in the hemorrhage, and at that time identified a ruptured aneurysm in the circle of Willis.

Up to this point, the doctors were proceeding judiciously and were to be commended for identifying the ruptured aneurysm; but there was a serious basic flaw in their medical knowledge.

They attributed the ruptured aneurysm as being a direct result of the fight. The first degree murder charge was reduced to first degree manslaughter. In the interim following the preliminary hearing, McIntyre's attorney entered into "an arrangement" with the district attorney, whereby McIntyre was given complete immunity from prosecution for his agreement to testify on behalf of the State at the trial of Cole and Williams. McIntyre did testify that while Wallace was unconscious on the pavement, the other two boys kicked him and beat him on the head with their fists.

Cole and Williams were granted separate trials, and it was in Cole's jury trial that Dr. Helpern and Dr. Snyder testified for the defense.

The prosecuting attorney, judge, jury, and the State's medical witnesses all appeared to be completely startled by the crucial portions of Dr. Helpern's testimony.

After Cole's attorney had carefully and patiently led Dr. Helpern through an explanation of what an aneurysm was, he continued:

Q. Dr. Helpern, what causes an aneurysm in any one of these arteries which comprise the circle of Willis.

A. These aneurysms are congenital in nature. By that I mean that they result from defects in the formation of the blood vessels in the brain of the embryo, and these defects are present at the time of birth.

Q. Do you mean that the aneurysm itself is always present?

A. No, I do not mean to indicate that the aneurysm itself is present, but the defect in the arterial wall is there which permits the aneurysm to develop over a period of years. The continuing pulsating flow of blood may stretch the defective arterial wall so that eventually a bulge or sac or pouch is formed. In other words, a person is not born with the aneurysm, but with the tendency for the blood vessel to develop and produce an aneurysm.

Q. At what age do these aneurysms develop?

A. At varying ages. If you examined the brain of an infant or a young child, it would be unusual to find an aneurysm. However, the stage is set for the development of an aneurysm later on. Usually, you don't see aneurysms in the vessels of the brain until the person is in his late teens; then you see them with increasing frequency over the years. You see them in the twenties, the thirties, the forties, the fifties, and in almost all age groups.

Q. Can you tell us any more about why this tendency to develop aneurysms happens?

A. In the first few weeks of the embryo's development, the circulatory system to the brain is a rather crude meshwork of vessels. Some of these dry up, while others are forming the normal circulatory system. During this formative process, some of the vessels simply do not develop in a normal manner. When this happens, the result is a congenital defect which sets the stage for the appearance of the aneurysm in later life. This is another one of those birth defects which we cannot explain; but we do know it happens. It is just like a person born with an abnormal heart or a withered limb or clubfeet or mental retardation.

Could the fight have *caused* the development of the aneurysm at the base of John Wallace's brain:

Q. Pardon me for interrupting, but does trauma or injury cause aneurysms?

A. On this particular question, all of the medical authorities who have made any study in the field at all are unanimous in the opinion that aneurysms of this nature are not produced by trauma or injury. These arteries are located deep inside the head and are well protected by the substance of the brain which surrounds them. Even if you had a penetrating, stabbing, slashing type of wound that cut open one of these arteries, it still would not produce the type of defect that you see in an aneurysm.

Up to this point, Dr. Helpern's testimony did not disagree in any respect with that given by the State's medical witnesses. Now came the critical difference of opinion as to why the aneurysm ruptured, and whether the fight could be incriminated as the cause:

Q. Doctor, all of the medical witnesses seem to be in agreement that the cause of John Wallace's death was the rupture or bursting of this aneurysm in the circle of Willis at the base of his brain. Do you have an opinion based upon reasonable medical certainty as to what caused this aneurysm to rupture?
A. Yes, I have an opinion.
Q. Will you please state that opinion?
A. It is my opinion that in all probability the aneurysm ruptured spontaneously.
Q. By "spontaneously" do you mean that the death of John Wallace was a result of natural causes?
A. Yes, that is exactly what I mean.
Q. Will you please explain the basis of this opinion?
A. In the great majority of these cases, the rupture of the aneurysm is not directly related to the unfortunate person's activity at the time. Many of these ruptures occur while the person is sitting in a chair reading, while he is at complete rest in bed, while he is sitting at his desk in an office, or while he is walking about or engaged in relaxed and pleasant activities. In other words, the rupture of the aneurysm is not associated with any unusual or strenuous activity, or with an accident; nor is it due to trauma.

All those in this Oklahoma City courtroom were perhaps even more startled at Dr. Helpern's analysis of the time at which the aneurysm ruptured:

Q. Now, Dr. Helpern, based upon all that you know and have observed about this case, and based further upon reasonable medical certainty, do you have an opinion as to when this aneurysm actually ruptured?
A. Neither I nor anyone else can say with any degree of certainty the exact moment this rupture of the aneurysm took place. It may have taken place during the scuffle. On the other hand, there is a strong probability that the rupture took place before the entire fracas actually started.

Q. On what do you base that statement?

A. On the activities and behavior of the deceased, John Wallace, as he emerged from the automobile in the parking lot of the restaurant. In most instances, when these aneurysms rupture, the person becomes agitated, excited, aggressive, and belligerent. His behavior is wild and unreasonable. He seems to lose control of himself. His social inhibitions disappear. He cannot understand what is happening to him. There is an uncontrollable tendency to violence and anger; and the person becomes combative. This type of behavior fits into the common pattern of these ruptured aneurysm cases.

Q. Then it is your opinion that John Wallace's conduct and behavior after he emerged from the car in a belligerent and combative manner is evidence of the fact that the rupture of the aneurysm occurred prior to the time that the fight began?

A. That is correct. We cannot be absolutely certain that the aneurysm did not rupture during the scuffle. It is possible that in a scuffle or in an argument, even without any blows being struck, the heart rate may increase, the blood pressure may go up, and an aneurysm which is about ready to rupture will burst sooner than it would have otherwise without this physical or emotional stimulus. I would say this: From looking at this aneurysm, and from the way it was described, its rupture was imminent.

Q. Do you have an opinion based upon reasonable medical certainty as to whether any blow or physical injury received by John Wallace could have caused the aneurysm to rupture?

A. Yes, I have an opinion.

Q. What is that opinion?

A. I am quite certain that this aneurysm did not rupture as a result of any particular blow or bruise or physical injury that Wallace received.

Q. On what do you base this opinion?

A. The rupture of an aneurysm of this nature due to direct physical trauma does not occur. The aneurysm ruptures spontaneously from within.

What about prior symptoms?

Q. And this is true even though prior to or just a few minutes before his death, John Wallace did not even know that he was suffering from an aneurysm?

A. That is correct. You are dealing with a disease process or a defect in the body which is extremely dangerous, even though its presence may not have been known to the deceased or to anyone else. In most of these cases, perhaps in a great majority of them, the aneurysm develops and exists for some time without causing any symptoms whatsoever up to the time of the rupture.

The jury debated long and earnestly before finally returning a verdict of not guilty. It was a touch-and-go situation.

"You see," Dr. Helpern explains, "this is a situation where the body sometimes defies the logic of our senses. You have a set of facts where the 'victim' ends up being struck or beaten up by another man. Almost immediately, the 'victim' slumps down to the floor and dies. It is certainly reasonable and logical to draw the inference that the blow to the head is in some way directly related to the cause of death.

"Lawyers, doctors, judges, and juries all go along with this 'logical' explanation, which is the only thing that makes sense to them. They may refuse to accept the 'illogical' fact that the fight had absolutely nothing to do with the victim's death. The real sequence of events is, first, the rupture of the aneurysm. Next, the 'victim' becomes aggressive and combative. He starts the fight. The 'defendant' or the 'accused' defends himself, or strikes the 'victim.' The 'victim' slumps down and dies a short time later. The 'defendant' is then charged with murder or manslaughter.

"It is a tricky and difficult proposition to get across. Too much depends on the courtroom ability of the lawyer and the medical witness to convince the jury of the true medical facts. The outcome of the case is really up for grabs. I have just about concluded that a ruptured aneurysm case should never, and I repeat never, serve as the basis of a homicide prosecution."

The concept of the spontaneous rupture of an aneurysm in the circle of Willis is difficult to sell. Cole's civil attorneys were scared to death of it. When Wallace's widow brought a $1,000,000 wrongful death civil suit against Cole, they recommended a $50,000 settlement rather than take their chance on trying the civil case before another jury.

Even though they were not convicted of manslaughter, Williams, Cole, and McIntyre still live under something of a stigma. Cole's family was extremely wealthy and prominent in the business and social circles of Oklahoma City. For this reason, the case attracted tremendous publicity. Its minute-to-minute developments were page-one headline items for a period of several weeks. A great many people continue to believe that Cole's family was able to pull off some type of shenanigan that resulted in their son's acquittal. This feeling was greatly enhanced by subsequent bribery scandals that rocked the entire judicial system of the State of Oklahoma a few years later, resulting in the resignation, impeachment, and subsequent conviction of two justices of the Oklahoma Supreme Court.

What of the pathologist and neuropathologist who testified for the State and gave their opinions that the fight caused the rupture of the aneurysm at the base of John Wallace's brain?

"You see," Dr. Helpern explained, "this is another example of medicine becoming so highly specialized that it gets fragmented. It's simply impossible now for the medical specialist to keep up with new developments in any field other than his own specialty.

"You see, what actually happens is this: At autopsy, the brain is removed and preserved in a formalin solution so that it can be studied separately. It is carefully labeled and delivered to the neuropathologist who may get around to looking at it two weeks later. He may be looking for tumors, or he may be writing a paper on some esoteric subject like degenerative changes in the brain as a result of apoplectic stroke. That is his great interest at the moment. He may never even think to look for an aneurysm in the circle of Willis. Sometimes they are hard to find.

"In this case, they did find the aneurysm, which had clearly ruptured; but this neuropathologist had not had enough experience, or had not studied the medical literature enough, to know what caused the aneurysm to rupture. This is where he got off base. He handled step one beautifully by identifying the aneurysm, but he stubbed his toe when he came to the next question of what caused it to rupture. He was trapped, just like everybody else, by the fact that the body sometimes defies the logic of our senses. John Wallace had been hit on the head. Therefore, the blow on the head must have caused the aneurysm to rupture.

"This same thing happens in other situations that do not involve aneurysms. For example, I remember a case where a man's brain had actually been severed from the spinal cord by a bullet. This brain was preserved in formalin and taken to a neuropathologist. The only trouble was that nobody got around to telling the neuropathologist the history of the bullet wound injury. He assumed that the brain had been separated from the spinal cord by the autopsy surgeon's knife at the time of the autopsy. He found a perfectly normal brain, and his report never once mentioned trauma or injury.

"In this age of tremendous medical specialization, forensic medicine must be considered as a separate and distinct branch of medicine. We must have highly trained men who know what to look for, and how to interpret it. Otherwise, these miscarriages of justice are not only going to continue, they are going to increase drastically."

Dr. Helpern undoubtedly has the largest personal collection of aneurysm cases that exist anywhere in the world. He has piled up over 400 of them, and has personally photographed approximately 150. The potential results in these cases are frightening.

There is the case of Albert Katz, a doorman in a swank apartment house on Park Avenue. One of the tenants had a fourteen-year-old son who was completely undisciplined, a brat in the worst sense of the word, and totally obnoxious to all the persons in the building. One rainy day, this boy persisted in roller-skating up and down the length of the lobby at full speed, even though the doorman requested him several times to stop it. After the boy almost crashed into an elderly lady, the doorman grabbed him by the shoulders, shook him, and finally slapped him with his open hand across the side of the face. The boy collapsed and died on the lobby floor before medical help could be called. The boy's parents were stunned and thoroughly indignant. They called the police and the district attorney's office, and a homicide charge was filed against the doorman. At autopsy, a ruptured aneurysm about the size of a large pea was found in the circle of Willis and was the cause of death. Because of Dr. Helpern's personal intervention with the district attorney, the charges against the doorman were dropped. His fate might well have been otherwise except for Dr. Helpern's knowledge of aneurysms, and the professional respect given his opinions by the district attorney's office.

The death of Dr. Ralph Stone is another case in point from Dr. Helpern's files. Dr. Stone was a thirty-nine-year-old physician who graduated from medical school in 1940. He moved to a small community in one of the New England states, and began to establish a general medical practice. It was a tough row to hoe, for in the days before the war not all doctors were getting wealthy; this particular community was old and staid but not particularly prosperous. Along came World War II, and most of Dr. Stone's colleagues were called into service. He was exempt because of a withered leg which resulted from a bout with polio when he was a child.

In a relatively short time after Pearl Harbor, Dr. Stone was swamped with patients, working a twenty-hour day, and earning more money than he ever dreamed possible. Mrs. Stone's brother was in the insurance business and was agent for one of the large New York life insurance companies. He was able to sell Dr. Stone on the idea that the best way to build an estate for his wife and two small children was through the mechanism of life insurance. The premiums which Dr. Stone could not have dreamed of paying six months earlier could now be made without the slightest financial strain on his household and office budgets. He took out an initial life insurance policy of $50,000. Three months later, he purchased an additional policy of $50,000, which was more elaborate in that it contained annuities and retirement benefits. Two months later, a final $50,000 term policy was added.

One Friday night, during that period when the Allies were still being pushed back on all fronts and could not even seriously consider mounting anything resembling an offensive, Dr. Stone took time out from his exhausting chores to attend the meeting of his Masonic lodge. His lodge brothers reported that he was in excellent spirits and apparently in the best of health.

The following morning, Dr. Stone's two lively children got up around eight o'clock. Mrs. Stone went down to prepare breakfast for them and to try to subdue some of their vigor so that their father could get a well-deserved rest. At approximately nine o'clock the telephone rang. From her position in the kitchen, Mrs. Stone could hear her husband in the upstairs bedroom talking to a patient. This was a long drawn-out conversation that lasted for approximately fifteen minutes. She assumed that he would be down for breakfast shortly, and prepared some bacon and waffles. When he did not appear in another ten minutes, she sent the two children up to wake him. Their mission failed, because their father was dead.

Mrs. Stone called another local doctor, who was a close personal friend. He certified the cause of death on the death certificate as a coronary occlusion, and advised Mrs. Stone that there was no need for an autopsy. The body was embalmed and taken to Dr. Stone's home town in Maryland for burial.

Mrs. Stone signed the necessary papers furnished her by her brother, so that the claim for death benefits could be filed with the insurance company on the three policies which totaled $150,000.

In the interim before the company paid out the claims, all kinds of vicious, insidious rumors fermented in the atmosphere of this small New England community. How could this young doctor, who appeared to be in the best of health and spirits the night before, and who had just completed a long telephone conversation with a patient, die from natural causes? The speculations grew in geometric proportions as they passed from mouth to ear to mouth again. One camp held that the death obviously must be a suicide. Another countered with the theory that Mrs. Stone, in some way, had killed her husband, probably by an undetectable poison which he inadvertently had told her about at some time during his medical career. Still a third legion injected a more dramatic twist to the plot. Since Mrs. Stone's brother was the seller of the life insurance policies, he obviously was involved in a conspiracy with his sister to kill the crippled doctor and enhance the family fortune. As a matter of fact, they continued, he was probably the "brains" behind the whole nefarious scheme.

Some community leader felt morally obligated to bring these "facts" to the attention of the insurance company in New York. The company backed off and delayed payment of the death benefits. The policies were worded in such a way that the company could demand an autopsy only if the double-indemnity clauses were invoked on the claim that the death was accidental. The company could not insist on an autopsy, even though there was a suspicion of suicide.

Six months went by, with the rumors running rampant. The company wrote Mrs. Stone that it was "dissatisfied" as to the cause of her husband's death. The patients who had relied on Dr. Stone's medical skills in life deserted his widow and children after his death, and refused to pay their bills. Mrs. Stone was in extremely strained financial circumstances.

Finally, her brother succumbed to the pressures of the rumor mill. He confronted her directly to ask if she had anything to hide concerning Ralph's death. When she recovered from the shock of this veiled accusation, she sat down and wrote a letter inviting the insurance company to arrange for an exhumation and an autopsy of her husband's body.

Dr. Helpern has a vivid recollection of his entrance into the small Maryland town where the exhumation was to take place. He was riding in a car driven by the death claims manager for the company. Just as they turned onto the main street, some kind of gas explosion took place underneath the street, and two manhole covers up in front of them were blown about three feet into the air above the level of the pavement.

Dr. Helpern dictated the autopsy protocol to his secretary at the grave site. Dr. Stone's heart in his well-preserved, embalmed body was normal in every respect. There was no sign of any clot or plug or anything else that would produce a coronary occlusion. When he opened the head, Dr. Helpern found a classic case of a ruptured aneurysm in the circle of Willis. In the brief interval between the time that Dr. Stone had concluded his conversation with his patient and the time Mrs. Stone sent the children up to tell him that his breakfast was ready, and while he was still lying in bed, the aneurysm obviously had ruptured. Its deadly course was so rapid and overwhelming that Dr. Stone did not even have an opportunity to call for help.

Randolph Hayes' widow, Robert Williams, George Cole, Henry McIntyre, Albert Katz, and Mrs. Ralph Stone were all comparatively lucky. The ruptured aneurysm in the circle of Willis which seriously threatened their peace of mind and, in some cases, their liberties was discovered and correctly interpreted. No one will ever know how many others have not been so fortunate. If the facts could be known, the number might be shocking.

Take the case of two young theater ushers, both in their early twenties, in a large city in the Midwest. They heard a disturbance toward the center mezzanine section of the theater one night during the performance of the feature film. When they went to investigate, they found a man in his early thirties seated near the aisle. He was thrashing around in his seat, groaning and mumbling unintelligibly, and punctuating his gibberish with profanity. He refused to leave his seat, and the two ushers lifted him bodily and half-dragged him up the steps in the mezzanine and out into a corridor. Their task was not easy. He wrenched his body from side to side, and vigorously resisted their attempts to propel him forward.

When they reached the corridor, the man had a wild, mad look in his eyes, continued his swearing, and finally swung at both of the ushers. They reacted by swinging back. One of them, and probably both, landed blows on the "victim's" head. This "drunk" person slumped down to the floor, and was dead on arrival when the ambulance delivered him to an emergency hospital. This city did not have a medical examiner's office, but operated under the old politically motivated coroner's setup. No autopsy was performed.

Both of these young ushers were convicted of second degree murder and are now serving life sentences. Some years ago, the pathetic, widowed mother of one of them came to Dr. Helpern and sought his help.

"I did all I could, but what could I do?" he says sadly. "The 'victim' had an excellent reputation. He was described by the State's witnesses as being retiring and of a peaceful nature. The jury concluded that the two burly ushers beat him to death. From the history of what took place, it appears to be a rather classic case of a ruptured aneurysm in the circle of Willis, but there is no way to demonstrate it physically. By the time the mother came to see me, the body had been buried for some five years, so that there would have been no soft tissues left to examine."

CHAPTER 8

"Death Has Created Its Own Superstitions"

"I am a firm believer in life's coincidences," Dr. Helpern often says in the course of a lecture to some interested medico-legal group. "I learned long ago that it is wise to look out for the impossible, the unsuspected, the situation that simply cannot happen, but which does happen."

His "Case of the Incredible Coincidences" began in Manhattan on a rainy Friday morning. The excavations for a skyscraper office building were being dug at the corner of 40th Street and Second Avenue. At exactly the same time, some fifty blocks uptown, the foundations were also being readied for a towering apartment house.

The construction work was performed by two separate companies, each employing a different engineering method for its footings and retaining walls.

At 10:58 A.M., one of the retaining forms in the uptown building collapsed. Allessandro Nicoli was pinned under heavy debris and crushed in the process. He was extricated as rapidly as possible and taken to the emergency room in Metropolitan Hospital.

At 11:05 A.M., a collapsing form in the downtown building project pinned Maurice Levine against a retaining wall. He was rushed to the emergency room of Bellevue Hospital as soon as his fellow workers could dig him out.

Both were pronounced dead approximately fifteen minutes after their arrival at the two separate emergency hospitals. Since their deaths were accidental, they became medical examiner's cases; and both bodies reached the medical examiner's mortuary at Bellevue at virtually the same time.

Both men were thirty-nine years of age, their bodies measured five feet seven inches in height; Levine weighed 158 pounds, and Nicoli 160 pounds. Both men had dark brown, wavy hair, brown eyes, and swarthy complexions. The one distinguishing feature of their physical appearance was Nicoli's thick, black moustache. Levine was clean-shaven.

Autopsies were performed on each of the bodies by the same assistant medical examiner, after the receiving personnel placed identifying name bracelets on each wrist. The autopsy findings were not remarkable. Both men died of the same type of violent crushing injuries that shattered bones, dislodged internal organs, and snuffed out breath. The bodies were then put in separate crypts to await routine identification so that they could be delivered to a mortician for the burial preparations.

The time element was critical, for Maurice Levine's family were Orthodox Jews. Their deep religious beliefs and rituals, which go back well over two thousand years, proscribe burial on the Sabbath, which would begin at sundown only a few hours away. If Levine's body could not be buried before the beginning of the Holy Sabbath, his interment would have to be delayed for at least twenty-four hours, and probably longer. This presented a paradox, because there is another tenet in Orthodox Jewish belief that a body must be buried, if at all possible, before sundown on the day of death.

David Kesselman, Levine's brother-in-law, was given the unsolicited duty by the family of proceeding to the medical examiner's office to identify Maurice Levine's body. He made the identification to Miss Cavanaugh, although he broke down completely at the shock of seeing his brother-in-law dead.

Levine's body was delivered to an undertaker who had been alerted to the emergency. The race against time continued all the way to Staten Island where the family had assembled to participate in the burial ritual before the beginning of the Sabbath.

Time was not a critical religious factor in the case of Allessandro Nicoli. He was a first-generation Italian and a devout Roman Catholic. The identification of Nicoli's dead body was made by a funeral director, a long-time friend of the family, as he told Miss Cavanaugh. He took the body to his mortuary in the Bronx to embalm it, and to prepare it for the Rosary and the High Requiem Mass.

It was late afternoon when Nicoli's widow, still in a state of shock, was led into the room in the funeral chapel where her husband's body rested. She collapsed completely into the arms of her male in-laws as she approached the casket. They all experienced varying degrees of shock. The carefully prepared body which they viewed was not that of Allessandro Nicoli.

Frantic phone calls and scurrying emergency investigative procedures soon immersed the Catholic funeral chapel in the Bronx, the medical examiner's office in Manhattan, and the Jewish mortuary on Staten Island. Since the casket is not opened at an Orthodox Jewish funeral service, no error had been detected when the body of Maurice Levine was put into the ground on Staten Island.

Dr. Helpern's vigorous investigation of the mix-up in the bodies of Maurice Levine and Allessandro Nicoli finally cleared the air, although no one has ever been able to explain satisfactorily how the name-tag bracelet of Maurice Levine ended up on the wrist of Allessandro Nicoli, or how Nicoli's identifying bracelet was placed around Levine's wrist. It has never happened before or since.

The Italian undertaker's mistake in identifying Levine as Nicoli is not too difficult to understand. Although he claimed to be a long-time friend of the family, he was stretching this "friendship" a bit thin in order to guarantee himself the funeral business. He was acquainted with the Nicoli family, but only casually.

Dr. Helpern was more concerned about David Kesselman's erroneous identification of his own brother-in-law.

"But you saw this body with a heavy, black moustache?" Dr. Helpern asked him. "Didn't that look strange to you? You knew that Levine didn't wear a moustache."

"That's right," Kesselman explained sheepishly, "but I had

always heard that hair grows on a body after death, and I thought this moustache must have grown after Maurice was killed. I guess I was excited, and it didn't occur to me to ask anybody about the moustache."

The bodies of Maurice Levine and Allessandro Nicoli now rest peacefully, each in its respective Jewish and Catholic cemetery, and time has assuaged the wounded feelings of the living survivors.

"The trauma of death has created its own superstitions," Dr. Helpern says, "but they are superstitions of the living, not the dead. One of the most common of these old wives' tales is that the hair and fingernails grow after death. This is not true at all, although you can readily see how the superstition got started. The skin and soft tissues of a body may shrink after death, while the hair and the nail lengths remain the same. This gives the illusion or the appearance that the hair and nails have grown."

There are a great many other beliefs that fall into this category of superstition. Some are relatively harmless, like the one that a pregnant woman who looks at a dead body, will in some way "mark" the child she is carrying. This is not true.

Others, however, are not so harmless.

Dr. Helpern was particularly disturbed about a murder case in the mountain section of one of the southern states less than a decade ago. A lean, rangy mountaineer was on trial for first degree murder. The prosecutor's evidence was overwhelming and incontrovertible. The defendant, after telling three witnesses of his plans, lay in wait for the victim, and deliberately plunged a six-inch knife blade into his chest, almost cutting the heart in two. The killing was the product of one of the traditional family feuds in the area that went back over several generations. Every ingredient of murder with deliberation and careful premeditation was abundantly present.

The prosecutor, however, had not allowed for the defense attorney's ability to exploit one of the old superstitions of death.

"Gentlemen," the defense attorney said in his closing argument to the jury, employing the oratorical flourishes of a William Jennings Bryan, "here is the knife the State would have you believe was a murder weapon. They claim it was used in the killing. I want you, Mr. Ashton, to take this knife with you to the jury room after His Honor tells you that you can go. I want you to examine it very carefully. I want you to show it to Brother Smathers and to Jim Taylor there, and to every other member of this jury. I want all of you to examine it patiently and with great care; and when you do, you are going to come out of that jury room with a unanimous verdict of 'not guilty.'

"How can I be so positive that you're going to vote 'not guilty' after you retire to the secrecy of that jury room? Because you know as well as I do that you can't wipe murder blood off a knife. You can't wash it off. You can't boil it off. You can't get it off any way. Once murder blood gets on the murder weapon, it's there to stay as long as anything is left of that weapon.

"Now when you get in that jury room and look at this knife, if you can find the slightest trace of blood on it, I want you to vote a verdict of 'guilty.' This is what you should do. But you aren't going to do that, because you won't be able to find one little drop, one little flyspeck, one little mite, one little atom of blood on that knife. This killing wasn't a murder killing. If it had been a murder killing, then you could find some blood."

The jury retired and presumably carefully examined the knife. They returned in less than ten minutes with their verdict of "not guilty."

"You don't have to charge off into remote areas," Dr. Helpern explains, "to find myths and superstitions that interfere with the medical facts of death. A lot of these are accepted by doctors who apparently have relied on 'data' furnished them by the mystery writers.

"A common misconception is that a body will not bleed after death. This just is not true. A body *can* bleed after death. True, it isn't the same physiologic process that you get during life when the heart is functioning and the blood is circulating. After death, the 'bleeding' results from a stasis or settling of the blood which is caused by gravity; but the important point is that the postmortem bleeding may look exactly the same as the 'premortem' bleeding. The doctor or investigator who does not understand this can be led into a fatal trap that distorts the entire case."

Dr. Helpern can give countless examples which illustrate his point.

One particularly sad case involved the death of an eleven-month-old Puerto Rican baby in Spanish Harlem. It started out as an "infant crib" death, one of those tragic, puzzling phenomena that claims the lives of perhaps 25,000 children each year in the United States, and for which there is still no satisfactory medical answer. The baby was put to bed around seven-thirty in the evening. As far as the parents could tell, it was normal, happy, and healthy. When the mother awoke at six o'clock the next morning and went in to check the child, it was dead.

The body was brought into the medical examiner's office for autopsy about two hours later.

"Chief," the assistant autopsy surgeon said as he called Dr. Helpern to the mortuary, "I'd like to have you take a look at this one. It could be a 'battered child' case that got out of hand, and it's now a murder case."

"The whole thing just didn't feel right to me," Dr. Helpern says, as he recalls the events vividly and in great detail. "Here you had this Puerto Rican couple in their late twenties. Her mother and father lived with them in the same apartment. This was their only child. The Puerto Ricans have the inherited Latin trait of taking care of their children and their old people with a love and tenderness that takes on the attitude of a religious duty. Still, here was this child with a two-inch gash across the back of its head that was matted with blood, and there were bruises on the side of the face and across the back of the shoulders.

"I called the father in and questioned him to see if he could explain what had happened to the child. Finally, through tears and broken English, he told me that he saw the ambulance attendants drop the body on the curb just as they were loading it into the ambulance to bring it in for autopsy.

"I called in the driver, and he admitted dropping the body and that this was what caused the cut and the bruises. I gave him holy hell! Not for dropping the child! Anyone can have an accident. What I really chewed him out for was his failure to report it. This could have led to tragic consequences.

"But here, you see, you have a pretty well-established example of wounds bleeding after death. We don't know precisely how long the child had been dead, several hours at least; but the wounds had the same gross appearance as those which are inflicted before death. The blood vessels around the bruises were engorged with blood which had 'flowed' as a result of the force of gravity. The same thing happened when the blood flowed out of the cut on the back of the head, to get matted with the hair.

"We see this happen all the time. We try to be as gentle and careful with dead bodies in our mortuary as we would be with a living person in a hospital; but occasionally, an elbow will get bumped against the side of a crypt door, or as it is transferred from a gurney cart to the autopsy table. The blood vessels break, and blood moves into the area by gravity to cause a bruise just as though the person were alive.

"I remember another case of a man in his early fifties who died while sitting in a chair in his living room watching TV. The autopsy showed a massive thrombosis which was undoubtedly the cause of death, but there was a great lump underneath the scalp at the back of the head. The capillaries and other blood vessels were engorged with blood, and it looked like we had an antemortem (before death) blow to the head to account for. This, of course, always opens up legal possibilities. Did someone hit him over the head while he was sitting in the chair watching TV? As I recall it, there was a $50,000 accidental death insurance policy on this man; so if his death was from other than natural causes, his family would be entitled to a considerable sum of money.

"We checked this one out and found that thirty minutes after the man went completely limp in the chair, a doctor arrived and pronounced him dead. While the doctor was making this examination, the body somehow slid forward out of the chair onto the floor. The doctor and the man's wife tried to lift the body onto a davenport. While they were struggling with it, the head was dropped to the floor again, and it received a hard bump. This, in all probability, accounted for the lump on the back of the head which looked for all the world just like the result of a blow received before death."

Resuscitation procedures, which are now used routinely by doctors, nurses, and first-aid technicians in an effort to reestablish heart action and breathing, can cause confusion to the inexperienced autopsy surgeon.

"It seems," Dr. Helpern explains, "that every advance in medicine almost invariably produces counter-results that are troublesome until we recognize them and learn to live with them. These resuscitation procedures can and do cause postmortem bleeding and bruising that look exactly like antemortem injuries. A pulmotor apparatus which produces artificial respiration by forcing oxygen into the lungs and then sucking out air can cause injuries in the throat area that look exactly like injuries you see in 'mugging' cases. We've had a number of cases where the police thought they had a 'mugging' on their hands; but when we got the complete history, we found out that a pulmotor had been used and that this, in all probability, caused postmortem bleeding and bruising."

In an attempt to indicate that a clear delineation cannot be made as to whether the wound was caused before death (antemortem) or after death (postmortem), Dr. Helpern has coined a new word to describe the situation. It is perimortem (*peri*—around; *mortem*—death: "around the time of death").

In cases where it can be anticipated from the history and other circumstances that the future legal problems may require a determination of whether the wound was antemortem or postmortem, Dr. Helpern insists on a microscopic study of tissue from the wound site. In life, the body begins its incredible reparative processes within hours after injury. These processes result in microscopic changes in the tissue. If they have already begun, it may be possible to conclude that the wound did take place at least several hours before death.

There is another superstition that rigor mortis causes goose pimples on the skin, and this criterion is sometimes used erroneously by investigators in that illusory problem of establishing the time of death. Rigor mortis does *not* produce goose pimples. However, it may "fix" them once they develop.

Dr. Helpern once had a personal experience with the development of goose pimples after death, so he speaks from firsthand experience. He was in the vicinity of Pennsylvania Station one night in early February, when the thermometer stood at a few degrees above zero. He was startled to glance up and see something hurdling through the air at him, to land almost at his feet. It was the body of an elderly man who had been struck by a speeding automobile at an intersection approximately thirty feet farther up the street.

Dr. Helpern bent down and quickly determined that the man was dead. The impact of the accident had literally undressed him. While Dr. Helpern stood over the body looking down at it, goose pimples formed over the areas of skin which were exposed to the cold.

"The same physiological mechanism that causes goose pimples in life causes them after death," he explains. "The skin muscles can contract after death. Many of the body's tissues continue to absorb oxygen and give off carbon dioxide long after the breathing and circulation stop."

Another myth is that if the victim of a murder gets a good look at his killer, the image of the murderer will be permanently imprinted on the retina of the dead person's eye.

"This would certainly be a great boon to homicide investigators," Dr. Helpern says. "Unfortunately, this one has even less of a foundation in fact than most of death's superstitions."

There are dozens of superstitions that deal with dreams and death. Their origins make for interesting speculation, but they are otherwise of little value.

"Some of my good Irish friends tell me," Dr. Helpern says, a mischievous twinkle filling his eyes, "that according to Irish mythology, the deceased always has a good time at his own wake. No one can prove or disprove the answer to this one. It may well be true, and I sincerely hope that it is."

CHAPTER 9

"We Are Just Beginning to Probe the Body's Secrets"

The dedication of the new building to house the medical examiner's office in September 1960, was a grand event for Milton Helpern. He was fifty-eight years old, and had achieved this physical, tangible goal of a new building after six years of his term as Chief Medical Examiner. It started as the dream of Dr. Charles Norris when the office of medical examiner was created in 1918. Dr. Thomas Gonzales had talked wistfully of new office space during the interim period when he held the post. It was Dr. Helpern's lot to see these dreams come true.

At Dr. Helpern's insistence, the dedication ceremonies were simple and were carried out with dignity but without ostentation. Mayor Robert Wagner issued a proclamation naming this second week in September as "Forensic Medicine Week" in New York City. This coincided with the meeting of the Second International Congress of Legal Medicine, Pathology and Toxicology, which Dr. Helpern hosted in New York. Seven hundred leaders in the field of forensic medicine from some forty-three countries from all parts of the world gathered to exchange ideas and to see Dr. Helpern's new physical plant.

The six-story building, appropriately housed between the grizzled old facilities of Bellevue Hospital and the modern complex of New York University's Medical School, served as an effective link between the old and the new, the archaic past and the hopeful future, the practical and the theoretical, the drab, slow-moving historical techniques and the exciting, challenging atomic age. The building with its cheerful exterior of gray brick, aluminum, and tinted glass, cost $3,700,000. Its special equipment, including 128 storage crypts, a main autopsy room with eight tables, a special autopsy room for decomposed and diseased bodies, and a still more specialized single-autopsy room for those persons who follow a particular religious belief, ran to another $700,000.

The new physical facility created the proper climate for establishing a world center of forensic medicine. Instead of treating the new building and its facilities as the culmination of his life's work, Dr. Helpern considered it only the beginning. Outstanding and revered centers of knowledge in any field come about, not from modern buildings and stainless steel equipment, but through the quality, dedication, competence, and integrity of those who utilize the physical tools available to them. Years earlier, Dr. Helpern had already assembled the nucleus for his cadre of experts who would build the reputation of this center of forensic medicine. This dedicated group, who had struggled valiantly amid the discouraging circumstances at the old Bellevue morgue, took heart at the move into the new building, and began many new research projects which they had dreamed of for years but which could not be implemented in the cramped Bellevue laboratory space.

One of Dr. Helpern's prime goals in the new building was to give Dr. Alexander Wiener an opportunity to expand his work in the closely related fields of serology and hematology. The two subjects definitely come into the field of forensic medicine.

Serology is the science that concerns itself with the reaction between antigens and antibodies. An antigen is a foreign substance which gains entrance to the body and stimulates the formation of antibodies. The antibodies are the defense mechanisms which the body creates to fight and destroy the invading antigens. Any allergic reaction such as hay fever is an example of the antigen-antibody struggle. Another example is the severe shock reaction which some people experience after getting a penicillin shot. Still another form of a "controlled" antigen-antibody fight within the body is the immunization shot given to prevent disease, such as a flu shot which many people get each autumn.

Hematology is the science of blood. Since the techniques of serology as well as some of its terminology (antigens-antibodies) are employed in hematology, the two fields overlap. The same holds true for still another highly specialized branch of medicine called immunohematology. This is the science which deals with blood diseases in which the cause is investigated and proved by studying the reactions between antigens and antibodies. These are all highly complex subjects, and only a few doctors in the entire United States devote their time to these specialty fields.

Dr. Helpern has long recognized that serology and hematology are important adjuncts to forensic medicine. The solution of a murder case may turn on the question of whether a given stain is human blood, and whether it can be identified as belonging to a specific blood group or type.

For over a quarter of a century, Dr. Wiener's tests for the medical examiner's cases and many of his research projects were carried out in a one-room laboratory-office in the old Bellevue morgue. Uncounted thousands of mothers and their children the world over should be thankful that Dr. Wiener did not give up in disgust over his limited working space. The same holds true for millions of persons who have received blood transfusions without any serious reaction. They owe their debt to Dr. Wiener because he discovered the Rh factor in blood.

Man has been fascinated with his own blood ever since he has been able to think, but it has only been a little over three hundred years since the acceptance of William Harvey's revolutionary theory that the blood circulates in the body. The classification of blood into groups or types is much more recent.

Dr. Wiener is a protégé and collaborator of Karl Landsteiner, who received the Nobel prize in 1930 for the International A-B-O system of blood grouping, which was announced in 1901. Dr. Landsteiner's discoveries opened up one of the most fabulously interesting chapters in all medical history, although a systematic method to group blood was not at all what he set out to accomplish. He noticed that certain mixtures of blood caused clumping, which is also called agglutination. The next step was the observation that some blood cells contained properties that differed from those of other blood cells. He labeled these properties in blood cells "receptors" or "antigens" or "agglutinogens."

There were also certain special properties in the blood serum, the clear fluid portion of the blood which separates from the clot and the corpuscles in the clotting or clumping process. He called these properties in the serum "agglutinins," and concluded that the clumping of the blood was caused by a reaction between the agglutinins in the serum and the antigens or agglutinogens in the cells.

The different agglutinogens (antigens) in the cells were called A and B, for the simple reason that there was no better name for them. The corresponding agglutinins in the serum were identified as Anti-A and Anti-B.

Landsteiner's A-B-O blood grouping system looks no more complex on paper than Einstein's three-letter formula ($E = mc^2$) on which the discovery of atomic energy was based.

A person with only A antigens in his blood cells was labeled Group-A; with B antigens only, Group-B; with both A and B antigens, Group-AB; and with neither A nor B antigens, Group-O. It followed that regardless of the type of antigen in the blood cells, the corresponding agglutinins in the serum were absent—otherwise, the person's own blood would clot or agglutinate. Therefore, if a person was in Group-A, with antigens A in his red blood cells, he could not have Anti-A in his serum. His serum antibodies would have to be Anti-B. This made it possible to work out combinations and tests to classify blood in its proper group or type.

The simplest blood grouping procedure divides the unknown blood specimen into two parts. Known Group-A cells (agglutinogens) are added to the first portion, and known Group-B cells to the second. The technician then observes the clumping reaction which permits him to determine the blood group. There are four possible reactions which permit the following conclusions within the basic A-B-O classifications:

Part I (A cells added)	*Part II (B cells added)*	*Blood Group*
Clump	Clump	O
No clump	Clump	A
Clump	No clump	B
No clump	No clump	AB

There are many other blood grouping procedures, and variables within each procedure. There are hurdles and pitfalls which can be guarded against only by special training and experience. Just as no person can build an atomic bomb by simply memorizing Einstein's formula, the theoretical mastery of Landsteiner's precepts does not guarantee accurate blood grouping. There are all sorts of problems in preparing the correct solutions and proper strengths of solutions, in judging reactions and the vigor of the reactions.

It was soon discovered that Group-A was divisible into subgroups such as A-1, A-2, A-3, and so on. Next came the MNS subclassifications, to be followed by the Kell, Lutheran, and Duffy systems. No contribution to the entire field of hematology has proved more important than Dr. Wiener's Rh-Hr factors, which he whimsically named for the rhesus monkeys that were used in his research. It is now possible to speak in terms of fifteen major blood groups or categories under the basic A-B-O system, and of some five hundred subgroupings or subclassifications. Up until the time of Dr. Wiener's discovery of the Rh factor, medicine simply could not explain why some babies were born "blue," and why they either died or were so mentally retarded that they never developed an intellectual age of more than one or two years. Doctors also could not explain why certain people whose blood had been typed O and who were transfused with blood that had also been typed O, suddenly developed fever, chills, kidney failure, and jaundice. They went on to die rapidly; or if they lived, they suffered permanent kidney impairment.

The medical name given the "blue" baby condition is sneezed out as erythroblastosis fetalis. It is the result of the antigen-antibody, agglutinin-agglutinogen battle that goes on within the womb of an Rh-negative mother who has been impregnated by an Rh-positive father; approximately 13 percent of all mothers are Rh negative. Medicine's technical explanation of erythroblastosis fetalis is that it is a form of anemia in newborn and young infants characterized by the presence of erythroblasts (immature red blood cells) in the blood, and by extensive destruction of the normal, mature red blood cells. It occurs in an Rh-positive infant carried by an Rh-negative mother, because the Rh substance in the infant causes the formation of the fighting antibodies in the mother which destroy the red blood cells of the infant. The presence of the immature or young red blood cells represents the attempt of the infant's body to replace the losses of its normal, mature red blood cells by calling up immature "recruits" (the erythroblasts).

Dr. Wiener devised methods of anticipating the "blue" baby emergency before it is born, so that total blood transfusion exchanges can be made immediately after birth to save the baby from death or pathetic mental retardation. The addition of his Rh system permits a more finely honed blood grouping classification, so that blood used for transfusions is more compatible between the donor and the recipient.

Dr. Wiener's extension of the basic A-B-O grouping system through the addition of the Rh factor is important not only for the preservation of life. It offers many fascinating possibilities in forensic medicine which Dr. Helpern delights in describing.

A case in point had a rather routine beginning in Hospital Gnade in Basel, Switzerland.

Konrad and Marie Mueller had been married for two years and were expecting their first baby. There was no great surprise when Marie gave birth to twin boys, because Marie's mother was a twin, as was Konrad's father. The twin births were comparatively easy and both Marie and the young boys did well. They were christened Hans and Eric a week later, when the two family clans gathered for this traditional ritual in the German-speaking part of Switzerland.

The two boys developed beautifully into robust, mischievous little devils. Marie Mueller went to Mass every morning to thank God for her good fortune in life—she had been given a kind husband who was doing well as a dealer in secondhand books; her two young sons were delightfully impish, smart, with good senses of humor, and relatively easy to manage.

As the boys grew older, Konrad Mueller was subjected to continuous kidding by his father-in-law and other members of the family because Hans and Eric were not identical twins. Anyone, they taunted, could sire nonidentical twins, particularly in two families where twins predominated, but somehow Konrad did not have the exact touch. The true sign of a man should be his ability to produce identical twins any time he so desired. The gibes and jests were always good-natured on the part of the kidders, although Konrad Mueller found them somewhat overbearing and tiresome at times.

Hans and Eric had just celebrated their fifth birthdays when their mother and father were invited by a mutual friend to the apartment of Ralf and Irene Schnug. It was the beginning of *Fasching,* that wild pre-Lenten celebration native to Munich, but also observed by Bavarians in other parts of the German-speaking world; the Muellers and Schnugs were only one generation removed from Munich.

The Schnugs were gracious and generous hosts, freely pouring schnapps and dark Bavarian beers for the six or seven couples assembled in their apartment. This particular *Fasching* seemed to be launched in classic, festive style.

Konrad and Marie Mueller were stunned, however, when Irene Schnug presented her son Willi at around eight o'clock in the evening, to say goodnight to the guests. Willi was strikingly similar in appearance to their own son Hans. The evening's celebration progressed into the hours of the following morning as the group moved to other and even more lively homes and *hofbraus.* Even though Konrad and Marie halfway enjoyed themselves, when they awoke later in the morning after only two hours of restless sleep, they decided that they must call Ralf and Irene Schnug. The Schnugs agreed to bring Willi to the Mueller home, for in the course of the telephone conversation, it developed that Willi had been born at the Hospital Gnade on the same day that Hans and Eric were born.

There was a great wrinkling of brows, and a haunting aura of doubt descended on the four parents as they watched Hans and Eric and Willi for an hour. Hans and Willi were identical in physical appearance in every respect, while Eric was totally dissimilar. Marie Mueller finally voiced the question that permeated the entire room.

"Could Hospital Gnade possibly have made a mistake?" she asked in a tone that was barely audible.

All four parents and the three boys rushed immediately to Hospital Gnade. As could have been anticipated, the director of the hospital vigorously denied even the remote possibility that Willi and Eric could have been mixed up and given to the wrong parents five years earlier.

The weeks after *Fasching* passed by, but the Muellers and the Schnugs could not dispel their depressing gloom. Together, they sought legal and then medical advice, in an effort to resolve their dilemma. Blood tests were made in Switzerland, but they proved inconclusive. The Swiss doctors used only the A-B-O and M-N groupings for their tests.

While no expert any place in the world can come up with a "positive" assertion that a child is the offspring of a certain father and a certain mother, the Swiss doctors were laboring under a limitation, as they attempted to "exclude" certain hereditary possibilities. They were working only with the fifteen major blood group systems, and not with the subgroups.

An individual's blood group is inherited from his parents. The blood pattern follows the Mendelian law of heredity and involves genes and chromosomes. This means that the heredity source of any individual's blood group must be computed by "negative" patterns. Depending upon the blood groups of the parents or putative parents, it is possible to "exclude" either one or both parents as being the father or mother of a child. This "negative" or "exclusionary" approach is accompanied by a corollary proposition which permits the doctor to say that a child "could be" the offspring of a questioned father or mother. It does not, however, permit the "positive" conclusion that the child definitely *is* the offspring of either an alleged father or mother.

Konrad and Marie Mueller, Ralph and Irene Schnug, were saddened when they learned that all of the tests performed on Hans and Eric and Willi must fall within the "inconclusive" category. They resolved, however, to make the best of the situation. They dearly loved the sons whom they were raising, but still . . . still . . . the inter- and intra-family relationships would never again be the same.

Several months passed by, and the Swiss doctor who had performed the blood tests in Basel casually mentioned the case to another hematologist in Zurich. He suggested that the Muellers and the Schnugs contact Dr. Alexander Wiener in the office of the Chief Medical Examiner of New York City. The case intrigued Dr. Wiener; within two weeks time, seven carefully labeled vials of blood were flown across the Atlantic to New York City. By using his Rh-Hr system in the blood grouping determinations, Dr. Wiener found:

Hans Mueller's blood group was $A_1MNRh_1Rh_2$
Eric Mueller was A_1MNrh
Willi Schnug was $A_1MNRh_1Rh_2$ (the same as Hans Mueller)
Marie Mueller was $A_1NRh_1Rh_1$
Irene Schnug was A_1MNRh_1rh

Working out these combinations on a chart, Dr. Wiener was able to state positively that Hans and Eric could *not* be brothers. Further, Eric could *not* be the child of Marie Mueller. Willi could *not* be the child of Irene Schnug. Willi *could* be the child of Marie Mueller, and Eric *could* be the offspring of Irene Schnug. Willi and Hans *could* well be brothers.

Dr. Wiener's carefully documented conclusions were flown back to Basel, where Swiss doctors submitted the three boys to a battery of additional tests. They found that both Hans and Willi were color-blind, whereas Eric was not. Skin grafts taken from Eric's body were rejected by both Willi and Hans, which indicated an incompatibility with the "foreign" substance from Eric's body. However, Willi's body "accepted" skin grafts from Hans, and Hans "accepted" the grafts from Willi.

By this time, the Muellers and the Schnugs were convinced beyond any reasonable doubt that Hospital Gnade had indeed switched Eric and Willi some time before, possibly at the time that Marie Mueller and Irene Schnug were discharged with their babies. The evidence, particularly that furnished by Dr.

Wiener, also convinced a Swiss court that a switch in children had been made.

Hans and Willi Mueller and Eric Schnug are now eleven years old. They, as well as their parents, seem to be well adjusted to their new family alignments. All have expressed personal thanks to Dr. Wiener for his important role in unraveling the perplexing puzzle; and Konrad Mueller is no longer kidded by his father-in-law for his inability to sire identical twins.

Rh factors in blood are only one aspect of Dr. Wiener's work. The one-room office-laboratory, where he labored for over a quarter of a century, in no way cramped his inquisitive mind. He began to speculate as to whether the individual characteristics which permitted the typing or grouping of blood might also be present in other body fluids and secretions. After years of painstaking investigation, he arrived at a positive answer. About 80 percent of all persons are what Dr. Wiener calls "secretors." This means that the same components or "receptors" which permit blood grouping are also present in the saliva, semen, perspiration, and gastric juices of these secretors. This makes it possible for Dr. Wiener to determine the secretor's A-B-O blood type, provided he can obtain a sufficient quantity of saliva, semen, or perspiration.

Dr. Wiener's ability to group semen introduces fascinating new possibilities in rape and sex cases. Semen is the viscid, whitish fluid manufactured by the male reproductive organs. It floats the spermatozoa. These spermatozoa, which are also called sperm or sperm cells, resemble microscopic tadpoles with their oval heads and flapping tails, the tail being roughly ten times longer than the head. An average of 300,000,000 spermatozoa are discharged by each male ejaculation, the climax of sexual intercourse in the male. The ejaculation fires them into the receptacle of the female vaginal canal. They would not get very far were it not for the bed of seminal fluid in which they swim and float. This semen carries the sperm cells into the uterine cavity, near the exit of the fallopian tubes, where they lie in wait for the ovum which is discharged by the female. An interesting battle takes place. The spermatozoa are short-lived, and millions are killed by the acid secretion in the vagina; but the ovum is fertilized when one spermatozoa spins its head into the shell of the egg, and a pregnancy can take place.

Approximately one teaspoonful of semen is expelled by each ejaculation. Sometimes it misses its target and lands around the pubic area of the female. It may reach the inside of her thighs, and frequently stains her clothing. When semen dries, it becomes stiff and starchy, and turns gray or white in color. Dried semen may or may not be visible to the naked eye, but there are ways of locating it, such as through the use of ultraviolet light.

One of the early semen cases involved fifteen-year-old Marian Samuels who went to a movie one Saturday night with her sixteen-year-old boy friend, Paul Monroe. When Marian did not return at her usual time, Mrs. Samuels became anxious and opened the door of the apartment on the Lower East Side of Manhattan where she and Marian lived. She heard a moaning sound from the floor below. Since the automatic elevator in the building stopped only on alternate floors, Mrs. Samuels rushed down the fire exit at the end of the hall to the next floor. She found Marian near the elevator in the hall, unconscious, bleeding from the head, with her dress torn and pulled up above her waist. Her black panties rested slightly below her thighs.

An ambulance rushed Marian to the hospital, where she remained unconscious for the better part of two days. The police assumed that she had been assaulted and raped at the time she left the automatic elevator on the floor below her own apartment. This supposition was confirmed by the New York Police Crime Laboratory, which identified the stains on her black satin panties as semen. A laboratory technician contacted Dr. Wiener to see whether he could type or group the seminal stains. The police were limited in their investigation of the case because Marian still remained unconscious, and could supply no clues that might help identify her attacker.

At the time that Dr. Wiener agreed to attempt to type the semen on the black panties, the police were holding Paul Monroe as their chief suspect. They considered his story somewhat suspicious. Although he had taken Marian to a movie on six or eight previous occasions, this was the first time he had failed to walk her directly to the door of her apartment. On this particular evening, he said that she had gotten off the bus at a bus stop to wait for a crosstown bus. The weather was extremely cold and she had insisted that he continue on to his home without getting off the warm bus to accompany her.

When Dr. Wiener concluded his tests, Paul Monroe was immediately released from custody. The reactions obtained indicated that the seminal stains came from a person whose blood was Group-B. Both Marian and Paul belonged to blood Group-O. The police then turned their attention in other directions, and apprehended a forty-eight-year-old man who was seen prowling around another apartment house just across the street from where Marian and her mother lived. Even before Marian regained consciousness, he confessed not only to her rape but to eleven similar rape cases which had completely stymied the police.

The semen grouping techniques have presented Dr. Wiener with a great many problems. He was given some rough moments by the Consuela Costa y Lima murder case.

Consuela was thirty-one years of age and employed as a maid by the socially prominent Fitch family on Park Avenue. She had a bubbling and cheerful personality, and the Fitches were especially fond of her. Consuela lived in an apartment on the West Side of Manhattan, which she had shared with her husband Carlos up until six months ago. She did not understand what the doctors meant when they described Carlos as "manic-depressive"; but she did know that he had acted strangely and was now committed to a state mental hospital. The doctors said he would be confined for at least a year and probably longer.

On this particular morning, Consuela, due at work at seven-thirty, had not arrived by nine o'clock. Mrs. Fitch became alarmed because Consuela had always been punctual and reliable in the past. She telephoned Consuela's apartment, and was even more disturbed when a man answered the telephone. The anxiety deepened when he said that Consuela had gone to work, and gave the address of the Fitch apartment where she was long overdue.

Just after this call, Mrs. Fitch learned that Carlos had escaped from the mental hospital three days earlier. The hospital's information was that he had boarded a bus for Miami.

Mrs. Fitch took her two grown sons, hailed a cab, and rushed to Consuela's apartment. They explained their concern to the superintendent of the building, who let them into Consuela's quarters with a passkey. When they entered the bedroom, they saw Consuela lying in the center of the bed. She did not respond to their calls, and they thought that she was unconscious. They immediately removed her from the bed, placed her on the floor, and began to administer artificial respiration while the superintendent called the police. Within ten minutes, police officers arrived. They observed the two boys giving Consuela artificial respiration, and joined in the operation which lasted for another thirty minutes, until a doctor arrived and pronounced Consuela dead. There was no obvious external signs of injury, and the police considered the death the result of natural causes.

Consuela's body was taken to the medical examiner's office for autopsy, where Dr. Helpern observed a few superficial abrasions on the external skin of the neck and pinpoint hemorrhages in the eyes and about the face. These alerted him to the possibility of death by asphyxia. The autopsy confirmed death by manual strangulation. The hyoid bone in the neck was fractured, and there were internal injuries in the structures of the neck and larynx.

Dr. Helpern called Dr. Wiener to the autopsy table. On examining the vulva, he had noticed that the pubic hairs were matted together by some dry, gray material which he thought might be semen. There was also a flaky, dried stain on the inside of Consuela's right thigh.

Dr. Wiener carefully collected his specimens and took them to the laboratory. He found spermatozoa when he examined the substances under the microscope, which confirmed the stains as semen. He next began his procedures for typing the semen, and concluded that it had been deposited by a man with Group-A blood. Consuela's blood was typed and found to be Group-O.

In the meantime, the police had turned up two possible suspects other than Carlos. They were released within a few hours after their blood groups were established as Group-O and Group-B, respectively.

Through the help of Miami police, Carlos was located in Florida and was eager to confess to the crime. After he escaped from the state hospital in New York, he took a bus to Miami, but he was seized with an overpowering urge to see Consuela. He boarded another bus and rode all the way back from Florida to New York. When he knocked on the door of their apartment, Consuela refused to let him in. He then went around to the rear of the house and entered their bedroom through a fire escape window. When she attempted to scream, he strangled her on the bed, after which he had intercourse with her and left her. He went directly to the bus terminal in New York and took another bus back to Miami.

Dr. Helpern explained, with some pride, to the district attorney and the police detectives in charge of the murder case, that Dr. Wiener had been able to identify semen on Consuela's body, and also to type it as Group-A. The district attorney was properly elated. This would enhance the quality of his proof against Carlos, and it would also be the first case in which the grouping of semen would be presented as evidence in court.

Carlos was returned to New York after waiving extradition from Florida, and was placed in the ward for the criminally insane at Bellevue Hospital.

A week before trial, Dr. Helpern received a frantic call from the deputy district attorney who was preparing the case against Carlos.

"Doctor," he almost screamed, "this new scientific stuff may be all right; but it's about to cost us a murder prosecution."

Carlos' attorney had found out about the grouping of the semen found on Consuela's body, and believed that it gave him a perfect defense. He was attempting to get the district attorney to dismiss the murder charge against Carlos, and threatened to call Dr. Wiener as a defense witness if the State did not do so. The problem was simply stated. At the time of Carlos' arrest, his wallet contained an identification card from the Chilean Navy in which he served during World War II. The card proclaimed for all to see that Carlos' blood type was Group-O. If, as Dr. Wiener had indicated, the semen was from a person of Group-A blood, obviously Carlos was not the perpetrator of the strangulation murder and rape.

Dr. Wiener was puzzled momentarily but not deterred. He immediately asked for a sample of Carlos' blood, which was drawn with his consent. This sample was quickly typed as Group-A.

The real error had not been in Dr. Wiener's procedures of grouping the semen, but in the procedures in Chile in grouping Carlos' blood at the time of his service in the Navy. This is not an unusual finding, because it is now admitted that between 10 and 15 percent of all blood groupings during World War II, including those that were made on service personnel in the United States Armed Forces, were made in error.

Dr. Wiener's "secretor" discovery was used in an Arizona case. A forty-five-year-old divorcée was last seen alive around 11 P.M. when she left a Tucson bar in the company of one of her many boyfriends. She was reported missing two days later by her landlady. Her boyfriend stuck to his story that he had taken her home, spent three hours with her in bed, but left her in good health except that they were both a little drunk. Little was known of the woman's past history except that she came from the "east."

Six months passed before a family prowling the desert in a jeep in search of rocks found the bones of what turned out to be a human female body of the approximate age of the missing divorcée. Desert animals had helped the sun strip it of all soft tissue. The remnants of clothing were rather nondescript, and there was nothing to aid a personal identification.

Sheriff's investigators brought in the dismembered bones, after observing that the back of the skull had been crushed. They scooped up a bucket of sand a few feet from where the head was found since it was a different color from the surrounding area. The stains in this sand proved to be dried blood in sufficient quantities to permit it to be typed Group-A.

Three days later, another family of rock-hounds found a similarly dismembered set of human bones approximately twelve miles from the spot where the first one was discovered. The two human skeletons were amazingly similar when they were assembled. On the basis of the information then available, either could have been the remains of the missing divorcée. There were no fractures or other evidence of injury in the bones of the second skeleton.

Someone suggested that the officers examine the divorcée's clothing which was still hanging in plastic sacks in the sheriff's office. The perspiration shields were removed from her dresses. She proved to be a secretor; and her "receptors" were so strong that her blood could be typed from the perspiration residues as Group-A, even at this late date.

This discovery did not, of course, prove that the first body with the crushed skull was that of the divorcée. It established merely that it "could be"; but it was enough.

Sheriff's deputies confronted a second boyfriend with the fact that the divorcée's body had been found with the head crushed. The suspect confessed to her murder. He had recognized the car of the first boyfriend at her apartment and lay in wait for him to leave. He then inveigled the woman to take a ride with him. When they reached the desert, he forced her out of the car and clubbed her to death with a tire tool.

"We are just beginning to probe the body's secrets," Dr. Helpern says with enthusiasm as he guides visitors through Dr. Wiener's laboratories which occupy space on the fifth floor of the new Medical Examiner's Building. "Ten years from now, we will look back on the Rh factors in blood, and the secretor concept in semen and sweat, and treat them as mere stepping-stones. Dr. Wiener tells me that there is no reason in the world why we cannot develop refinements and extensions in the blood grouping procedures so that each person's blood can be shown to be just as unique and individual as his fingerprints. Think what that would mean to the homicide investigator!

"I'm convinced that there are other body substances that will eventually lock a murderer to the scene of his crime in much the same manner as fingerprints now do. But we haven't even begun to think and experiment in these terms. If each man is individual and special, as I think he is, there are more individual traits and characteristics in his body that we haven't even begun to dream about."

Dr. Helpern's expression then sobers as he continues: "But the hell of it is, I don't know of a single, solitary, major research project under way any place in the field of forensic medicine.*

* Dr. Helpern emphasizes the word "major." At the present time he has scrounged money from grants and other sources to initiate research projects in infant crib deaths, coronary disease, narcotics deaths, traffic accident fatalities,

There isn't any money available to research death. I don't have any quarrel with the billions which are being spent to explore space and send people to the Moon and Mars. I do think that we are missing a bet here on earth which is a little closer to home, even though it is considerably less glamorous.

"Take this question of determining the exact time of death. We haven't made any progress with this problem since I first got into this business. The body has the answer for us, just waiting to be discovered. But who has the time or money to do it? No one, absolutely no one!"

"Take toxicology," Dr. Helpern continues as he guides his guests into Dr. Charles Umberger's twenty-eight room toxicology department. "There isn't a better toxicologist to be found any place than Dr. Umberger; but he does not have enough staff. The laboratory equipment and instruments for analysis are the finest. We use basic techniques of trying to locate poisons in a dead body; and don't forget that 25 percent of all our medical examiner cases involve some form of drugs and narcotics. These run all the way from the Greenwich Village addict who gets an overdose of heroin, to the Park Avenue society matron who loads herself up on sleeping pills and alcohol. We're in a sleeping pill and alcohol society; so our problems here are going to get an awful lot worse before they get any better."

What about Dr. Umberger's ability to identify LSD in a dead body?

"LSD," Dr. Helpern continues, "is the glamor drug of the moment. The prescribed dose of LSD for a regular 'trip' of around eight to ten hours is 1/30,000 of a grain. You can get some idea of the size of the dose if you visualize a five-grain aspirin tablet. You cut this into five equal pieces, and then take one of the pieces and divide it by 30,000. A person goes off on his 'trip' and he walks out of a fifth-story window, or in front of a bus on Second Avenue at 5 P.M. LSD seems to dispel any fear in some people of heights or speeding automobiles. They bring

radioactive fallout, sudden natural death, fatal boxing injuries, operating room deaths, electron microscope studies of central nervous system injuries, and new human blood factors. The amounts available, however, are "pennies and peanuts. They don't even begin to get us off the launching pad, in view of what is really needed in the field of forensic medicine."

this body in to us. There isn't any way in the world for us to find LSD in that body. We have to rely entirely on the medical history to alert us to the possibility of LSD. This may change a suicidal death to an accidental death.

"The whole point is that if we can send two men up in two little capsules to rendezvous miles out in space, we can find a way to identify all of the drugs in the body if we want to spend the time and money to do it."

Are poison murders still going undetected?

"Who knows?" Dr. Helpern says. "But I am certain that they are.

"We frequently request what we call a 'general unknown' search for drugs. Now, this sounds real impressive. We're being thorough. We're leaving no stone unturned to uncover murders by poison, or deaths from industrial poisons. The problem with the 'general unknown' is that the time and labor required to carry out this extensive analysis are out of all proportion to the staff that is available to do the work. When the laboratory caseload is around 4500 cases per year, and a minimum of two organs and preferably three are required in each case for a complete chemical examination, and considering that it takes about three weeks to process one single sample just to get ready for the chemical testing—if all possibilities are to be considered—this gives you twenty-seven separate samples per case to be tested for anywhere from 100 to 5000 possibilities.

"The laboratory question is where and how to make shortcuts and still carry the workload. Laboratory processing has to be something of a guessing game in which the most common poisons are the most probable cause of death if it is a chemical cause. Consequently, barbiturates and other central nervous system depressants that go into 'sleeping pills,' the amphetamines, the central nervous system stimulants that go into 'pep' pills, the common tranquilizers, and the narcotic class of drugs are about the limit in this so-called general unknown, unless it is indeed a special case. You see, toxicology doesn't have any real blanket techniques that permit us to test for hundreds of 'unknown' drugs at the same time.

"If we get a history that indicates that some specific drug should be searched for, the laboratory problem is quite different. When processing and testing is directed toward a specific substance, it is not difficult to confirm or rule out the suspected agent. Without a history to give us a clue as to what to look for, there is no guarantee as to the extent of the 'looking process' in one of many isolated cases.

"To return to the question of undetected poison murders, they are probable; but for anyone contemplating a homicide by poison, don't count on it, because your case might be that exceptional one that will receive *full* treatment.

"I'm a firm believer in that old aphorism that man can do anything he dreams of doing, provided you extend it to include 'if you give him the proper tools.' These tools involve research; and research calls for money, as well as manpower and motivation. We know very little about the body's secrets. The discouraging thing is that we really haven't begun to probe them, especially in the field of forensic medicine. I'm convinced that there are secrets in the body that will completely revolutionize the entire concept of crime detection."

CHAPTER 10

"Death May Have Its Own Sign"

Dr. Helpern hurriedly descended the spiral steel stairway that links his office on the first floor of the new Medical Examiner's Building with the mortuary in the basement. He dislikes the term "morgue" because many people find it offensive and are repelled by the image it conveys of a grim room filled with dead bodies. The aura that surrounds Dr. Helpern's mortuary actually differs little from that found in a surgical operating room of a major hospital. There is no levity. The body on each of the surgical tables is treated with genuine respect. The autopsy surgeons go about their medical tasks with a detached, scientific approach in a manner reminiscent of other quests for knowledge in a physics or chemical laboratory.

The spiral stairway, which Dr. Helpern insisted on having incorporated in the architect's plans for the new building, leaves him no more than thirty seconds away from the main autopsy room, his first love. His assistants are no longer startled to see him literally pop out of the wall at the far end of the room two or three dozen times each day to personally check on almost every one of the 7500 autopsies that are performed each year. He much prefers the role of forensic pathologist to that of administrator of his office, with its annual budget of approximately $1,000,000, and the supervision of 130 full-time employees.

On this particular morning, Dr. Helpern had just returned

from the annual meeting of the American Academy of Forensic Sciences in Chicago. Of all the medical and professional associations, groups, and societies that have interested him over the years, he feels that the American Academy of Forensic Sciences offers the greatest potential in the field of forensic medicine.

Dr. Helpern was instrumental in its formation. Dr. R. H. B. Gradwohl, the author of the book *Legal Medicine,* invited a group of practitioners in forensic medicine to meet in St. Louis in 1948 to explore possibilities of forming a society that would be made up of those persons concerned with the problems of medical and scientific proof in the courtroom. The American Medical Association sent two representatives to observe the proceedings. Dr. Gradwohl explained his goals, which were ". . . to encourage the study, improve the practice, elevate the standards, and advance the cause of forensic sciences; to promote the standardization of scientific techniques, tests, and criteria; and to plan, organize, and administer meetings, reports, and other projects for the stimulation and advancement of these and related purposes." He proposed an organizational format.

The two AMA representatives deferred an endorsement, saying that they would have to report back to their directors in Chicago before they could endorse and participate in the formation of this new organization. Dr. Helpern's response was characteristically vocal and forthright.

"I've belonged to the AMA for a great many years," he said. "I respect the organization. I have cooperated with it and participated in many of its projects, but I do not propose to let it dictate to me whether I can participate in a new organization in my field of practice, if I think this organization is needed. I think that we should establish this Academy now without any further delay, so that we can get on with the business of improving the quality of medical and scientific proof in the courtroom."

With Dr. Helpern's enthusiastic backing, the American Academy of Forensic Sciences came into being. It divides itself into six separate sections or disciplines. These are criminalistics, jurisprudence, pathology and biology, psychiatry, questioned documents, and toxicology. Its membership is exclusive and limited only to those men who are actively engaged in the courtroom application of all phases of medicine and related sciences. Lawyers and judges with problems in forensic proof turn to the roster of membership of the American Academy when they need help on a difficult and complicated case.

Dr. Helpern has served as President of the American Academy of Forensic Sciences, and his work behind the scenes has contributed greatly to the professional respect it has attained through the years. The pathology and biology section is one of the largest in the Academy, and Dr. Helpern's contributions in the form of papers, pathological slides and pictures, and common-sense suggestions have made up a substantial part of each one of the annual programs of the Academy during the years since it was established.

On this particular morning when Dr. Helpern entered the autopsy room after his return from the Academy meeting in Chicago, the appearance of a body on one of the autopsy tables captured his attention. It was that of a man, probably in his early fifties. The head and chest were huge although not particularly obese. The shoulders were extremely broad, and the chest was almost as thick and deep as it was wide. The long, light-brown hair rolled in waves and ringlets. The face was covered with a full, well-combed beard which also rolled in gentle waves. The arms and legs were powerful and well muscled. It was one of the most impressive bodies that Dr. Helpern had ever seen, and it reminded him of some character actor in the movies who might be made up for the part of a pirate or sailor in "Mutiny on the Bounty," "The Black Swan," or some other role from the days of the old four-masted sailing vessels.

"What's the story on this man?" Dr. Helpern asked the autopsy surgeon at the table.

"Not very much," the assistant answered. "He was found dead last night on the steps of St. Agnes Church over on East 43rd Street. His clothes were in tatters and were pretty filthy. The only identification on him was a card that listed the name of Lief Helgesen, and a flophouse address some place down in the Bowery."

The autopsy disclosed a massive coronary thrombosis as the cause of death. The enormous fatty liver, which was approximately two and a half times the normal size, was almost conclusive evidence that the man had been a chronic alcoholic for a long period of time.

Most people would probably have dismissed this case as just another Bowery bum or unfortunate derelict. However, the evidence of physical power and strength that still remained in this body after death aroused Helpern's curiosity. He went immediately to the office of the police lieutenant from the missing persons bureau of the New York City Police Department, who maintains a continuous vigil at the medical examiner's office, to help with the problems of identifying the unknown dead. Dr. Helpern asked that he be furnished with all the information that was uncovered concerning Lief Helgesen. Several days went by before the report was completed.

The police began their investigation at the flophouse on Bowery Avenue where Helgesen had lived for almost ten years. His room, cubbyhole No. 14, was no larger than the space required for a sleeping compartment on a train. The matted, paper-thin mattress that served as a bed was foul. A one-by-six board was nailed to the wall above the head of the bed, to serve as a shelf. An unbaited, empty mousetrap, covered with dust, guarded one end of the shelf, which also held nine volumes of texts and references in structural engineering. An address in one of the books led the police to one of the largest architectural firms in New York City. Here, they learned that Lief Helgesen had worked for almost twenty years as a respected structural engineer. His computations of spans and weights and carries had contributed to the design and erection of many of the city's tallest buildings.

He was a lonely man, almost a total introvert, without wife or family, but he was brilliant in his field of engineering and a highly valued employee of the architectural firm.

One morning almost ten years earlier, Lief Helgesen failed to appear at work. His associates thought that he was ill, and after the second day's absence, they attempted to contact him at his apartment near Central Park. A week went by, and then two weeks, and he was reported missing to the New York police. He had been carried in the missing persons file during all this period.

The clerk at the Bowery flophouse checked his records to confirm the fact that Lief Helgesen had lived in room No. 14 for almost ten years. He was known as just another Bowery wino. He always had enough money to pay his room rent punctually. He bought a few meals at cheap restaurants from time to time, although he prepared most of his food, making purchases at a neighborhood grocery store in the next block. During all this time, he never ran out of the one thing that was most important in his life, the two or three bottles of cheap, red wine that he consumed every day.

He was considered an excellent tenant in the area, friendly enough but never aggressive or really outgoing. Sometimes he would join the other flophouse residents in the room on the first floor, off the lobby, that served as the recreation hall, to watch a movie or a television program. He would sit by the hour with one of his engineering books, and stare at or over the open book without ever turning the pages. In many respects, his lot in life was far more rewarding than that of many of the Bowery derelicts and winos, for the simple reason that Lief Helgesen always had enough money for the necessities of his life, the bottles of cheap, red wine.

At around ten o'clock on the morning of the day before the night that he was found on the steps of the Church of St. Agnes, Lief Helgesen, in his soiled and ragged clothing, came up to the clerk at the desk in the flophouse.

"I'll tell you good-bye now," he said, extending his hand. "You've been real nice to me."

"Where you going?" the clerk asked. During his tenure as superintendent of the flophouse, he had seen hundreds of Bowery derelicts come and go, move and pass on, only to return again.

"I'll be going now," Helgesen continued. "I've got to get uptown today."

"What do you mean, you've got to get uptown today?" the clerk persisted, looking at Helgesen's unattractive appearance.

"I've got to get uptown today," Helgesen repeated.

"But the police . . . the police will pick you up," the clerk cautioned. "You'd better stick around here where everybody knows you."

"Not today. Not any more," Helgesen said as he turned toward the recreation room. "I've got to get uptown."

The clerk watched him say good-bye to three or four other long-term residents of the flophouse, and then wondered what was passing through the mind of Lief Helgesen as he stepped out onto Bowery Avenue.

Helgesen turned north to head uptown. His massive body dressed in tattered clothing, his great chest, the large head covered with wavy hair and his neatly combed beard, coupled with his painful, plodding gait, created an image along the route that dozens of people saw and remembered.

At the corner of Bowery Avenue and Jones Street, he stopped at a delicatessen and bought a loaf of bread and packages of Cheddar cheese and sliced salami to go with the two bottles of red wine acquired elsewhere. Habitués of the benches in Cooper Park talked to Helgesen shortly after noon. He was eating his meal of bread, cheese and salami, washed down with generous pulls from one of his wine bottles, and looking longingly at the old Cooper Union building.

"I've got to get uptown today," Helgesen said as he painfully lifted himself off the park bench, picked up his sack of staples, and shuffled across the park to Third Avenue.

By the time he reached Gramercy Park in the afternoon, his pace was so slow that it took him at least ten minutes to cover a single block. He had lost his right shoe, and dark stains of blood were matting the horizontally striped blue and gray stocking on that foot.

Although Gramercy Park is locked except to area residents, park regulars were startled to see him ease himself onto a bench and sleep until dark. Still, no one called the police. Other park visitors watched spellbound as he raised himself from his weary, drugged sleep to finish the last of his bread and cheese, and drain one of the bottles of red wine.

"I've got to get uptown today," Helgesen mumbled as he struggled to his feet, supporting and steadying himself with his hands on the back of the bench until he could gain his balance.

His progress was now so painful that he had to use his hands to move one thigh in front of the other. No one knows exactly where he spent the night, although it could have been in a darkened corner of the park.

At about ten o'clock the next morning, Lief Helgesen was seen struggling up Third Avenue at around 27th Street, only two blocks west of Bellevue Hospital. He no longer carried the paper bag with its wine bottle. He had probably consumed the wine to gain endurance to continue his pilgrimage. It was now taking him between twenty and thirty minutes to traverse each block. The foot of the horizontally striped blue and gray right sock was now completely gone. His own foot was swollen, raw, and bleeding. Each step looked like it would be his last as he struggled to force one leg in front of the other.

"I've got to get uptown today," he told a newspaper vendor at the corner of Third Avenue and 32nd Street, just two blocks west of New York University Medical Center.

"But you're in pretty bad shape," the news vendor said. "Let me call the cops, or at least an ambulance to help you."

"No, no," Helgesen protested. "I'll make it all right. Don't need any help. I've got to get uptown today."

He plodded painfully on, completely oblivious to the crispness of the weather which was now around the freezing point. The news vendor recalled watching him continue up Third Avenue for over an hour, until he was finally lost in the crowd of hurrying pedestrians who gave way, with scarcely a second look, so that Helgesen could pass through.

What happened to Lief Helgesen the remainder of the day is not known. Presumably, his pilgrimage required the better part of the day and early evening. He probably mingled with and was passed by thousands of people in the crowded area south and east of Grand Central.

At around nine o'clock that night, a young honeymooning couple from Iowa, on their first visit to New York, started down the rather dimly lit block of 43rd Street, east of Grand Central. The street was practically deserted at this hour in view of the cold weather, with the thermometer now in the low twenties. They were startled when they saw a huge shadow of a man sag down on the steps of the Church of St. Agnes. He eased himself down on his back across the church steps. After a moment of indecision, the young couple walked over to ask if anything was wrong and if they could help Helgesen.

"No help needed," he replied. They recalled that his face was bathed in an angelic smile that was so peaceful it transfixed them. "I've made it back uptown!"

Lief Helgesen's head, the contented smile still on his face, then rolled to the side against the cold concrete steps. It was then that he died.

Out of curiosity, the investigating officer checked the parish records of St. Agnes Church. Fifty years earlier, almost to the day, Lief Helgesen, the son of Danish immigrant parents, Peter and Margaret Helgesen, had been christened in the church. He had served for two years as an altar boy, and for over thirty years was carried on the membership rolls as a member of the parish.

"There may not be any great medico-legal significance to this case of Lief Helgesen," Dr. Helpern says in describing it, "but on the other hand, it offers an interesting speculation. Death may have its own sign. Medicine has a name for it. It is called the thanatognomonic sign, which is defined as 'indicating the approach of death.' William Cullen Bryant used the same word root in his 'Thanatopsis.' You can certainly speculate that the awesome compulsion which Helgesen obviously felt 'to get uptown' the day before he died fits into this category."

There are countless examples of medicine's thanatognomonic sign.

Franklin Roberts retired after forty years as an executive with a large advertising firm. He and his wife were one day out of New York harbor after completing a nine-month world cruise. Roberts was in the bathroom of their cabin, shaving before dinner. The ship lurched and Roberts fell to the floor. His wife assisted him to a standing position, and noticed that he was shaking all over, although he protested that he was all right and assured her that he did not have any broken bones or other serious injuries.

He sluggishly dressed for dinner, but looked pale. His wife insisted that he lie down on the bed for a few minutes to rest.

"Come here, Mabel," he said tenderly as he reached for her hand and pulled her down on the bed next to him. "I'm going to die; and I want you to be prepared for it. We've had a wonderful life together. I want you to know how much you have meant to me."

Mabel Roberts was first stunned, then shocked. Never in her thirty-eight years of marriage had her husband made such a statement. He was always hesitant, almost embarrassed to speak in direct terms of affection. She protested that he shouldn't talk such nonsense about dying; but she did call the ship's surgeon. He examined Roberts and could not find anything wrong. Franklin and Mabel Roberts went on to dinner, and returned to their room. At three o'clock the following morning, Franklin woke Mabel.

"I love you," he said, squeezing her hand affectionately; and he died.

Did Franklin Roberts receive a thanatognomonic sign?

Or Susan Martin? She was visiting her sixty-year-old sister with whom she had been extremely close since the earliest days of childhood. The two women were sleeping in separate rooms when Susan called to ask her sister to come to her at five in the morning.

"Will you just lie down beside me for a minute, and put your arm under my head?" she asked. "I want you to know it has always been so good when I am near you."

Susan Martin then died peacefully, with a smile on her face.

Or John Piper? For months, he suffered excruciating pain while in the terminal stages of a long illness from cancer. At dusk one evening during a particularly colorful sunset, the pain seemed to disappear completely.

"What a perfectly beautiful sunset," he said to his wife and children, who were especially startled because Piper had been unable to really notice and appreciate anything for the preceding several weeks. "Everything is going to be fine now."

He continued happy until he died fifteen minutes later.

"I don't make any effort to explain it," Dr. Helpern concludes. "I do know that there is enough hard evidence to support the proposition that death *may* have its own sign."

CHAPTER **11**

"I Reject the Idea of the Common Grave"

A clean, new snow was falling on the mall in front of the New York University medical complex as Dr. Helpern slipped out of his surgical gown. It had been a long day, although no longer than most, but he still had to attack the staggering pile of mail on his desk, letters which pour in from each one of the fifty states, and from many foreign countries. The great bulk of the letters request information and guidance on specific cases. These requests have been so voluminous over the years that they now fill an entire filing cabinet in his office.

STATION HOSPITAL
MORRIS FIELD
CHARLOTTE, NORTH CAROLINA

DEAR DR. HELPERN:
I am taking the liberty of writing to you concerning a patient of mine. He is twenty-nine years old, married, a South Carolina farmer, and at present a private in the U.S. Army. He was brought to the hospital complaining of severe pain in the left lumbar region, and radiation of pain down to the left testicle. Admitting temperature was 101, pulse 100. Physical examination was essentially negative. For several days, urine showed occasional red blood cells and white blood cells. The white blood count was slightly elevated. After one week, symptoms subsided and the patient became afebrile. It was at this time that he showed me a most remarkable phenomenon.

By rubbing the thumb and forefinger together, a faint wisp of smoke appeared. This definitely had the odor of phosphorus. Because of this, I observed him in a dark room and, lo and behold, a definite luminescence appeared wherever friction was made on the body. The glow would also appear across the knuckles when the skin was stretched. The glow is transient, lasting only a few seconds.

Naturally, we suspected some trick, but we have now observed him for some time and have never been able to discover how he does it. We have on two occasions had him take a bath, change into clothes he had never seen, and [we] put [him] into a strange room under lock and key for several days. Everything was taken from him, and still he was able to produce the phenomenon. He has been observed by a number of individuals, some of whom are convinced that he is malingering; others are convinced that this is some extraordinary physiological manifestation.

As for myself, I am still puzzled. I have observed this man for several months and do not believe he is clever enough nor sharp enough to be pulling the wool over our eyes. He has been under constant observation of everyone in the hospital, including the patients themselves. No one has discovered how he does this.

Complete X-rays and fluoroscopy examinations are negative. Intravenous pyelograms are negative. The bony structure appears intact. Repeated blood work-ups yield essentially normal values.

The urine has revealed a luminescence on frequent occasions. If it is collected in a closed container, a vapor forms over the liquid which is also luminescent. The vapor has the odor of phosphorus. The vapor as well as the urine turns silver nitrate paper black. When the vapor is collected in a condensing chamber after boiling the urinary sediment, a positive test is given for phosphorus.

I have done a considerable amount of research of the literature for comparable cases but am unable to find any. I am totally unable to find any physiological explanation for this phenomenon. I have consulted several biochemists, and have talked with Dr. E. N. Harvey of Princeton, the luminescence authority. They have all been extremely interested but have been unable to offer any suggestion.

I would greatly appreciate any suggestions from you and any further ideas for working up the case. I do not believe that the patient is faking, though I do not know how to explain it on any other basis. It does seem to me scientifically necessary to exhaust every possibility from every point of view.

BARRON, WISCONSIN

DEAR DR. HELPERN:
I have been referred to you by a local pathologist for advice on the etiology of a case of acute glomerulonephritis in an eight-year-old girl.
I am making the inquiry on behalf of the parents of the child, who have found it necessary to solicit an expert opinion as to whether or not exposure of the child to a dusting powder used for chickens on her father's farm might or could have caused this disease, and to inquire whether you would be available as an expert witness in the event of a trial of an action for damages resulting from the disease.

The next letter which Mrs. Helpern, who serves as her husband's secretary, had placed near the bottom of the pile that particular day was the continuous recital of an old familiar refrain. It was from the editor at Appleton-Century-Crofts, Inc., Dr. Helpern's publisher.

DEAR MILT:
I know how snowed you are every minute of every hour of every day, but we simply must get out the next edition of *Legal Medicine, Pathology and Toxicology*. I have tried every type of argument that I know, and here is one which I do think is valid. So much of your time is consumed by letters asking for help from all over the world that if we could get all of the free advice that you give out assembled into book form, many of the inquiries could simply be referred to an appropriate page or section in your book. In effect, you are dictating several books a year which now take the form of letters to persons who need help in the forensic medicine field. Let's change the format. Let's dictate these answers into sections and chapters for the revised edition of the book. . . .

Dr. Helpern smiled. It was a new argument and it made sense. The revision of the book was extremely important, but he had no ready solution to the time factor.

The last letter in the day's mail was a sample of those terribly unexpected events that happen from time to time, to send all planned schedules and agendas spiraling off the desk and into wastebaskets.

This letter was from the Civil Aeronautics Board in Washington, D.C.:

DEAR DR. HELPERN:
Enclosed for your information and to complete your file, is a copy of the Civil Aeronautics Board's report on the:
American Airlines, Inc., Boeing 707-123B, N7506A, Jamaica Bay, Long Island, New York, March 1, 1962 accident.
On September 19th, 1962, when I stopped in your office, I was given copies of sixty-three of the completed autopsy protocols. I wonder if the thirty-two remaining ones have now been transcribed. If so, I would appreciate it if you could send me copies to complete my file of these.
On a little less formal basis, I would like to repeat what I said in my Human Factors report, that I surely did appreciate all the fine cooperation between your organization and the Civil Aeronautics Board's team. It made my job much easier. Thank you.

As he thumbed through the staid, formal report which described the tragedy in cold technical language, Dr. Helpern's own vivid recollections of the events returned:

On March 1, 1962, American Airlines Flight One, a Boeing 707-123B, with eighty-seven passengers and a crew of eight, was given taxi instructions to Runway 31L, at 0954. The flight was issued an IFR clearance nonstop to Los Angeles International Airport at 1002. The clearance contained local departure procedures and included the then-prescribed statement ". . . in the interests of noise abatement do not delay turn to heading two niner zero." In the run-up area adjacent to Runway 31L at 1005:05, American One advised Idlewild Tower, "Ready for takeoff," and was immediately cleared for takeoff. Flight One then taxied to the runway and was aligned with it at 1006:29. At 1006:51 the tower requested Flight One to "advise rolling" and one second later while in the takeoff roll, the Flight so advised the tower. . . .

The takeoff was routine, the huge plane lifting gracefully and responding to the pilot's command for a gentle left turn at one hundred feet. At 1007:54, the pilot started a second turn to the left; and the tower instructed him to report out when he reached 2000 feet. He did not report and the plane vanished from the radar screen because American One, less than two minutes after takeoff:

. . . then entered a "nose-low attitude" and plunged earthward in a nearly vertical dive. The airplane struck the shallow waters of Pumpkin Patch Channel of Jamaica Bay approximately three miles southwest of the Idlewild Control Tower at 1008:49. Floating debris and fuel ignited a few minutes later and burned fiercely. . . . The crater made by the aircraft in the bottom of the bay was approximately 130 feet long and 8 to 10 feet deep. On impact, the wings were fragmented and the fuselage crushed accordionlike, breaking into many sections. Part of the horizontal stabilizer and elevator of the tip of the fuselage attached was the largest piece of structure recovered. . . .

What caused the crash?

"Reconstruction" of the wreckage was made in a hangar for detailed study. . . . The Board determined that the probable cause of this accident was a rudder control system malfunction producing yaw, sideslip, and roll, leading to a loss of control from which recovery action was not effective. . . .

Dr. Helpern thought back to the gray, cold, dismal morning ten months earlier when he received the emergency call. While the Civil Aeronautics Board's task as reflected by the official report was the "reconstruction" of the physical scraps and pieces of metal that only minutes before had been a silvery, shimmering jet airliner, he had directed a major "reconstruction" project of his own. The physical materials with which he worked were once alive and animated, but they were now as pathetically fragmented as the scraps of metal which floated or slanted upward in ragged spears from the mud and silt of Jamaica Bay. The torn bodies were now as inanimate as the shredded metal that had comprised the aircraft.

March 1, 1962 had been planned as a day that New Yorkers should long remember. American One left Idlewild barely an hour before Lieutenant Colonel John H. Glenn, Jr. arrived at La Guardia Airport to begin his triumphal entrance into New York City in celebration of his historical orbit around the world. Other New Yorkers would have even more poignant recollections of the day.

"I just happened to turn my head and look out the train window," John Petersen of Bayport, Long Island, said. He was riding a Long Island Railroad train into the Jamaica Station just as American One took off from Runway 31L. "I saw this giant airplane climbing—and then heading straight down to the ground. I didn't see it hit. I didn't see any fire while the plane was heading down. I couldn't believe my eyes. It went absolutely straight down—on a ninety-degree angle. I was so shocked I could hardly move. I'll bet I was maybe twelve miles away from the scene."

"It shook the whole house," Mrs. Ivan Church said. "Oh, it was loud. Such force. The first thing that entered my mind was that it was a plane, because they fly right over the house when the wind is blowing a certain way."

"I could smell the odor of burning flesh in the air," Mrs. Joan Brett, a registered nurse, said. "My house shook something fierce. At first I went out and could see nothing. But I put my baby in the playpen, then went out to look again. This time I could see the smoke."

Friends and relatives who had just said good-bye to the passengers who boarded American One were still in the American Airlines Terminal when the news of the disaster came back. While they were taken to Hangar 10 to await word of the fate of their loved ones, police, fire, and Coast Guard crews rushed to the crash scene. Dozens of policemen were called off assignments connected with Colonel Glenn's arrival to work on the problems produced by the tragedy.

A Coast Guard helicopter, one of the first to reach the scene, radioed back: "There is no sign of life"; and American Airlines soon announced that all ninety-five persons aboard the giant aircraft had perished.

Soon after he reached the icy waters of Jamaica Bay, Dr. Helpern made his own announcement which was reported in the press and also sent back to the shocked occupants of Hangar 10, who clustered in their mutual grief over coffee, Coke, or just plain memories.

"No one, particularly relatives, will be asked to view any of these bodies for the purpose of identifying them," Dr. Helpern said. "It would be too brutally cruel. I urge all relatives to go back home and do something that will help us to help them. They can contact the doctors and dentists of the victims and get the most detailed medical history possible for each one of the persons aboard the airplane. These should be brought or sent to the medical examiner's office as soon as possible. We will then contact the families or their representatives just as soon as the identifications are made."

Dr. Helpern's experience with the grim business of disaster is vast. By way of example, on December 16, 1960, a mid-air crash of two airliners over Staten Island took a toll of 134 lives, and was the worst air disaster in history. This was followed four days later by an explosion in the Brooklyn Navy Yard that claimed another forty-nine lives. Dr. Helpern has worked out techniques of identification which are now accepted the world over.

"The identification of mutilated and incinerated bodies," he explains in his frequent lectures on the subject, "must be considered as a team approach. It involves local police agencies, the fingerprint division of the Federal Bureau of Investigation, the missing persons bureaus of police departments, and coroners and medical examiners. Someone must take charge and correlate all activities in these situations of tragedy. The proper official charged with the legal responsibility of making the ultimate determination of cause of death and identification of each victim is the coroner or medical examiner. Therefore, he should direct all the activities."

The recovery of the ninety-five bodies was slow and painful. It was the worst single plane disaster in history. The bodies had to be searched for and dragged up out of the waters of Jamaica Bay before they could be carried to the facilities of the new Medical Examiner's Building. This was the first major disaster involving Dr. Helpern since the new building was completed.

"In a society based on speed," Dr. Helpern warned at that time, "we must learn to expect more of these affairs, and be prepared to handle them."

Just as soon as the first bodies were brought in, Dr. Helpern and his assistants began their work, which was to last for forty-eight consecutive hours. They methodically put into operation Dr. Helpern's carefully devised procedures.

The first tool was fingerprints. If there was enough skin left on any finger or thumb so that a readable print could be obtained, this was delivered to the FBI agent who was on the scene, so that it could be forwarded to the FBI identification division in Washington for search and comparison. Since most Americans at one time or another have had their fingerprints taken and sent to the FBI for filing and future reference, fingerprints are the "easiest" and surest way of determining identification.

In incinerated bodies, however, where the fire is extremely intense and reaches high temperatures, the hands and feet are frequently destroyed. This eliminates the possibility of fingerprint identification. Many of the bodies pulled from Jamaica Bay were incinerated.

The next resource is an examination of the teeth. These are carefully X-rayed so that they can be compared with dental charts, which offer a comparatively easy, safe, and sure means of identification. Four days after the crash of American One, Dr. Helpern publicly thanked all of the dentists for taking the time to search out the dental records of the victims, and either airmailing them directly to his office or personally bringing them in to aid in the comparison for identification purposes.

Still, in many instances the fire is so hot that the jaws are burned away, or more often the gold and platinum and other metals, which are alloyed into the fillings for cavities or hold partial or full dental plates, are melted. When this happens, identification through the use of dental records is a much more laborious and hazardous procedure.

The last structures of the body to be destroyed by incineration are those that lie deep in the chest and abdominal cavities, and those that are encased by the bony vault of the skull. It was for this reason that Dr. Helpern requested the surviving family members of the victims to obtain the complete medical records as soon as possible.

One by one, the grim process of identification proceeded.

Mabel Schofield, who had worked for only two weeks in a defense plant during World War II and, as far as anyone knew, had never had her fingerprints taken again, was identified by fingerprints. Seaman Second Class James Nesbitt, whose fingerprints had perhaps been taken half a dozen times, now had no hands left to fingerprint. He was identified by the dogtags around his neck, one of which had melted. The other was burned into the skin of his chest as though stamped there by some giant die-press. Michael Shay had no fingerprints left, but a plain gold wedding band on his left finger was only partially melted. The inscription inside could still be read: "To Mike with love, Sally—March 17, 1923." The wallet, amazingly intact, found in the left back pants pocket of Stewart Anderson contained all of his identification cards.

These were the easy ones.

The hours flowed into days, and the days merged imperceptibly into nights. All lights burned around the clock in the Medical Examiner's Building, and the exhausted autopsy surgeons could not tell from the artificial lights of the autopsy room whether it was the sun or the moon that shone outside on the mall of the New York University Medical Center.

There remained only two badly charred bodies which lacked hands, rings, wallets, jewelry, watches, jaws, or any of the more normal means of identification. An internal examination of the charred trunks clearly indicated that the bodies were male. Although the external sex organs had been burned away, the internal anatomical design of the genitourinary systems permitted a conclusive determination of sex.

The problem now was to determine which body was that of Paul Hendel and which was Charles Atwood. It was Dr. Helpern's personal task to make the last two identifications.

Paul Hendel was sixty-three years of age, and operated his own public accounting office. It was something of a marginal operation, as most things during Paul Hendel's life had been. The fact that he was even on American One that morning was typical of his fate in life.

He and his wife Martha had originally been booked on United Airlines Flight 819. At the last minute, it was learned that United could not furnish a jet plane for the nonstop flight from New York to Los Angeles, but one seat was available on a TWA nonstop jet, which Paul urged Martha to take. Paul was alone and a stranger to the other eighty-six passengers on American One.

Paul Hendel graduated from Dartmouth College in 1930 as the third man scholastically in his class. The math courses in those days were not so complex as they are now, but he was considered by his classmates as a "whiz" in any math subject. He had learned the principles and mechanics of bookkeeping through part-time jobs which had helped defray his college expenses. He easily mastered the deeper concepts of accounting, and a bright future was predicted for him by faculty members who knew him and by his classmates.

Even though the stifling years of the Depression were beginning, Paul Hendel had no difficulty in finding a job in the accounting department of one of the large international oil companies whose head offices were located in Manhattan. He possessed a technical competence which accompanied a friendly, outgoing personality that was mellowed by a great sense of humor and a genuine empathy with other people. He clearly seemed to be a young man destined to rise to the top in record time.

Paul and Martha Hendel had been married for eighteen months, and their first child was only six weeks old, when Paul was riding with a friend in one of the first Model-A Ford automobiles. The car was struck from behind by a truck whose brakes failed; Paul immediately complained of pain in his neck and right arm. This was almost two years before the medical term "whiplash injury" was coined, but Paul Hendel had obviously received a genuine, bona fide whiplash. X-rays revealed a hairline fracture in the fifth vertebra in the neck. The pain in his neck and arm was so intense that it completely wiped out his ability to concentrate. Four months after the accident, he and his employer mutually agreed that he could no longer satisfactorily perform his duties in the office of the company's comptroller.

By 1936, Paul and Martha's lot was perhaps no worse than that of millions of other people. They had three small children, and Paul was doing reasonably well as the manager of the accounting department in the warehouse division of a large shipping company. He still suffered fatigue, headaches, and pain in the shoulder girdle from his old whiplash injury, but he had made up his mind that he could live with it and accepted its partially disabling sequelae as part of his fate in life.

Paul was riding home from work late one Friday afternoon

with another friend, this time in a 1936 Chevrolet. The friend lost control of the car and it rolled over three times after failing to negotiate a curve. Paul suffered bruises, lacerations, and abrasions over his head and shoulder, and sustained five badly fractured ribs on the right side.

After Pearl Harbor, Paul was turned down when he volunteered for military service, because he honestly attempted to give a full medical history. A year earlier, after suffering for several years with an incapacitating duodenal ulcer, he had undergone an operation. This was noted on his medical chart as a "laparotomy," which is the term used generally to describe abdominal surgery at any point in the abdominal region.

Paul's professional services were in great demand during the years of World War II. He and Martha and their four children enjoyed their greatest moments of financial prosperity. But then, in early 1945, approximately six weeks before Germany finally capitulated to the ultimatum of unconditional surrender, he was felled by a severe gallbladder attack which resulted in a cholecystectomy, the surgical removal of the gallbladder.

Three years later, after he had moved his family to Brooklyn and opened his own public accounting firm, Paul Hendel submitted to a routine, unglamorous appendectomy.

By this time, Paul's medical plights had developed into a running joke among Paul and Martha and all those who knew him. "What next?" was the continuing theme of the macabre jest, and there always seemed to be something next. The family fortunes—financial, social, spiritual, and otherwise—ebbed and flowed in direct relationship to Paul's physical illnesses. Still, he was one of those rare individuals who learned to roll with life's punches. His keen sense of humor never left him. If anything, his empathy with other people increased through the years.

Finally, in 1955, something serious happened to Paul Hendel. He suffered a severe heart attack, with major myocardial infarction. The area of the infarct, the dead, scarred tissue which resulted from the plug in one of the major coronary arteries which blocked off the blood supply to this part of the heart muscle, causing it to die, was clearly discernible on Paul's EKG examinations. He was laid low for eight months, but then gradually returned to work, first for an hour a day, then two, then three, until he was finally working six or seven hours a day. If he suspected that his former clients continued to employ him as their accountant out of charitable motivation, he never let on.

In 1960, Paul Hendel suffered a stroke. A stroke is the physiological event which medicine calls a cerebral vascular accident (CVA), when a blood vessel in the brain either becomes plugged or ruptures, so that the normal blood supply to a portion of the brain is interfered with. Paul's stroke was only partially disabling. He gradually regained the use of the right side of his body, which had been paralyzed initially. His ability to speak returned, along with his mental powers. The stroke in no way impaired his optimistic, cheerful outlook on life.

By late 1961, Paul's oldest son, who was living in Los Angeles, had scrimped and saved enough money to buy a round-trip ticket from New York to Los Angeles for Paul and Martha. They had agreed to come to California for the Christmas holidays and to stay at least until Easter, when the cold weather on the East Coast would be gone for another year. But the trip was delayed. Just before the Thanksgiving holidays, it was discovered through X-ray examination after a barium enema that Paul Hendel was probably suffering from cancer of the ascending colon, and the malignancy had invaded the surrounding tissues within the peritoneal cavity. Because of the widespread appearance of the malignancy and Paul's now somewhat debilitated physical condition, an operation was postponed, and then definitely decided against.

Now, on this first day of March 1962, just before Colonel Glenn's triumphant entry into New York, the trip to Los Angeles for Paul and Martha Hendel was definitely on. Paul was in better spirits and physical condition than he had known in several months, but they all knew that if he did not get to Los Angeles soon, it would probably be too late. Martha agreed to leave him and take a separate flight on a different airplane only because United Airlines canceled its flight.

Dr. Helpern finished the autopsy on the first of the two charred bodies which remained unidentified. There was not much to go on. The autopsy disclosed that this person, in life, had undergone an appendectomy and had a small hernia in the area around the navel. The heart was also enlarged. These were rather standardized, general findings which, standing alone, would seldom warrant a positive identification.

He now approached the last body, which had already been opened by one of the assistant autopsy surgeons. Paul Hendel's medical and personal histories were clearly interwoven, so much so that one was inseparable from the other. Dr. Helpern looked carefully at the fifth vertebra in the neck, and found a deposit of calcium in an old fracture line. The calcium had been poured out by the body in an effort to heal the facture which could have been caused by a whiplash injury in 1932.

There were similar outpourings of calcium in five ribs on the right side of the body, obviously the result of healing of prior rib fractures which could have been caused by an automobile rolling over in 1936. This person had clearly suffered a duodenal ulcer, which had been operated upon by laparotomy. The gallbladder and appendix were gone. Despite the fact that the heart was shrunken, the scar of the old infarct area on the right front portion of the heart muscle was clearly visible. The top of the head, including the calvaria, the very top portion of the skull, was burned away; the brain appeared as a soft organ diminished in size and tightly enclosed in the shrunken dura mater, the outermost layer of the three layers of meninges that surround the brain and spinal cord. A careful examination of the soft, heat-shrunken brain disclosed evidence of a prior stroke, or cerebral vascular accident. Sections of the ascending colon and the surrounding retroperitoneal tissues were removed for microscopic examination. These were clearly saturated with malignant cells.

The incredible number of medical adversities which Paul Hendel had suffered in life now made his identification in death a positive certainty. This unanticipated traumatic way of death undoubtedly saved him from the trauma of unbearable, excruciating pain in life, which would have been his lot when the cancer cells finally began to take their toll.

"I reject the idea of the common grave," Dr. Helpern explains patiently when asked why he goes to such extravagant lengths to insure the correct identification of each and every person who perishes in a common disaster. "Every man is separate and individual in life. He occupies a special place on this earth. He is entitled to individual recognition, respect, and consideration in death. The most horrible image that has ever been produced in my mind results from the pictures out of Auschwitz and Buchenwald, where the Nazis bulldozed deep trenches into which they could dump millions of broken, emaciated bodies that had been reduced to little more than skin and bone.

"The common grave is the ultimate symbol of the perverse idea that all men are alike and that they can be computerized into mathematical symbols, and given the status of nothing but a tattooed number. No matter what you call it, Nazism, Fascism, Communism, or state socialism, it is a totally unnatural philosophy that is doomed to failure. Man is an individual. Each man is special. If he is special in life, it follows that he must be special in death. With all the strength that I have, I reject the idea of the common grave."

CHAPTER 12

"Life Is a Series of Arcs That Come Full Circle"

As infrequently happens, none of the surprise element had gone out of the function that took place in the halls and offices of the Medical Examiner's Building on the evening of April 17, 1962. Surprise or no, it was a rewarding occasion for Dr. Helpern.

More than three hundred of his friends assembled to celebrate his sixtieth birthday. There were judges, defense lawyers, and prosecuting attorneys, professors of medicine and professors of law, deans of schools of medicine and deans of schools of law, faithful employees of the medical examiner's office, city officials, and just plain friends. In addition, approximately five hundred letters from the leading figures in forensic medicine from all over the world poured in from admirers of Dr. Helpern, alerted by Mrs. Helpern and Dr. Joseph Tamerin to the occasion.

It was the occasion of the dedication of the Milton Helpern Library of Legal Medicine-Museum. Authors who had written textbooks and articles in forensic medicine sent in autographed copies of their works. Many rare textbooks, long since out of print, were received, to serve as the beginning of what may well become the most respected library in forensic medicine to be found anyplace in the world. The books came in German,

Japanese, French, Italian, Russian, Arabic, and half a dozen other languages. The library was launched on a firm, practical basis.

The museum, on the other hand, needed no contributions of exhibits for its successful launching. These had been collected and preserved, although more or less haphazardly, in the forty-four years since the office of medical examiner was created in New York. It is perhaps the most unusual museum in the world. In the first place, it is closed to the public and can be visited—and only by special permission—by doctors, lawyers, judges, professors, police officers, and others with a legitimate interest in the field of forensic medicine. It is a museum of death in all of death's aspects—strange, subtle, violent, mysterious, and bizarre.

No names appear under any exhibit. A simple card in one or two sentences, sometimes a single paragraph, gives a thumbnail sketch to explain why the particular item merits attention. These numbered cards are cross-referenced to complete files which are kept under lock and key by James B. Schafran, the museum's curator.

Most of the physical items are dully familiar and deceptively innocent in appearance. There are electric heaters, a hot dog, a dull table knife, a plastic bag, a Mason jar lid, a small, wake-up electric radio, a television set. Each item, however, has been carefully selected from dozens of rivals for the poignant story it played in someone's life and death.

There is an ice pick, no different from millions of others that have been manufactured and sold at hardware and dime stores in every part of the country. The bottom quarter-inch of the point is broken and lies separated from the main shaft on its mounting.

What makes this particular ice pick unique? It was stabbed into the chest of a forty-eight-year-old man in a fight. After it was removed, he felt no ill effects and did not even consult a doctor. For seven months he worked, walked around normally, ate, drank, and made merry until he entered a hospital complaining of "the flu." A month later, he died and the autopsy disclosed that his death was due to endocarditis, an infection of the sac that surrounds the heart. The autopsy also produced the one-quarter-inch tip of the ice pick which had broken off and remained in the man's heart for eight months prior to his death.

There is another quite similar ice pick on exhibit. A fifty-one-year-old man was brought to a hospital unconscious, and died thirteen days later from what the doctors assumed was a stroke. Two autopsies, together with independent investigation, were required to incriminate this ice pick. It had been jabbed through the socket of the eye, the blade penetrating the complex layer of muscles in such a manner that the wound was not observed by the attending physicians, nor was it observed at the time the first autopsy was completed. Only an accidental remark by a relative of the deceased at the time she came to identify the body led to a reexamination of the eye, at which time the wound track was discovered and the death correctly attributed to the infection of the brain coverings caused by the wound, instead of to the natural disease process of a stroke.

Another exhibit consists of two familiar items, a surgical clamp and a surgical gauze pad.

They were involved in the fate of a thirty-five-year-old woman who entered a hospital for an appendectomy. Her postoperative recovery was uneventful, and she was sent home on the eighth day after the operation.

She called her surgeon the next morning to complain of abdominal cramps. He advised her that this was nothing unusual following abdominal surgery, and he prescribed simple medication for her symptoms. The cramps did not go away as the surgeon had assured her they would; so she consulted another doctor. He diagnosed her condition as an acute intestinal obstruction, and ordered her admitted to another hospital on an emergency basis.

This hospital was fifty blocks from the first one, and a different surgeon performed the second operation. He discovered that the first surgeon had left the surgical clamp in her abdomen. Some of the coils of the small intestine had become entangled with the clamp, causing gangrene. He removed the gangrenous section of the intestine, sewed the two healthy ends together, and closed the incision.

The patient's postoperative course following the second surgical procedure was far from routine. The incision wound refused to heal. She ran a fever, and before long the dread diagnosis of peritonitis was made. It was before the days of the "wonder" drugs, and two days later she was pronounced dead.

The autopsy by the medical examiner's office listed the cause of death as "Septic peritonitis due to the presence of a foreign body." The postmortem investigation revealed that the second surgeon in the second hospital had left a surgical gauze pad in the abdominal cavity.

There are presently over six hundred separate exhibits in this highly specialized museum, each one with its own distinct story in some person's life, some person's death.

There are also the rare anatomical anomalies, many of which illustrate man's ability to overcome the physical handicaps of his birth.

Exhibit 283 consists of a single ovary, a fallopian tube and uterus, and a tube running to the anus. This is an unusual anatomical arrangement in any woman, but this particular specimen came from the body of a fifty-five-year-old man who was killed in an automobile accident. He functioned well as a day laborer during all of his adult life, and was a good husband and father to his two children. His wife described him as "not much of a doctoring man"; and fortunately for the medical profession, he did not seek medical treatment or advice during life for his single ailment. His problem was, his wife explained, that "about once a month" he suffered from "those bleeding piles." This condition gradually corrected itself when he reached the age of about forty-seven or forty-eight. The episodes of bleeding became spaced over longer and more irregular periods until they ceased altogether. The autopsy disclosed no hemorrhoids of any size sufficient to account for a long history of "bleeding piles." Presumably, his anatomical anomaly caused him to menstruate until he apparently went through a menopause, at which time the menstrual periods ceased altogether.

One of the exhibits which intrigues Dr. Helpern consists of a prize, bloodstained, Japanese samurai sword. Servicemen who fought against the Japanese in the South Pacific during World War II, in that peculiar type of fighting known as island-hopping, brought back hundreds, perhaps thousands of these swords as souvenirs.

This particular one was returned by Huxley Charles Leighton. Hux Leighton never wanted to be a Marine. In fact, in those years before Pearl Harbor, the glory and glamor of the United States Marine Corps had not captured the imagination of too many college men; but Hux Leighton was more or less forced into the Marine Corps.

In the spring of 1941 he was a senior at Duke University, majoring in chemistry, when it suddenly occurred to him that he should check with his draft board in New York City to see if there was any danger of his being drafted within the next year or two. Like many of his contemporaries, he believed the possibility of war with Japan highly remote, an event that was speculated upon only in newspaper headlines when the "phony" war in Europe failed to produce any item of great news interest.

Hux Leighton was shocked two weeks later when he received a letter from his draft board, advising him that he was then enjoying a 1-D status, which had been granted only because he was a student, and that this status would lapse immediately after he graduated in June. He would then be reclassified a highly available 1-A. In formal, friendly tones, this "board of your friends and neighbors" went on to advise that he could expect to be inducted into the service sometime the following July. This startled him out of his complacency, and he began a search for some avenue that would prevent him from being drafted into the Army as an ordinary private.

Although he knew less than nothing about the Marine Corps at that time, he believed that he had perhaps found his solution when a news item appeared the following day in the student newspaper. A Marine Corps recruiting officer would be on the Duke campus a week hence to interview and receive applications from senior men. If accepted, they would be sent to Quantico, Virginia, for Officer's Candidate School for three months, then commissioned second lieutenants in the Corps. After advanced training, they would be assigned to duty aboard ship, or perhaps to guard duty at one of the United States embassies in a glamorous foreign country. Hux Leighton immediately applied. The possibility of being an officer in any corps was much more appealing than the prospect of being drafted as a private under the terms of the Selective Service law. Only ten men were selected from each of the major college campuses, and Hux Leighton was one of those chosen from Duke University. By June 26, 1941, he found himself a member of the third officers candidate class in the neat, polished, brick barracks of the Quantico Marine Corps base.

He hated every minute of his tenure at Quantico. He conformed only in a grudging way to the iron regimen imposed by the highly competent noncommissioned officers who were career veterans, with a background of service in China, Nicaragua, and Haiti. He found that he was still basically a foot soldier and treated worse than any private drafted into the Army. He longed for release, particularly after hearing that several of his classmates had obtained commissions in the Navy and were pleasantly ensconced in training missions, some already assigned aboard ships.

Almost every weekend, Mildred and Charles Leighton, Jr., came down from New York to Washington to visit their only son. Charles was a successful stockbroker in New York City, maintaining a large apartment on Park Avenue and a summer place on Long Island where the Leightons sailed their thirty-eight-foot sloop almost every weekend of the year.

They suffered through Hux' every move during his training school, and Charles went so far as to contact the United States Senator from New York, in an effort to get Hux released from the Marine Corps so that he might apply for a commission in the Navy. The Senator was never quite able to pull off this request.

The possibility of interservice transfer was completely obliterated by the Japanese bombs at Pearl Harbor. As the island-hopping operation from Pearl Harbor to Japan got under way, Mildred and Charles Leighton lived in terror with each newspaper headline, that special terror known only to parents of a son on the battlefield during a major war.

It began August 6, 1962 with a Marine landing at Guadalcanal. They received the Navy Department's wire that Hux had been wounded in action a week before they received his first letter attempting to reassure them that his wound was not serious. Perhaps it was a good omen, they wishfully told themselves. It might mean that their son would be relieved of additional combat assignment; but the Marine Corps was not relieving any personnel of front-line assignment, particularly a man like Hux Leighton who had distinguished himself sufficiently to be awarded a Silver Star to go along with his Purple Heart.

The long days and weeks passed by, with Mildred and Charles Leighton living between the newspaper accounts of the war and Hux' letters. He was now a first lieutenant, and was back with a fighting unit.

On November 20, 1943, the newspapers reported Tarawa, but it was several weeks later before the Leightons received the full story. Hux' landing barge had run aground on the coral reefs five hundred feet from Betio Beach, and capsized. He managed to lead most of his struggling company onto the beach, where they were pinned down by stifling Japanese fire for the better part of twenty-four hours. Once more he distinguished himself and was awarded a second Purple Heart. His superiors recommended him for the Congressional Medal of Honor, but he received the Navy Cross instead; once more, Mildred and Charles Leighton prayed that this might mean that Hux would see no futher combat action.

They were terrorized by Einewetok in vain. Hux was not in this action, but he was in the thickest fighting on Saipan the following June. He was now Major Leighton, and went in with the first wave from the landing barges, meeting little opposition. Then came the rugged, well-executed Japanese counterattack that almost drove his unit back into the sea. It was on the third day of the engagement that he picked up the wound that led to his third Purple Heart.

It was about this same time that Mildred Leighton read a long article in one of the Sunday papers which bothered her for several days. It was written by a leading psychiatrist in New York City, attempting to alert the families of servicemen who had seen combat to some of the problems they might encounter after the war was over, when the servicemen were discharged and returned to civilian life. No man could go through the rigors of mortal combat, the psychiatrist explained, without receiving serious damage to his psyche. There were going to be severe cases of neuroses and psychoses which the family members must learn to expect and recognize. The combat veteran who came back whole in body, in all probability, would not be whole in mind. Parents and spouses should be prepared to see and accept the worst. They should anticipate the specific symptoms so that they could then direct their combat veterans toward a psychiatric clinic before dire results occurred.

Mildred and Charles Leighton arranged an appointment with the psychiatrist who had authored the article. Yes, he said, he would accept a retainer from them now, even though no one could anticipate just when Hux Leighton would return to the United States, or to civilian life. He would be available and on call around the clock, to render his professional services in the event that Hux exhibited any signs or symptoms of psychotic behavior; and as parents, they were wise and foresighted in making this arrangement in view of Hux' arduous combat record. Mildred and Charles Leighton were somewhat comforted by the arrangement, but they lived under a cloud of depression for the next fifteen months. Even if Hux did return whole in body, they could probably look forward to a long period of adjustment as he was eased out of the military way of thinking and back into a normal, docile civilian life.

They both shed tears of joy at the news of Hiroshima and Nagasaki. Hux Leighton would be spared the landings on the islands of Japan. They would not be put through the ordeal themselves.

On September 2, 1945, it was all formally over when MacArthur signed the surrender agreements aboard the *Missouri*. Day by day, they waited for word as to when Hux might reasonably expect to be returned home. Three months passed, and Hux was still on Okinawa. Only a miracle could get him home by Christmas, and this did not seem to be forthcoming.

Charles Leighton was no longer a young man. He was sixty-nine years old. Mildred was fifty-five. Although Charles was semiretired, he still went to his brokerage office for two or three hours each day when the market was open. Mildred was shocked to receive a call from Charles' secretary one morning reporting his collapse in the office. He had not felt well for the preceding ten days, and for the last two days he had been particularly distressed. They both attributed it to a bad cold which might have been bordering on flu. Mildred feared a heart attack at the time she received the secretary's call. She rushed to Presbyterian Hospital, where Charles had been taken by ambulance, to await the verdict of the doctors.

The diagnosis was not long in coming. It was lobar pneumonia. This was the old type of "walking" pneumonia which was so prevalent before the days of penicillin and which accounted for a great number of deaths certified by the medical examiner's office.

The penicillin supply available to the civilian population in those days was negligible. The same was true for the other "wonder" drugs which were then being used experimentally in the treatment of pneumonia. The prognosis for Charles Leighton was grave, particularly because of his age. Mildred Leighton launched an emergency campaign to have her son returned to the United States because of his father's critical illness. Her ally was the American Red Cross. Mildred assured Charles that Hux was on his way home, although she could not be sure at first whether this news had penetrated his mind which was clouded by delirium from time to time.

Early in the morning of December 22, 1945, Charles Leighton successfully passed the crisis of his disease, that critical point in the course of a disease when the struggle for life remains in balance, awaiting the mustering of the body's own antibody defenses to see whether they can overcome and defeat the invading bacteria. Six hours later, Mildred Leighton received a call at Presbyterian Hospital. Hux Leighton had arrived in Washington and would take the next train to New York. The incredible miracle had occurred. Charles Leighton appeared to be well on the way to recovery, and Hux was safely home before Christmas. Although neither Mildred nor Charles mentioned it, there was a reservation in their elation. Hux was home safe in body, but only the next few hours would tell whether he was also safe in mind.

Mildred Leighton almost overwhelmed her son with her greeting in one of the crowded mazes of Grand Central. He acted rationally enough, although she immediately sensed a change in his personality and behavior. He was certainly more restrained, even somewhat distant, as they hurried up to Presbyterian Hospital in a taxi. It was enough to make her wary and to stimulate her haunting fear that he might be suffering from some form of mental aberration.

Charles Leighton was also confused by Hux' attitude and behavior. He and his son had always warmly embraced each other at every reunion opportunity. This time, Hux attempted only a formal handshake and seemed to resent—or at least be embarrassed by—his father's efforts to pull him down toward the pillow so that he could hug and kiss him. The reunion visit in the hospital room, which lasted for approximately an hour, was strained and not at all what the parents had anticipated and hoped for after this period of waiting. At one point, Hux seemed to stare off into space and mumble as though engaged in conversation with a person who was not in the room.

Hux seemed perfectly amenable when his father suggested that he was undoubtedly exhausted from the long trip home and that he and his mother should go to the apartment on Park Avenue so that Hux could sleep for a while. Charles noticed a sort of wild stare in Hux' eyes as the two of them shook hands in a formal good-bye.

Mildred whispered to Charles that she was worried, and Charles urged her to contact Dr. Brownfield, the psychiatrist, and arrange an appointment just as soon as Hux went to sleep.

Hux did not go to sleep. An hour after they reached the apartment, Mildred slipped out to a neighbor's and tried to call Dr. Brownfield, but he was not available. She told the neighbor that Hux was acting strangely, as though he did not know where he was. He seemed to be hearing voices and was carrying on conversations with Marine officers who certainly were not present.

The neighbor promised to attempt to locate Dr. Brownfield. She heard Hux' loud voice coming from the Leighton apartment for the next hour, and then everything was suddenly quiet. He had, in all probability, fallen asleep. At ten the next morning, when the neighbor still had heard nothing from Mildred Leighton, she knocked on the door of the apartment. There was no response, so she summoned the building superintendent, who used his passkey to enter. The scene was not pretty. Mildred Leighton lay dead in the middle of the living room floor, stabbed by the samurai sword. Hux' body was only a few feet away. He had fallen on the sword in the Japanese fashion of hara-kari.

The fears of Mildred and Charles Leighton proved justified in the extreme. The newspapers gave the story exaggerated space. It was one of the first of the tragedies of the returning veterans: "Combat Hero Stabs Mother, Kills Self With Japanese Sword."

When Dr. Helpern opened Hux Leighton's chest cavity at the autopsy table, he saw a familiar entity when he examined the right lung. It was "heavy" and saturated with fluid, so that the alveoli, the tiny air sacs in which the oxygen and carbon dioxide are exchanged to maintain the life-sustaining oxygen cycle, were so "drowned" that they could not perform their necessary task. Hux Leighton was the victim of a severe case of lobar or "walking" pneumonia.

One of the characteristics of the disease is that the person frequently goes into periods of delirium. He acts insane; his conduct exactly mimics that of a person who is "out of his mind," or drunk to the point of passing out.

The Marine Corps conducted its own investigation into Hux Leighton's tragic death. At no time did he ever have a history of mental instability. Dr. Helpern concluded that the murder-suicide that claimed his life and that of his mother was, in all probability, the result of the delirium of lobar pneumonia, the same disease from which his father recovered without physical defect and the one that was responsible for Hux' hurried trip home from the Pacific.

"This case shows," Dr. Helpern frequently says in his lectures, "why you do an autopsy in *every* homicide case, even the obvious ones. If you fail to do an autopsy, you are left with only the superficial conclusions based on 'facts' that are really no more than guesswork.

"Here, everything in this man's superficial history pointed to the fact that he had gone mad while in the service. Actually, the odds are overwhelming that his 'madness' was nothing more than the delirium brought on by lobar pneumonia. He probably would have been dead in a few hours from this disease, even if he had not killed himself."

Dr. Helpern uses the case to illustrate another premise.

"It shows," he says, "how many things in life come full circle. Life is a series of arcs that come full circle, from birth to death, birth to birth, and death to death. These separate arcs that themselves come full circle are the most fascinating segments out of the whole span."

CHAPTER 13

"Those Who Deviate from the Norms Should Understand the Risks"

Dr. Helpern hurriedly put on his surgical gown and descended the spiral steel staircase to the autopsy room. A young assistant autopsy surgeon had alerted him to a case that might prove of interest.

The view of the body that had once been the person of Winston Paulson was not pretty. The subsequent autopsy protocol attempted to describe bits and pieces of the scene:

The body is that of a well-developed, well-nourished, young adult white male who appears his stated age of 26, height 5 feet 9 inches, weight 150 pounds. The hair is brown in color, slightly wavy, and receding. There are gaping, longitudinal, anterior-to-posterior lacerations of the scalp of the left frontal, temporal, and lower parietal and anterior occipital areas. There are multiple loose fragments of scalp with small fragments of cranium protruding from this wound. Its greatest dimensions are 5½ inches in length and 2¼ inches in width.

There is a single gaping laceration in the hairline of the midportion of the scalp which runs slightly right to left but is generally vertical in its orientation. It measures 2 inches in length and ½ inch in width. The cranium is palpable and can be observed through this wound; but there is no evidence of depressed skull fracture in this region. There are two gaping lacerations in the posterior occiput. . . . These wounds are 4 inches in length and each has a width of $\frac{3}{4}$ inch. . . . There is a superficial laceration, which has maroon edges, which is located above the left eyelid and just below the left eyebrow. Its length is $1\frac{3}{16}$ inches, and its width is $\frac{3}{8}$ inch. There is a laceration above the right eyebrow . . . there are lacerations. . . .

The autopsy protocol was unusually long because page after page was required to describe the sixty-nine separate and distinct wounds about the head and upper portion of the body, to say nothing of less serious bruises and abrasions in the area of the buttocks, the pubic region, and the lower limbs. If ever the cliché about being "beaten to a bloody pulp" applied, its use was appropriate in this case.

"What's the history?" Dr. Helpern asked simply as he looked at the uniformed patrolman standing at the head of the autopsy table.

"Well," the patrolman began, looking at his notes, "he was found in his own apartment over on Sheridan Square in Greenwich Village, about three o'clock this afternoon. He had complained a few days earlier to the handyman of his apartment house about the lock on the front door not working right. When the handyman went up to check on it, the lock cylinder spun around when he tried to put in the passkey. He opened the door and saw blood all over the apartment, from one end to the other. It was even on the ceiling and the top of the walls. I was the first officer there after the handyman called the police."

"What kind of a place was it?" Dr. Helpern asked.

"Beautiful," the patrolman responded, a tone of envy creeping into his voice. "I sure wish I could afford furniture like that for my family; and great big oil pictures all over the walls. Even some of them were spattered with blood, and on this modern art stuff the blood seemed to blend right in with the artist's paints."

"You found the weapon?" Dr. Helpern continued.

"Yeah, it looks like it's this," the patrolman replied, holding up a blood-covered, fourteen-inch barbell.

"That would do it," Dr. Helpern observed. "Anything else in the room?"

"Yeah," the patrolman responded, looking again at his notes. "There was a quart bottle of Four Roses on the coffee table in the living room. It was about three-quarters full. There were two crystal glasses on the table, about half-full of something that smelled like bourbon."

"We can probably give you the cause of death in just a minute," Dr. Helpern said. "It will be 'multiple, depressed skull fractures with contusions and lacerations of the brain.' "

"Anything else?" the patrolman asked, after writing this entry in his pocket-sized notebook.

"Yes," Dr. Helpern continued, "you can tell the Homicide detectives that they should start looking for a homosexual murderer."

The detectives in the Homicide Bureau did begin to look for a homosexual murderer, but first they conducted a thorough investigation into the life and activities of Winston Paulson.

They found that Winston Paulson was a particularly brilliant and sensitive young man who had received his Doctor of Philosophy degree from one of the leading eastern universities two years earlier. Only twenty-three years old at the time, he had been courted by the personnel recruiting agents of more than two dozen of the country's largest business firms. The starting salary offer began in the range of $1000 a month, because Winston Paulson showed promise of becoming a truly creative mathematician—and this type of mind and talent are rare and valuable commodities. Paulson signed on with a company whose large international headquarters was located in Rockefeller Plaza, and he was immediately assigned to a highly intensified training course in cybernetics. His ultimate position with the firm would be to attempt to improve and simplify the language of the computers.

The police investigation disclosed that Winston Paulson was considered to be one of the brightest prospects in the firm's great stable of promising young Ph.D.'s. For a while, he had dated a fellow employee, but she broke off their relationship because "he was unreliable and often stood me up." Since no one at Paulson's place of employment could shed any real light on his private and social life, the police were thrown back to the apartment building on Sheridan Square for their sources of information.

A pattern soon began to emerge. Winston Paulson obviously had a great many friends who visited him often. They were described as men between the ages of twenty and fifty. They arrived around six in the afternoon of the weekdays, and departed at one or two the following morning. Over the weekends, his guests arrived and departed at all hours of the day and night. Their physical descriptions ran the entire gamut from tall and slender to fat and pudgy, blond, brunet, and redhead. A handsome, well-dressed Chinese had attracted the attention of many of the residents of the building.

After Winston Paulson's body was discovered, a detective had remained in the apartment to monitor any incoming telephone calls. At 8:45 P.M., the following conversation was reported in the police files on the case:

In Male Voice:	*Hello.*
Out Male Voice:	*Is Alex there?*
In Male Voice:	*No, he is not. Who's calling?*
Out Male Voice:	*I'll see him at work tomorrow. Tell him Richard called.*

The police had, hopefully, confiscated three reels of magnetic tape on top of Paulson's expensive stereo set; but when they played the reels through, they found that they contained nothing but classical music performed by the London Philharmonic under the direction of Sir Malcolm Sargent.

The police also found the usual personal telephone book. It contained approximately one hundred and fifty names, with addresses and phone numbers. Out of the entire list of names, only seven were female; one hundred-and-forty-plus male names posed a staggering investigative problem.

Perhaps a more promising lead was an eight-by-ten picture taken in the Finale Restaurant two days before Paulson's murder. He sat proudly and regally in the center of a group of nine men who flanked him, five on his right and four on his left. Paulson had written on the back of the picture: "Richard's birthday party at Finale Restaurant. Left to right . . ."

Paulson then listed the first and last names of all those

present. The handsome Chinese face was identified as Ernest Wong.

The police also made a perplexing discovery in this same bureau drawer that contained the address book and the picture of the birthday celebration. There were fourteen lock cylinders, each approximately an inch and a half long and half an inch in diameter. Each cylinder could be fitted into the Segal lock on the front door of Paulson's apartment, the same lock which the building's handyman had described as "spinning" when he went up to repair it just before he discovered Paulson's brutally beaten body. Each of the fourteen lock cylinders had a professionally lettered identifying number on its side: "K-469," "M-182," "B-521."

The homicide detectives next made a list of all the code numbers found on the fourteen lock cylinders, and they began a search of Paulson's address book. It took only a few minutes to match all fourteen code numbers on the cylinders to fourteen names in the address book:

"Ernest Wong—891-2345-E-1672."

Obviously, Paulson's sensitive, brilliant, mathematical mind had worked out some sort of a cybernetic first.

The ultimate solution of the case required almost six weeks of methodical, painstaking police work. Winston Paulson, the promising Ph.D. mathematician who was destined to do great things in the field of cybernetics was an active homosexual. He recruited his partners stealthily, and believed that he had worked out a foolproof method whereby each partner would think that he was the only person involved in a physical relationship with Paulson.

To accomplish his purpose, Paulson had purchased a master lock set. He worked out an arrangement whereby each one of the fourteen lock cylinders could be slipped in and out of the single lock in the front door to the apartment at will. He then gave each one of his fourteen homosexual partners a key that would only fit its matching cylinder. Each of the men involved with Paulson was egotistically gratified to receive this special and select token of his affection and esteem, his own personal key to Paulson's apartment.

Ernest Wong, a wealthy real estate broker in Manhattan, was

so elated over the arrangement that he bought Paulson a new cream-colored Chevrolet convertible. Another member of the select fourteen, a doctor of medicine employed in the research department of a large, pharmaceutical company in New Jersey, took Paulson on a paid three-week vacation trip to Paris. A prominent, promising Greenwich Village artist had presented Paulson with what he considered to be his finest works, which now decorated the walls of Paulson's apartment.

Twenty-three-year-old Albert Hastisohn was also a member of the select fourteen, and had been favored with one of the personalized keys to Paulson's apartment. But something had happened on this critical 17th day of August 1965. Hastisohn received a call from Paulson inviting him to come over around six in the evening. When he arrived, he followed his usual pattern of slipping his own key into the door, unlocking it, and opening it unannounced. This time, however, Hastisohn's key would not unlock the door. Hastisohn, who had been discharged from the Army only three months, where he was assigned to military police duty, immediately became suspicious, and began a surveillance on Paulson's apartment.

Around eight-thirty that night, one of the men whom Hastisohn had met at the birthday celebration in the Finale Restaurant the night before, entered the apartment building. Fifteen minutes later, this man and Paulson came out and drove away in Paulson's Chevrolet convertible. They were back a little after eleven o'clock, and reentered the building. Hastisohn's careful surveillance was paying off. It was almost one o'clock the following morning when the man left.

Hastisohn then entered the building and made his way to apartment 17-D. This time, he did not rely upon his special personalized key to gain entrance. He pounded on the door, and when Paulson opened it, Hastisohn rushed by him into the room. Hastisohn confronted Paulson with his suspicions. Paulson poured the two of them the drinks of Four Roses. The discussion became heated. Before they could even finish one drink, Paulson admitted his infidelities and philandering. It was more than Hastisohn could bear, particularly the sneer on Paulson's face which was calculated to make Hastisohn jealous. In his confession to the police, Hastisohn said that he remembered eying the two barbells which Paulson used in his regular daily workouts to keep his beautifully proportioned body taut and in excellent condition. He seized one of the barbells; the autopsy protocol on the body of Winston Paulson tells the rest of the grim story.

As it is with computers and cybernetics, electronic devices and all man-made machines, Winston Paulson had not been able to eliminate the possibility of human error from his carefully devised mode of operation. When he called Hastisohn to invite him to the apartment, he failed to select the lock cylinder that would respond only to Hastisohn's key. Ernest Wong or the doctor friend or the artist might have thought nothing of being unable to gain admission to the apartment at that particular time on that particular evening; but Albert Hastisohn's exposure to military police procedures in the service made him immediately suspicious. This human factor, which cannot be eliminated from even the most elaborate plans of man, brought the destruction of both of these men.

"When we see these brutal, multiple wound cases in a single victim," Dr. Helpern says, in explaining why he could tell the patrolman almost immediately after seeing Paulson's body that the murderer was a homosexual, "we just automatically assume that we are dealing with a homosexual victim and a homosexual attacker. It's not my role to condemn homosexuality as such, and I leave it to the psychiatrists and psychologists to try to figure out why people practice homosexuality. Maybe it's because, as they say, the man hates his mother and thereby all women, or he loves his father abnormally, or he loves this and hates that, and this leads him into a different type of sexual and emotional relationship with other people. I'm glad that I don't have to try to figure out the motivation. This is another subject about which probably more is *not* known than is known at the present time.

"I do think, though, that it is high time that those who deviate from the norms should understand the risks. I don't know why it is so, but it seems that the violent explosions of jealousy among homosexuals far exceed those of the jealousy of a man for a woman, or a woman for a man. The pent-up charges and energy of the homosexual relationship simply cannot be contained. When the explosive point is reached, the result is brutally violent.

"Any one of a number of these wounds could have killed Winston Paulson. His skull was pulverized, his brain contused and lacerated, but here you had sixty-nine separate and distinct wounds. It's hard to imagine the torment inside the man wielding that barbell that caused this kind of attack. It appears utterly senseless to us, as impartial observers. We simply cannot understand what went on inside the mind and body of Albert Hastisohn.

"But this is the 'normal' pattern of these homosexual attacks, the multiple stabbings, the multiple senseless beatings that obviously must continue long after the victim dies. It's certainly none of my business if people elect to practice homosexuality; but I do think they might do well to recognize some of the risks involved when they decide to walk this path."

CHAPTER 14

"The Affluent Society Is Exacting Its Own Toll"

The cover letter from the supervisor of claims of one of the nation's largest life insurance companies, attached to the thick packet of reports, Xerox copies, photographs, and an autopsy protocol, read:

DEAR DR. HELPERN:
I enclose our entire file in the Edward Martin case for your review, to assist you in arriving at your opinion as to the cause of death.
The one policy involved is for a face amount of $100,000. It contains our usual Double Indemnity Clause for accidental death. In addition, there is a Suicide Exclusion Clause which provides that no benefits are due and payable at all if the death is suicidal within a two-year period after the policy becomes effective. This policy had been operative for approximately thirteen months at the time of the deceased's death.
We would appreciate very much your early attention to this matter, and your opinion as soon as you can give it. Our sales representatives in Graham County, Iowa, are hounding us for payment of the Double Indemnity feature, saying in effect that we cannot very well expect them to sell new business if we do not pay off promptly on all claims. As you know from past experience, it is our established policy to settle all legitimate claims promptly. We have adequate reserves out of which to pay these claims, but we do not intend to be imposed upon regardless of the amount or size of the claim.

The name "Graham County, Iowa," rang a bell with Dr. Helpern. He turned to the certified copy of the death certificate and saw that it was signed by a Dr. David Dawson.

"Go through our 'request' file," Dr. Helpern said to his secretary. "See if you can find anything from a Dr. Dawson of Graham County, Iowa."

Within minutes, his secretary brought him a letter dated almost two years earlier, which read:

DEAR DR. HELPERN:
I have been engaged in the general practice of medicine in this community for almost twenty years. I am planning to run for the office of coroner this fall. I wonder if you could refer me to any books or other medical literature that might be of help to me in the event that I am elected to this office. I have only performed one autopsy since my medical school days, and this was done almost eighteen years ago. Naturally, I want to be as well prepared for the duties of the office of coroner as I possibly can, in the event that I am elected.

Dr. Helpern remembered thinking to himself when he read the letter, that at least some progress was being made in this particular county in Iowa. One of the candidates for the office of coroner was a doctor of medicine. Presumably, he would be a great potential improvement over the furniture dealer, general merchant, undertaker, or some other nonmedical person, who is frequently elected coroner in most of the fifty states.

Dr. Helpern reread the copy of his answering letter:

DEAR DR. DAWSON:
I am delighted to learn that you, as a doctor, are running for the office of coroner in your county. Unfortunately, only a limited number of voters have any real appreciation of the serious determinations which must be made as to cause and manner of death by the elected coroner.
To answer your specific inquiry, I hope it will not seem immodest for me to suggest our book *Legal Medicine, Pathology and Toxicology* as a reference work in this field. I would also recommend to you Dr. LeMoyne Snyder's book *Homicide Investigation*. I enclose a mimeographed list of books and articles in the medical literature on subjects of importance in this entire medico-legal field.
I extend to you my best personal and professional wishes. If you are

in New York City, I would be very happy for you to come by and see our facilities; and members of my staff will be happy to discuss with you some of our common problems and procedures.

As Dr. Helpern began his examination of the Edward Martin file, he was hopeful that Dr. Dawson in Graham County, Iowa, had done his homework well.

The first entry was the certified death certificate. His eyes automatically focused on Item 18:

Medical Cause of Death
Part I: Death Caused By: *Acute coronary thrombosis*
Condition, if any, which gave rise to above immediate cause: ______________________

Under Item 20-A on the death certificate, the words "Accident," "Suicide," and "Homicide" had been crossed out, and a typewritten entry inserted: "Natural Causes." There was certainly nothing on the death certificate to raise a problem with the double indemnity, accidental death feature of the policy.

Dr. Helpern was immediately disappointed when he turned to Dr. Dawson's autopsy protocol. It was sketchy and handwritten in large hieroglyphics of "doctor's script," and was barely legible. Over three-fourths of the protocol was devoted to a description of minor cuts and lacerations on the chin, outside chest wall, and the knuckles of the right hand, and a bruise on the right shin.

The critical finding was given only eight lines. Under the heading "Internal Exam," it read:

On opening the heart, there was seen a thrombus projecting from the opening of the left coronary artery. Opening the left coronary artery revealed this clot to be firmly attached to the inside diameter of the artery. The only other pertinent finding was a fracture of the right 6th rib in the mid-clavicular line, with a small extravasation of blood into the intercostal muscles. The brain & remaining organs were regular.

These were the official medical findings on which as much as $200,000 in insurance benefits to Edward Martin's widow and four minor children hinged.

Dr. Dawson labored under considerable difficulty. The autopsy protocol indicated that the autopsy had been performed at a private mortuary after the body had been embalmed. Dr. Helpern frequently tells his students that the autopsy surgeon always has two strikes against him and a curve ball on the way to the plate when he is forced to perform an autopsy after embalming.

Embalming is one of the luxuries practiced almost exclusively by those who subscribe to the "American Way of Death." No other country in the world routinely embalms its dead. While this social custom is a great financial boon to funeral directors and undertakers, it definitely impedes the investigation of the cause and manner of death.

The basic procedure for embalming is to remove the blood from the circulatory system, and the other fluids from the gastrointestinal tract, the bladder, and body cavities, and to replace them with embalming fluid.

This is accomplished by inserting a large, hollow needle called a trocar into strategic locations. The trocar is attached to a vacuum or suction apparatus, and the fluid is aspirated from the various body cavities. Hollow tubes called cannulas are placed in different blood vessels, and the blood is withdrawn from one cannula while embalming fluid is introduced through the other in order to infuse this fluid throughout the network of veins and arteries.

An abdominal trocar puncture may be made in the epigastrium. The trocar is then pointed in all directions to penetrate the organs and structures in the chest and abdomen so that they may receive the embalming fluid.

The embalmer may make surgical incisions over the large blood vessels in the neck, armpits, and groin to expose the vessels for draining out the blood and injecting embalming fluid.

The principal ingredient of embalming fluid is formaldehyde; the exact formula is fixed by law in many states.

The formaldehyde causes the protein in the various parts and organs of the body to coagulate. This causes the tissues, muscles, and organs to harden, shrink, stiffen, and bleach. If the embalming process is thorough and complete, these drastic changes extend throughout the entire body.

The embalming process is designed to produce changes in the dead body, not to preserve evidence as to the cause and manner of death. It obscures and confuses certain pathological entities. An inexperienced autopsy examiner may draw totally erroneous conclusions if he does not differentiate between the conditions that existed before death and the changes caused by the embalming process. For example, hemorrhages beneath the surface of the skin, which produce the characteristic black and blue marks of bruising, may be "ironed out" and diminished so that the extent of the bruising cannot be estimated accurately.

While penetrating wounds, stab wounds, bullet wounds, and injuries by blunt forces may be identified after embalming, it is not unusual for an inexperienced autopsy examiner to confuse the before-death wound with an incision made during the embalming process. In some instances, the reckless insertion and manipulations of the hollow embalming needles by the embalmer make it impossible to trace the exact course of the wound through the body, or to accurately measure its penetration into an organ. Massive hemorrhages into the chest and abdominal cavities are sucked out by the embalming trocar. This makes it impossible to measure the amount of internal bleeding which preceded death.

Changes in the size, weight, color, consistency, and gross appearance of the body organs are often indicative of various disease processes. Since the embalming fluid causes the organs and muscles to harden, shrink, stiffen, and bleach, accurate determination of these changes for diagnostic purposes may be seriously impeded.

The embalming fluid may create discrete and hardened areas in the lung. These look like before-death thrombi, which are "plugs" or "clots" in the blood vessels. The hardened area may also simulate pneumonia.

The embalming process prevents the discovery of air embolism, which is a bubble of air in a blood vessel which obstructs it, causing death.

Embalming may also preclude an accurate detection of many

poisons, such as alcohol, carbon dioxide, paraldehyde, chloral hydrate, ether, chloroform, and the cyanides.

Death by drowning, strangulation, and smothering, which under the best of circumstances are often missed routinely by the inexperienced autopsy examiner, may be completely obscured by embalming.

Still, a frighteningly large percentage of autopsies are performed after the body has been embalmed by coroners and their so-called autopsy surgeons in every one of the states which still operate under the coroner system. Dr. Dawson was indeed laboring under a handicap when he approached the body of Edward Martin in the private mortuary in Graham County.

On its face, the autopsy protocol described a typical "coroner's thrombosis," and the insurance company was undoubtedly justified in treating the death as being from "natural causes" as the death certificate indicated. Dr. Helpern wondered temporarily what the real medical problem was all about. It was true that the bruises and lacerations on the various parts of the body and the broken sixth rib still had to be explained, but there was really nothing to raise a serious question of accidental or suicidal death. The company could expect to settle for the $100,000 face value of the policy, but perhaps nothing more.

Dr. Helpern soon became aware of the medical and legal issues as he plunged into the extensive report of one of the company's chief investigators.

Edward Martin was fifty-five years of age, a big-boned, virile, athletic man, standing just under six feet and weighing 190 pounds. Twenty-eight years earlier he started out with a high school education, five years of sales experience in the farm implement field, driving ambition, and a few practical, common-sense ideas for making improvements on certain types of farm implements. He founded his own small manufacturing plant in an abandoned barn on the outskirts of his city. The other employee of this fledgling company was his wife, who worked side by side with him, twelve, fourteen, sixteen hours a day. The company flourished, even during the years of World War II, for then Martin manufactured components for the landing gear system of B-17 bombers under subcontract to one of the major aircraft companies. The end of the war brought diversification and high demand, and the early 60's saw the company's gross profits round off in the neighborhood of $10,000,000. The life insurance policy now in question had been taken out by Martin as part of an estate plan, to give his wife and children working cash so that the business would not have to be disrupted or face an emergency sale because of his death.

This critical Thursday morning in the middle of November began no differently from hundreds of others. Martin and his family lived on a farm approximately ten miles out of the city. He left home at seven thirty in the morning, driving his new Lincoln Continental which was in perfect operating condition. The weather reports cautioned against the threat of a snowstorm, so he advised his wife that he might spend the night in town at his club, which he frequently did during the winter months if the weather was bad. A national sales convention was in progress at the main hotel of the city, and Martin was scheduled to give a thirty-minute speech at three o'clock in the afternoon.

Mrs. Martin heard no more from him or about him until approximately eight thirty the following morning when a sheriff's deputy arrived to announce that a body had been recovered from a creek about five miles from the Martin home; it was believed to be that of her husband.

The insurance company's investigator began to compile and fill in the gaps on Martin's activities for the period of time that transpired after he kissed his wife good-bye at seven thirty Thursday morning. The fact that Martin, or someone, was dead was first brought to the attention of the sheriff by a truck driver who crossed a bridge over the creek at 6:32 Friday morning. He casually glanced out the window of the truck cab and saw what appeared to be an automobile partially submerged in the creek. When the sheriff's patrol car arrived, the deputies found that it was Martin's Lincoln Continental that had run down the fifty-foot bank from the road to the creek, to come to rest at the edge of the water. The water covered the motor and the hood and had reached the level of the dashboard inside the car. The right rear door was standing open. The right front window was rolled down. The rear lights of the car were on. The ignition switch was turned off, and the ignition key gone. Martin's glasses, which he always wore, were found on top of the dashboard. There were no footprints leading from the car up the bank, nor were there any along the bank; but thirty feet from the car, the deputies found Martin's body submerged in approximately six feet of water. The wristwatch on his left arm had stopped at 4:41.

The deputies called a doctor who lived in the vicinity. He arrived within thirty minutes and pronounced Edward Martin dead. The body was then taken to the funeral parlor and immediately embalmed. Dr. Dawson, the duly elected coroner of Graham County, was notified by the officers approximately one hour after the embalming was completed. He arrived two hours later to perform his official autopsy.

The insurance investigator, with permission and authorization from Mrs. Martin, began a careful background check into Martin's medical history. Over the preceding ten years he had received eleven physical examinations, including the one required by the insurance company at the time the policy under consideration was taken out. Outside of a hemorrhoidectomy, the medical history was basically negative. The periodic, yearly EKG's were well within the range of normal. He had never complained of any chest pain, shortness of breath, indigestion, arm pain, or any of the other symptoms of heart disease. All the doctors described him as being a moderate man. He had described himself to them as a "social drinker," and indicated that he never drank to excess.

The investigator received the same corroborating information from eight of Martin's friends and business acquaintances. It was only by accident that he talked to an out-of-town business contact who had lunch with Martin the critical Thursday, just before Martin was to speak at the convention. Martin had declined a cocktail before lunch, stating casually that he was "on the water-wagon." This chance, accidental remark stirred the inquiring brain of the insurance investigator, who wondered why Martin was on the wagon that particular day. He soon found his answer.

Martin had been a chronic alcoholic for the preceding ten years. As is true with a great many alcoholics, he had become increasingly adept in concealing this failing from his doctors. Martin also had undergone an operation for a detached retina of the right eye six months before his death. This had left him almost totally blind in this eye. Mrs. Martin had called the family doctor to apprise him of the fact that Martin's habits and outlook on life had undergone a drastic change since his eye problem. He was now depressed and seemed to be losing interest in his business. He no longer worked twelve and fourteen hours a day, but was content with a minimum of eight and sometimes only six hours. A month before his death, he had undergone a complete physical examination. Because of Mrs. Martin's telephone call, the family doctor had referred him to a psychiatrist for an interview. The psychiatrist made no outstanding findings. He reported that Martin was definitely concerned about his loss of eyesight, but he did not find any pathological psychoses or deep depression.

The investigator next discovered that soon after Martin delivered his speech to the convention, he fell off the wagon and began to frequent several of his old bars. He was last seen alive taking his car from a parking lot near the Gladiator Restaurant. The parking lot attendant described him as being obviously intoxicated at the time he entered the car, presumably to drive home. This was approximately one o'clock Friday morning.

No evidence was developed as to what happened to Martin between the time he took the car from a parking lot, and the time he was found submerged in the creek approximately five miles from his home.

Dr. Helpern put down the file and began to speculate on the possibilities of Edward Martin's death. The single medical finding of significance was the thrombus or "clot" in the left coronary artery, but this offered several possibilities. Did the clot in the coronary artery form *before* the car left the road to plunge down into the creek bed and therefore cause the accident? If this was true, then Edward Martin's death was a result of "natural causes," as Dr. Dawson had indicated on the death certificate.

There was also a possibility that the excitement and trauma of the accident had actually produced the clot and the "heart attack." If this were true, then the insurance company's position was quite different. It would mean that the death was the result of the accident, which would bring into effect the double indemnity clause in the policy. Instead of owing Martin's wife and family $100,000 on the face value of the policy, the insurance company would have to pay $200,000.

Dr. Helpern did not spend too much time considering the possibility of suicide, which would completely eliminate any payment under the terms of the policy even though the two-year suicide exclusionary feature still had eleven months to run. It was true that Martin had been depressed over the loss of his eyesight. He had been examined by a psychiatrist. The route that he had taken toward his home and by a creek was off his beaten path; but all of this evidence taken together would not come close to overcoming the legal presumption against any death being suicide unless overwhelming evidence were produced that it was suicide.

In his autopsy protocol, Dr. Dawson had made no attempt to describe the observable characteristics of this particular blood clot. This may have been because the body had been embalmed before he did his autopsy. Even on unembalmed bodies, the present state of medical knowledge, as it concerns a determination of the age of a blood clot, leaves much to be desired. Doctors can say that the blood clot does *not* form after death. They can say that it is "fresh," which means that it is "soft and red." This, in turn, indicates that it was probably not more than six hours old at the time of death. Beyond that, however, more specific estimations of the age of the clot are little more than rank guesswork.

Dr. Helpern's opinion, of necessity, had to be that the blood clot that caused the heart attack *could* have come before the car left the road to enter the creek. It could have caused the accident. On the other hand, the accident could have occurred first, and in turn caused the heart attack.

He quickly turned over the other evidence in his mind. Obviously, Edward Martin had climbed out of the car alive and under his own power, even though he might have been intoxicated, or stunned and in a state of shock from the impact of the car against the water. The key to the ignition was found in Martin's right-hand pants pocket. He had been conscious and able to perform this coordinated motor act of turning off the switch, removing the key, and placing it in his pocket. The only logical explanation for the rear right-hand door being open was that Martin crawled across the back of the front seat, opened the door, and got out of the automobile. Even though his reason was not apparent, it further seemed logical that Martin had walked in the water a distance of thirty feet from the car to the point where his body was found. He may have been dazed. He may have been drunk. At this point, in all probability, he simply collapsed and slid under the six feet of water.

Dr. Dawson's autopsy, even if he had been alert enough to look for the signs, was of no help as to whether the death was from drowning. The embalming process had forever eliminated the possibility of this determination. In drowning deaths, the contents of the lungs and heart often show definite pathological changes, but these observable changes will not withstand the assault of the embalmer's needle.

Dr. Helpern reached for the telephone and dialed the insurance company's chief claims superintendent.

"Jim," he said, "my best opinion is that you should pay off the full $200,000 double indemnity claim on the Edward Martin policy. My reasoning is this: Neither I nor anyone else can tell, on the basis of the evidence that now exists, whether Martin's heart attack happened before the accident or after the accident, or whether he actually drowned. Keep in mind that his body was found submerged in six feet of water. This is completely irreversible. No body can survive that type of insult. We are assuming that because of this thrombus or clot in the coronary artery he did suffer a heart attack; but a heart attack of this nature is not necessarily irreversible. More frequently than not, it does not cause death. The victim may recover and go on to live out his normal life span."

The following day, the insurance company processed a check in the amount of $200,000, payable to Edward Martin's estate.

"Our affluent society is exacting its own toll in the form of stress and pressures," Dr. Helpern says, "and we simply aren't prepared to cope with it. This is especially true in the medicolegal field.

"This Martin case is not exceptional in any way. As a matter of fact, it is a rather drab, routine, run-of-the-mill case. You know, only 2 percent of our medical examiner's cases involve any question of homicide. Granted, the homicides and suicides are the cases that make the headlines, and are the type that the public remembers; but 98 percent of our cases involve a dollars-and-cents problem of insurance benefits, Workmen's Compensation payments, automobile accident liability, burial insurance, hospital insurance, and almost any type of legal problem that you can imagine.

"The complexities of modern living enter the picture of modern death and modern dying. Death is no longer a simple process. The exact manner in which a man dies, and the exact single cause of his death may have grave legal consequences.

"Then, we have the problem of alcohol, which is the great 'masker of injury and trauma.' This is frequently compounded by the problem of barbiturates. Modern man's fight to retain his individuality against the overwhelming pressures of reducing him to a monotonous, unrecognizable digit in life continues on in death.

"When I talk about the fact that we are not ready to meet the demands imposed by modern death, I am not referring exclusively to the lack of trained personnel in coroners' and medical examiners' offices. This Edward Martin case is a good example of what can happen on that score. It seems incredible that the death certificate and the autopsy protocol in this case contained absolutely no mention of the possibility of death from other than natural causes, that old 'coroner's' heart attack. Still, this is the way these cases are reported and signed out hundreds of times every month.

"My main concern is over our lack of planning for the future, so that the demands of our modern affluent society can be at last partially coped with. I want to see some genuine, well-organized, well-financed research projects in every facet of this subject of death. This Martin case is a good example of the type of project I am talking about. I am reasonably certain in my own mind that with proper research, we could devise methods of determining the approximate age of a clot in a coronary artery. We could set up some safe guidelines that would permit us to determine this question of whether the accident comes first and causes the clot, or whether the clot comes first and causes the accident. Hundreds of millions of dollars in insurance claims every year hinge on this one simple question; but at the present time, we are operating purely by medical guess and legal gosh.

"There are dozens and dozens of other facets of this subject of death that must be researched. In our office alone, we now have detailed records on almost one million deaths. We don't have the personnel or money to make sufficient statistical arrangement of these deaths for research purposes. They are just filed away by name. A great many medical discoveries in the past have been arrived at through the proper use of medical statistics. For all anyone knows, the answer to cancer or heart disease, or a dozen other medical problems, may be lying right in our filing system in the medical examiner's office in New York. If we put all of this dormant, latent information on tapes and into computers, there is no way of even guessing at the discoveries that might be made.

"One of my major objectives before I reach the age to retire five years from now is to see some of these research projects launched, so that death can really begin to help the living in this affluent society of ours."

CHAPTER 15

"Be Careful What You Do to the World"

It was 2 A.M. Sunday morning when the telephone in Dr. Helpern's apartment rang. It did not awaken him because he had not been to bed. He was struggling over the final budget figures for submission to the fiscal officers of the city the following Monday morning.

"'Chief," the assistant medical examiner stationed in the Bronx said, after a few preliminaries, "I've got a subway suicide case out here. The family is Catholic, and you know how upset they are!"

"What's it about?" Dr. Helpern asked as matter-of-factly as if the call had been to his office at ten o'clock in the morning.

"Oh, the usual alcoholic Irishman," the assistant examiner replied. "Threw himself in front of a train. It's about as open-and-shut as that, except that the family doesn't want it classified as suicide."

The assistant examiner then rambled on for a full twenty minutes about his heavy workload, and his particular problems with other specific cases. Dr. Helpern listened attentively and courteously. He always listens to a subordinate's problem, no matter what the hour or location.

"Well, don't close out the case," Dr. Helpern said when his assistant finally talked himself out. "I'll be over around noon and take a look at it."

Dr. Helpern then returned to his charts and graphs and budget figures. He was now presiding over an office that had 130 full-time employees, and an annual budget of almost $1,000,000. He had a first assistant chief medical examiner who now earned $18,500. There were five full-time associate medical examiners at salaries of $15,000 each. Dr. Helpern's own salary was now $25,000, but the fight to get salary schedules upgraded to even these levels had been long and difficult. It was still the vicious circle of the chicken and the egg. Most pathologists simply would not go into the field of forensic medicine because of the long hours and the inadequate salary structure. Even if the salary schedules were suddenly raised so that they would become attractive to young promising pathologists, the number of men actually trained in forensic pathology remains so limited that there are not enough to go around. So, where to begin!

In New York, Dr. Helpern must fill nineteen positions of assistant medical examiner on a rotating, per diem basis. The doctors who serve in this capacity work from six to twenty-four hours a day for a stipend honorarium of $25. It is a labor of love and professional interest only for these men, since they could earn several times their per diem allotment by working at their own private practices. They are able to perform their forensic medicine duties for the city in an adequate professional manner because of their love of the field, and their respect and genuine affection for Dr. Helpern, who guides them with a firm but sympathetic hand.

Dr. Helpern would show the City Budget Examiner the next morning that each death falling within the jurisdiction of the medical examiner's office would cost the taxpayers approximately $33.33. It is an incredible dollars-and-cents figure, and one that is even more impressive when analyzed against the cost figures of counties that still operate under the ancient, dilapidated, archaic coroner's system.

Orange County, California, by way of example, can be used as a measuring stick. Orange County, situated along the coast between Los Angeles and San Diego, prides itself through chamber of commerce promotional statements on being the fastest growing county in the entire United States. Virtually every department in the county government, which has an annual budget in excess of $110,000,000, is organized along modern, twentieth century lines, with the exception of the coroner's office.

Here, there is no central morgue facility. Coroner's autopsies are performed on a "piecework" basis, at private mortuaries scattered throughout the county. They are performed by independent physicians, who frequently must travel substantial distances and carry their own surgical instruments with them. These physicians are not trained as forensic pathologists. Many of the autopsies are little more than what one observer has termed "stir jobs." He means that the doctor simply opens the chest cavity or the head, and counts the number of organs, stirs them around, closes the surgical incision, and guesses at a cause of death.

Still, the citizens of Orange County pay $60.20 for each coroner's case accepted, and an additional $41.26 for those cases which are autopsied in the "stir job" manner.

This figure of $101.46 for each autopsied coroner's case should impress the board of county supervisors when it is compared with Dr. Helpern's figure of $33.33, but the supervisors could not be less interested. Their concern lies in things tangible, such as airports, electronic traffic control equipment to handle the visitors to Disneyland or the Angel's Stadium, and data-processing equipment. The chairman of the board of supervisors dismissed a grand jury inquiry into the operations of the Orange County coroner's office by pointing out that, in his opinion, autopsy findings primarily benefitted insurance companies, and he did not see why the citizens of Orange County should foot the bill for insurance companies. He had no interest in improving the quality of autopsies in Orange County, and even the dollars-and-cents cost factors did not impress him.

Regrettably, his attitude is not unique. Death is still a difficult commodity to sell. Even its ability to help the living is not considered sufficiently attractive in the eyes of those who run for public office to stimulate them to upgrade the facilities and the personnel in forensic medicine.

Dr. Helpern finished his budget calculations, and slept for a few hours before going over to the Bronx to view the subway suicide of the alcoholic Irishman.

"I'm going to call it 'accidental,' " Dr. Helpern said after carefully examining the horribly mangled body which had been run over by the subway train. He had already checked the autopsy findings of his assistant medical examiner.

"I agree," the assistant medical examiner said. "I jumped to my conclusion too fast. I won't do it again."

Dr. Helpern made his determination of "accidental death" on the basis of three small burns. One burn was on the inside surface of the right thumb, one on the inside surface of the right index finger, and the third covered a somewhat larger area on the head of the penis. Although the body had been badly mangled by the train, the heart and brain were still reasonably intact. The autopsy had excluded stroke as a cause of death. There was no evidence of a clot in the coronary arteries. The autopsy, therefore, ruled out these two rather common causes of death, so it could not be classified as death from natural causes.

The train engineer had seen the body suddenly lunge backward, not off the platform above the rails, but rather from the ground level of the track on the side near the vertical supporting posts that divide the uptown and downtown tracks. The crucial question still remained, of course, as to whether the body lunged into the path of the speeding train voluntarily and with suicidal intention, or whether it fell there accidentally.

The history of Joseph Patrick O'Malley was also considered in arriving at the opinion that the death was accidental instead of suicidal. There are uncounted thousands of Joseph Patrick O'Malleys. Some are Irish, and some are not. Some would like to be Irish, and some would not; but whether Jewish, Irish, Dutch, or Scandinavian, they are Joseph Patrick O'Malleys all the same.

This particular Joseph Patrick O'Malley was a legitimate Irishman, forty-seven years old, lovable, kind, sometimes considerate, but frequently heartless in any matter that tended to separate him from his constant companion, alcohol. The unity between Joseph Patrick O'Malley and his "friend" began at an early age, when he attempted to follow the bricklayer trade of his immigrant father. When his friend would let him work, Pat O'Malley was a skilled artisan. But as the years and the friendship took their toll, his workless days began to outnumber the productive ones.

Patrick O'Malley's earnest bouts with the water-wagon were of progressively shorter duration.

He was blessed with a great and understanding family, dozens of aunts, uncles, cousins, brothers, and sisters, who understood Pat and were sympathetic to his problem. They supplied him generously with a place to stay, clothes, food, Irish whiskey and beer, asking only that he accompany some one of them to Mass every Sunday morning. It was a fair and equitable arrangement which never disturbed Pat in the least.

Like thousands of other Joseph Patrick O'Malleys, this Pat O'Malley would have periods of depression and give vent to some type of pent-up hostility about his lot in life generally. This un-Irish attitude appeared when his blood alcohol reached a certain saturation point on certain days.

"Urinate on it . . . urinate on it . . . urinate on it . . . !" he would mutter, sometimes smiling, sometimes feigning genuine hostility, sometimes appearing to be seriously mad and angry. It should be pointed out parenthetically that the word "urinate" was not a part of his regular vocabulary. The word that he used in its place was much shorter and more pithy.

There is another habit and custom practiced by many of the Joseph Patrick O'Malleys, which assisted Dr. Helpern in arriving at his opinion of accidental death. At certain stages of intoxication, many of these people seem to derive some particular form of euphoria from walking the cross-ties of a railroad track. It may be similar to the so-called consciousness-expanding powers of certain drugs such as LSD. Regardless of the mechanics of the physiology involved, it is not uncommon for intoxicated persons to walk the tracks in the New York subways. Many of them suffer no untoward results. There is sufficient space between the tracks for them to retreat in safety when they hear a train approaching. When the train passes, they resume their consciousness-expanding occupation and interrupt it only when the next train approaches, or when they are forced out by the police.

The fate of this particular Joseph Patrick O'Malley also involved the third rail of the subway. This is the "hot" rail through which the 600-volt electric current passes to furnish the energy for the subway trains. It parallels the inside rail of each track and is embedded in cement so that it is covered on three sides. The fourth side is open, facing the train, so that the contact wheel of the subway train can run against this "hot" third rail to pull in the electrical current to move the motors.

That this Joseph Patrick O'Malley's death was accidental involved a combination of facts derived from the history and from the autopsy. As Pat O'Malley's encounter with the train occurred some fifty yards away from any platform, in an area of a gentle curve in the track, it was physically impossible for him to have jumped from the platform into the path of the train. He had been known to walk the tracks in the past on several occasions. The burns on the head of the penis and on the thumb and forefinger were obvious electrical burns.

For one reason or another, this Joseph Patrick O'Malley elected to literally urinate on the world at this particular time. The stream of urine had come into contact with the 600 volts of the third rail. The current coursed up the stream to cause the burns on his body as the electricity entered it. In all probability, he was dead from electrocution before the train ever hit his body.

"I've always interpreted this case," Dr. Helpern says, his eyes flashing, "as illustrating the moral that you had better be careful what you do to the world. If you choose to be foul with it, it may foul you right back."

CHAPTER 16

"There Is Something Noble in Being Human"

It was 10:10 Saturday evening when the telephone rang in Dr. Helpern's apartment on East End Avenue.

"Chief," the duty man at the medical examiner's office said, "we are really jammed up down here. This hot weather, I guess! We're running three to five hours behind on calls, and the 32nd Precinct in Harlem is really yelling."

"What's their problem?" Dr. Helpern interrupted.

"One's a stabbing, and the other is a guy found dead on a stairway with needle marks on his arm. They say they're having trouble keeping the cockroaches and rats off the bodies."

"All right," Dr. Helpern answered. "Give me the information, and have them send a car over. I'll take care of them myself."

The thermometer stood at 95 degrees, with the humidity reading not too far behind, an all-time record for that particular day in July, as the police car drove Dr. Helpern through East Harlem, where he was born, on into Harlem proper. As the driver turned north off of 110th Street into Spanish Harlem, a police panel truck with two large loudspeakers mounted on top cruised the area while an officer inside admonished the people to stay close to home and not to assemble in large groups. The sidewalks and apartment stoops were crowded with Puerto Ricans from six months to ninety years, some wearing undershirts, some bare above the waist, some wearing ragged shorts, but all joined together in a common goal of seeking physical relief from the oppressive heat.

"Such a common factor as the weather," Dr. Helpern observed, "has a noticeable effect on life and death. Our caseloads rise appreciably during the extremely hot weather. It's particularly difficult for the elderly and the debilitated. They simply cannot take it, and they die unattended deaths which we must investigate and certify. This extremely hot weather *may* be a factor in suicides and homicides. I use the term 'may' advisedly since this is one of the many areas which has not been researched sufficiently to permit us to draw any valid conclusions."

The agitated Spanish conversations rose in rapid crescendo from the stoops and sidewalks, bouncing eerily back and forth against the walls of the buildings. There was practically no laughter as the depressing heat stifled spirits as well as bodies.

The pink-faced young driver, only six weeks out of the New York Police Academy, got lost as he turned the car across Lennox Avenue toward the address on West 138th Street. Somewhere along the route, the Spanish conversations and the tan faces had merged imperceptibly into Negroid features and the dialogue of Black Harlem.

"Doctors won't make house calls up here anymore," Dr. Helpern explained, as the youthful policeman continued his embarrassed search for the address. "Too many have had their medical bags stolen by narcotics addicts who are looking for morphine or codeine. Cabdrivers have quit coming in here, too. What recourse does the poor cabdriver have when his fare suddenly bolts from the taxi and disappears into a crowd like this? Almost the only thing he can do is to get out of the neighborhood as quickly as possible."

A swarm of black bodies grudgingly gave way to the police car as the driver inched it slowly along the narrow confines of West 138th Street. An ominous, hostile silence descended as Dr. Helpern alighted from the car to follow the police officer toward the front stoop of the building. There was almost a tangible, physical feel to the harbored resentment of the white men's presence. One of their own had fallen, and it should be solely their own concern, not that of the dictating white man.

The narrow opening in their ranks closed quickly behind Dr. Helpern, like a giant tube that squeezed him into the building.

The murder room was on the second floor of this particular variation of a brownstone house which had been quite fashionable in its day, a day that had crested and ebbed well over half a century ago. The mass of black humanity almost squeezed Dr. Helpern bodily up the stairs. Black faces with sparkling white teeth peered down dizzily from two flights of stairs above the landing. Nothing moved or even fluttered to interrupt the oppressive atmosphere which must have reached as high as 110 degrees inside the building.

"Boy, Doctor, we're sure glad to see you," the white police officer said eagerly as he unlocked the door to the apartment. "The cockroaches are about to carry us away."

The architectural design was that of the old railroad flat. In the beginning, the front door opened into a living room. A door in the rear wall of the living room opened into a bedroom. Another door in the far wall of this bedroom opened into a second bedroom. This hall-less design continued backward through a bathroom, then a dining room, and finally a kitchen where an exit door opened onto a fire escape in the rear of the building. This clumsy architectural design, which had been adequate for the needs of a single family unit, had been altered by cutting a narrow hallway from the front door to the rear door, along the side wall of all the rooms. Now, each tiny room had its own door opening onto the narrow hallway, to form four separate "apartments" which shared a common bathroom and kitchen.

"That's integration for you," Dr. Helpern said, as he pointed to the open girlie magazine on the grimy kitchen table. There were two female nudes on each of the facing pages of the magazine, both bodies beautifully proportioned, one chocolate-brown and the other pristine white.

"That's one of the most depressing scenes I know," Dr. Helpern said to the Homicide detective who was packing away his camera and fingerprint kit. He pointed to a greasy skillet on the one-burner gas hot-plate, in which two small, half-cooked pork chops lay in their own pearl-colored, congealed lard. "If I've seen it once, I've seen it a hundred times. There's something that tells its own story in pork chops in cold grease that have been interrupted by a murder."

"We have a perpetrator," the police officer said.

"What's the story?" Dr. Helpern asked in a professional tone.

"The perpetrator claims that the victim was drunk, and that when he got drunk, he was mean and aggressive," the officer explained. "He made some kind of threat against the perpetrator, and the perpetrator picked up this paring knife and stabbed him 'in self-defense.' "

"It's an old story," Dr. Helpern responded. "These people live here in these cramped, dirty, filthy quarters. They get on each other's nerves. Their mores are quite different from ours. Instead of talking out their problems, they resort to a knife or a gun or their fists."

"The body's in here," the police officer said, as he pointed toward the bathroom door.

The yellowed, chipped enamel of the bathub, resting fragilely on long, spindly legs, was covered with several years' accumulation of gray sediment that clung to the original enamel finish as though it had been baked on. A yellowed, moisture-wrinkled piece of cardboard was held against the wall above the tub by a single thumbtack. It had probably started out as the back of a writing tablet. One side now dipped at about a 40-degree angle. The printed, penciled message was all but faded away, the punch of its admonition completely gone. It read:

> Flush the toilet, after yous use it.
> It aint good for other people when
> you dont.

The body of Morgan Davis, a handsome, chocolate-colored Negro in his late thirties, sat atop the lid of the toilet seat, the eyes open, frozen in statuesque position by rigor mortis, the right hand supporting the chin, and the right leg jutting out in a rigidly straight line. The blood which emanated from the middle of the chest had flowed down the pants leg in a two-inch stripe, almost as though painted there with a brush.

Dr. Helpern brushed the cockroaches away from the body as he raised the brightly colored red and purple sports shirt so that he could examine the wound in the center of the body. It was deceptively innocent in appearance, no longer than three-quarters of an inch, and except for the crusted blood around the edges, it would appear to be only hairline thick.

"The knife blade probably penetrated the tip of the heart," Dr. Helpern explained. "Otherwise, it might not have done any serious damage at all. It was this man's fate, or luck, or whatever you want to call it, that the thrust of this particular blade penetrated a vital organ."

Great beads of sweat poured off Dr. Helpern's huge brow as he made meticulous notes on his observations. The heat and odors of the room were stifling, but he did not stop with his superficial examination of this major, fatal wound. He carefully inspected the rest of the body as he flicked off the cockroaches in an effort to discover other clues and evidence that might lead to a reconstruction of this man's demise. He noted the state of rigor mortis. He checked the neck for any signs of manual strangulation. He looked for bruises and abrasions about the face. He checked the whites of the eyes for signs of minute, petechial (pinhead size) hemorrhages.

"It's interesting," he observed as he continued his examination, "how many people who have been stabbed are found in the bathroom. A stabbing wound, particularly in the abdomen or stomach area, apparently makes them feel that they are going to have a bowel movement. They rush to the bathroom and die, either on the bathroom floor or seated on the toilet, as this man did."

Dr. Helpern then noted a small cut on the inside surface of Morgan Davis' right little finger, and a matching laceration on the bottom surface of the left thumb.

"You see these 'defense cuts'?" Dr. Helpern asked the police officer. "These may become vitally important in the trial. The perpetrator undoubtedly is going to claim self-defense. These cuts on the little finger and thumb indicate that the victim tried to protect himself from the knife thrust. He saw it coming in time to get his hands up in front of the stomach area."

Dr. Helpern's careful, thorough, deliberate examination of the body and the scene required the better part of thirty minutes. The police officer guarding the front door to the apartment opened it on a sea of surging black faces.

"Which one was it?" asked a spindly-legged, black girl with a shapely body, just entering puberty.

"The man in the third room down the hall," the officer answered politely.

"Him?" her companion of about the same age shouted. "Him? Oh, he won't be tryin' to get in yo' pants no moh."

The two girls giggled almost hysterically.

The crowd on the steps and out into the street opened reluctantly for Dr. Helpern to walk back to the police car.

The second call was approximately eight blocks away. The body of a good-looking, light tan, sixteen-year-old boy lay on its back against the third floor steps of a different apartment house, the right leg grotesquely bent underneath the left buttock. A triangular piece of white paper towel, perhaps an inch in length on all three sides, dangled from the left corner of the mouth. This scene was deserted entirely except for two police officers who stood guard over the body.

After a police laboratory man had arrived to take pictures, Dr. Helpern made another thorough, careful examination for any marks of violence. He quickly observed the fresh needle puncture marks inside the right arm, and noticed old needle-mark scars all over the interior surfaces of both elbows and forearms. There were fresh multiple puncture-type wounds on both legs in the bare area of skin which was exposed between the bottom of the pants cuffs and the tops of the socks. There were also similar puncture-type wounds around the neck, on both ears, and on the wrists and hands.

"What's the story?" Dr. Helpern asked.

"He'd just been released from a six-month's jail term for narcotics," the officer responded. "He lives with his mother about two blocks from here. His heroin supplier lives in this building. He came here for a fix before he ever went home."

"Did you see any rats when you got here?" Dr. Helpern asked of the uniformed officers.

"God, did we see rats?" the officer answered with a visible shudder. "They are all over the place."

"That probably accounts for these bite-type wounds on the exposed flesh areas," Dr. Helpern observed as he made his entries in his notebook.

It was just after midnight when the police car from the 32nd Precinct dropped Dr. Helpern off at his apartment on East End Avenue. It was the end of another day and another week.

Early Monday morning, Dr. Helpern hurriedly descended the spiral steel stairway to the autopsy room to check on the two Harlem cases which he had seen the preceding Saturday night.

He gave the young autopsy surgeon a stern lecture for not finding the defense cuts on the little finger and thumb of Morgan Davis, the stabbing victim.

"One of our big problems," Dr. Helpern says, "is to teach our men that each and every case, no matter where it comes from or no matter who is involved, deserves and must receive the same type of careful, thorough investigation as every other case. It is my goal that there will be absolutely no distinction in the autopsy and our medico-legal evaluation between a poor Negro who is killed in Harlem, or a prominent member of the elite set from Park Avenue.

"There is something noble in being human. I don't care if the accident of a man's birth places him in Harlem or on Park Avenue. There are plenty of squirrels living in fancy apartments on Park Avenue. Each man is born a special individual. He is an individual in life, and he is entitled to individual care and respect in death. It's sometimes hard to get this idea across to some of my young assistants. I don't go for the philosophy that 'It's just another Harlem stabbing,' or 'It's just another Negro or Puerto Rican murder.' No case is 'just another case.' I don't buy this 'just another man' idea. We are all different and that makes us all special."

The autopsy of the young narcotics addict was far from routine. The lungs were congested, so that death could have been caused by an overdose of heroin; but this same physiological result could have been produced by asphyxia. There was ample evidence of asphyxia, because three large paper towels were found in this man's windpipe. The police pictures showing the triangular piece of paper dangling from the corner of the boy's mouth now became of interest because somewhere in the process of moving the body to the medical examiner's office, this piece of paper had disappeared.

"This is no easy case," Dr. Helpern explained as he discussed it with the assistant autopsy surgeon. "Sure, you've got this great mass of paper in the boy's windpipe; but it brings into play about three separate questions. In the first place, was the cause of death narcotics poisoning, or was it the asphyxia produced by the paper? We may never be able to say for sure. Secondly, did the boy himself stuff the paper down his throat? Your first reaction may be that that's impossible. We've got a case upstairs in the museum where a man committed suicide by shoving an entire four-in-hand tie down his throat, and it ended up in the windpipe in just about the same way these paper towels did in this boy. His death was first signed out as 'natural causes.'

"Then you've also got the fact that when narcotics addicts overdose themselves, or get an overdose from someone else, there is a popular belief among them that jamming something down the throat will in some way relieve the overdose. We've had any number of cases like this. Sometimes they try pouring hot water, or hot salty water, or hot milk down the throat of the overdosed addict. Even if someone had been seen stuffing these paper towels down this boy's throat, it would not necessarily mean that he did it with a homicidal intent. He may well have been trying to help the poor guy.

"Then you have the possibility that this boy stuffed the paper towels down his own throat, not with any intention of killing himself, but actually attempting to relieve the overdose which he suspected or felt coming on.

"This is a good illustration of the fact that there are very few open-and-shut cases in the field of forensic medicine, or for that matter, in life. The dangerous practitioners are the ones who glibly and confidently say, 'Yes, the answer has to be this. It cannot be anything else.' These doctors who think they have all the answers and, in effect, try to play God, really haven't recognized the first premise about the human body or the human mind, human motivation or human behavior. None of us can jump back in time and actually share another man's experiences. We do the best we can in drawing our own inferences and conclusions from the observations that are available to us, but we must never lose sight of the fact that each man is different and individual, and that there is something noble in being human."

Afterword

Over the past ten years, some two dozen publishers and authors have solicited Dr. Milton Helpern for a professional biography. When he finally agreed that it should be done, it was with the firm understanding that it would be limited to a report of a few of his most interesting cases, so that the story of the important but neglected field of forensic medicine could be told.

The selection of the cases posed the most difficult problem of all. With literally thousands to pick and choose from, an effort was made to use those that were most representative of the subject, and of the man most intimately identified with it.

Dr. Helpern cannot be held responsible for the choice, because it was mine alone. Other writers undoubtedly would have selected other cases and blended the man and his field into something of a different mixture, but the end products would probably have been surprisingly similar.

I am sure that Dr. Helpern will permit a bit of personal biographical data.

He was born on 110th Street in East Harlem on April 17, 1902, the middle child in a lively group of four boys and one girl born to Moses and Bertha Toplon Helpern. His father worked as a cutter in a men's clothing factory in the old garment section of downtown Manhattan. Six days out of every week, except for holidays, he left the apartment promptly at seven in the morning and returned just as promptly at seven in the evening.

There were few luxuries for the family, but Dr. Helpern does not remember ever feeling deprived of anything of serious importance during his boyhood years.

Those were the days of horsecars, bonfires in the street on Election Night, Halloween, and other special occasions, where the kids on the streets gathered to roast chestnuts, marshmallows, and other goodies which had been begged, borrowed, or scrounged from dozens of sympathetic households. There were the block fights, but the weapons of that era were not the shivs of the modern jeans set. The favorite was an old sock filled with flour that inflicted damage to the victim's pride by breaking and marking him as too unskilled to keep from getting hit.

Doctors and surgical procedures were foreign to the culture, except in emergency situations, although Dr. Helpern does remember being called in from play one day by his mother.

"The doctor is here to take your tonsils out," she informed him perfunctorily. He submitted without any great to-do to the operation, which was performed on the dining-room table.

He did not particularly like it, but made a rapid adjustment; later on in the afternoon, he was back on the street buying ice cream for himself and friends with a quarter, which served as his own special reward.

His parents believed in looking after their children's physical and material well-being, but leaving them to follow their own intellectual interests without hindrance or help. By the time he was twelve, Dr. Helpern had a collection of fruit flies which he stored in the family icebox, and at about the same time he developed an interest in photography which has increased in intensity with each passing year. He learned how to convert the bathroom into a photographic darkroom, and after the usual experiments and failures, he produced acceptable black and white prints.

He entered Townsend Harris High School in 1915, where he completed its intensive course in just three years. His next stop was City College.

At the urging of a fellow student, Dr. Helpern consented to a visit to the amphitheater at Roosevelt Hospital to watch an operation. Anyone in those days could walk in and become an observer without the slightest question being asked. Dr. Helpern was not impressed. He did not like the hospital odors, the rustle of gowns and clank of instruments, and particularly the running banter which verged on the vulgar between the surgeons as they waited for the patient to be wheeled in. He liked it even less when the patient arrived, breathing stertorously, when ether began filling the air, and a pall of deadly silence suddenly enveloped the entire area. When the skin blanched under the scalpel and a line of red crept after it, Dr. Helpern decided then and there that all this was not for him. He left the scene quite early.

There was biology, though, which became his first area of sustained deep interest; biology, in turn, led to the Cornell Medical School, which was then located on 23rd Street and connected with Bellevue Hospital. During his medical school days Dr. Helpern taught biology three nights a week at City College.

When he started his rotating internship at Bellevue in pathology, surgery, and medicine, his leanings were in the direction of internal and diagnostic medicine; but his six months tour in pathology included doing autopsies at the Bellevue morgue. There he fell under the spell of Dr. Douglas Symmers, Director of Laboratories, and Dr. Charles Norris, New York's fabled first Chief Medical Examiner. There was the usual competition among the interns to see who could perform the greatest number of autopsies, and when the final count was in at the end of each week, Milt Helpern's name always led all the rest by at least one or two.

Dr. Norris held legendary beer-drinking sessions at Cavanaugh's, to which he invited the most promising interns for long periods of talk about medicine in general, but with subtly guided emphasis on forensic medicine. Milton Helpern became a regular attendant at these relaxed but highly instructive classes which Dr. Norris held two or three nights a week.

In July 1927, Milton Helpern and Ruth Vyner were married. He accepted the residency in pathology offered him by Dr. Norris; and to return the favor, he plowed even more relentlessly into his work, performing more autopsies than the rest of the autopsy team combined.

Forensic medicine was fascinating to him, but it still was not his goal. He aspired to a laboratory directorship in one of the large hospitals and to a teaching chair, hopefully at Cornell.

Dr. Helpern felt a deep sense of obligation to Dr. Norris, who had treated him as a personal protégé from the very beginning of their association. A great bond of genuine affection existed between the professor and the student; at the final minute of the eleventh hour of the last day for filing applications, Dr. Helpern submitted an application to be tested and interviewed for the position of Assistant Medical Examiner. He was appointed to his post in April 1931.

This was the way his career began.

Dr. and Mrs. Helpern had three daughters, Nancy, Susan, and Alice. Nancy is a graduate of Cornell, Susan of Barnard, and Alice of Wellesley. All are now married.

Ruth Vyner Helpern died in 1953 as the result of a rheumatic heart condition she contracted when a child.

On January 1, 1955, Dr. Helpern was married to Beatrice Liebowitz Nightingale, herself a widow of two years. Mrs. Nightingale has two sons, William and Stuart. Dr. Stuart Nightingale is presently completing a residency in pathology at Bellevue Hospital, walking the same ground that Dr. Helpern walked some forty years ago.

MARSH HOUTS

Appendix

Only the living have problems with death. Death is a mystery only to the living, and the living look to death for help:

CHARLESTON, WEST VIRGINIA

DEAR DR. HELPERN:

We had to deal, recently, with an unusually tragic death caused by the so-called pink belly treatment of a fourteen-year-old high school boy. Up to the time of this city-shaking event, nobody including myself knew what "pink belly treatment" was. An ample investigation showed that this consists of a fast rhythmic slapping of the upper abdomen of the "victim" with the flat hand, not necessarily rudely or viciously, up to a point where the affected skin assumes a pink color. It came up that this is one of the most widespread methods of induction of high school pupils into the school band, and is also practiced upon members of the Boy Scout troops, Sunday School classes, and country club youth members.

In the case under consideration, the healthy, vigorous boy underwent such treatment at 11:45 A.M. in an equipment room next to the gymnasium of the high school. He "passed out" and was admitted dead on arrival at 12:10 at our emergency room.

We did the autopsy and found only an incredible amount of sludged blood in the abdominal organs. No significant skin marks, no hemorrhages, no ruptured organs, no evidence of prior medication, no full stomach, no blood sugar, normal BUN, normal SGOT, normal everything, including no albumin in the urine and neither salicylates nor barbiturates, no alkaloids, or anything else I could think of.

We signed the case out as "Neurovascular shock." The school board, the police and the office of the prosecuting attorney started on a large-scale investigation conducted discreetly and efficiently, and discovered that this is not only a "custom" in Charleston, or, for that matter, in Kanawha County or any other West Virginia county, but seems to be a widespread national "disease." We learned furthermore that the "victims" are pledged to secrecy, and found out that up to that time a number of unexplained fainting spells, syncopes, and other peculiar reactions of varying degrees of seriousness—although non fatal—could be traced to this "fad."

In view of the serious implications, Dr. Ladwig and I felt that the "pink belly treatment death" should become the subject of a short article in one of the major national, medical periodicals. We hope that it may save the lives of other young people around the country.

El Paso, Texas

Dear Dr. Helpern:

A little while ago, I telephoned you to get some advice about a young border patrolman who was found dead, apparently in good health immediately preceding his death. Being a federal employee, the FBI laboratory did the toxicology and informed us that toxic levels of methyl alcohol were found. We have been unable to discover the source of this methyl alcohol, but at least we found the answer to his death. In view of the help you have given me in this case, I thought you might like to hear the final disposition.

Baltimore, Maryland

Dear Dr. Helpern:

We are the parents of an eleven-month-old baby girl, our first child, whom I found dead in bed when I went in to check her the first thing in the morning. She was absolutely all right the night before. She was happy, smiling, and had never really been sick. I have just read an article in the paper which says that you are attempting to find out what causes these "infant crib" deaths, and that there may be as many as 50,000 of them in the United States every year. What, oh what is it? What didn't we do that we should have done? We can't help but feel that it was all our fault somehow. We know you are busy, but would you please write and tell us what the cause of these "infant crib" deaths is?

SHERMAN OAKS, CALIFORNIA

DEAR DR. HELPERN:

The pathologist was unable to make a diagnosis in the case of the sudden death of the husband of one of my patients. I shall appreciate comments upon the history and findings given below and also any opinions regarding the possible effect of the marked change in climatic conditions which took place a few months before the young man's demise.

The subject in question was an Air Force major of thirty-five years, who spent about twelve months in charge of Supply and Maintenance at the U.S. Air Force Base in Thule, Greenland. He was then transferred to a base in Topeka, Kansas, where for the four and a half months before his death, he endured unusually hot and humid weather even for this mid-continental station.

At four o'clock one morning his wife was awakened by an outcry from the major. When she first observed him, he was apparently convulsing, and as she watched he became cyanotic, frothed at the mouth, and was incontinent of urine. Within five to ten minutes he died. An autopsy was performed that same morning, but the pathologist could find no cause of death.

The following are the significant gross and microscopic findings: . . . Toxicologic examination of the stomach contents was entirely negative for a wide variety of poisons and drugs. The body was embalmed prior to autopsy. No toxicologic examination was made of other tissues.

The major had been in apparent good health. An examination of his entire military health record, dating back to the beginning of World War II, showed no illness of consequence. His widow tells me that he suffered greatly from the heat after his return to the United States. He stayed on his job at the air base every day, but was tired and rarely felt like doing anything outside his duty hours.

He had no known allergies and had not been taking medicine or drugs of any kind.

The pathologist could not make a statement as to the cause of death.

I shall be most appreciative, as will the major's widow, if light can be shed upon the cause or causes of his death.

SONYEA, NEW YORK

DEAR DR. HELPERN:

From time to time I am called upon by the local coroner to perform autopsies in cases of medico-legal significance, mostly accidental deaths. To help me out, I frequently consult your book: *Legal Medicine, Pathology and Toxicology*.

Our most frequent problem involves cases of potential smothering. That is, I have to reach a decision whether the patient was the victim of an epileptiform seizure or seizures, or died as a consequence of asphyxia. Perusal of the usual pathology books yields very scanty and rather hesitant information with only sketchy descriptions of the organs, none of which is pathognomonic. Not even in the definitely proved cases of suffocation have I seen the often emphasized cyanosis of the face and upper part of the body. Similarly, I did not observe punctate hemorrhages of the conjunctivae and galea aponeurotica.

I do realize that you are more than somewhat busy, and the daily exigencies of your office leave very little free time. Nevertheless, I would appreciate it if you could find an opportunity to convey to me some of your reactions to the above observations.

PROSECUTING ATTORNEY'S OFFICE
SPOKANE, WASHINGTON

DEAR DR. HELPERN:

I hope that you will not feel that we are presumptuous in writing you, but through the years we have received substantial assistance from your book *Legal Medicine, Pathology and*

Toxicology, and for this reason we were in hopes we might ask your thoughts with reference to our problem.

Recently, a seventy-four-year-old man was found murdered in his store near Spokane, the event evidently having occurred in the course of a robbery. The autopsy was performed by a pathologist at Sacred Heart Hospital in this city. He found that the death had been caused by five blows on the head of the deceased. Three of the blows were in the area where there was no hair; two of them were on the forehead, in the area between the eyebrows and the hairline. The blows left impressions on the surface, three of them being 4 cm. in length, one 5.5 cm., and one 3.5 cm. In the pathologist's opinion, it was one of those on the forehead that actually caused death, which ensued, in his opinion, between half an hour and an hour and a half after the blows were administered. This particular one on the forehead fractured the skull. The other four blows, in the doctor's opinion, would have eventually caused the man's death, but not as quickly as the one described.

Six days after the crime, a man was taken into custody for another offense and confessed that he had struck the old man on the head with a tool, which turned out to be an adz. He took the officers into the country and showed them where he had thrown the tool following the crime. As you perhaps know, an adz is a tool roughly the weight of a pick, and has a long handle just as a pick would have. On one side of its head is a cutting edge similar to that of a grub hoe; on the other side of the head is a thick, flat surface such as might be used for driving spikes. It appears that the wounds were inflicted with this thick side of the head of the adz, not with the flat portion of the head, but rather with the corner edge, some of the blows from the top corner and some from the bottom corner. The defendant contends that after the crime he did not wipe off or wash off the adz, but left the scene and immediately threw it out into the brush in open country.

When the adz was recovered by the officers, no blood appeared to the naked eye on the tool. We sent it along with a sample of the dead man's blood to the Federal Bureau of Investigation laboratory in Washington, and were subsequently notified that the laboratory found no blood on the adz.

Recognizing the many, many instances where you and your staff have gone to the scene and examined instruments which have caused death, may I ask that you please inform me whether or not you have run into situations where instruments such as this one inflict mortal wounds, and thereafter no blood can be found on them? If you are familiar with any text material that we could obtain covering the subject, we would be very appreciative if you would give us the titles.

HORNELL, NEW YORK

DEAR DR. HELPERN:

The request in this letter may be somewhat unusual. I have a situation which intimately concerns me and, particularly, my sister. It has to do with the recent death of my father, who was also a doctor, and more particularly with his ability to execute a will about three weeks before his death.

I have discussed the case with a local pathologist, and he immediately referred me to your excellent book and suggested that I contact you for your thoughts on the matter.

My father attempted suicide by gas poisoning in 1958. Following his discharge from the hospital, the attending physician made a diagnosis, among other things, of encephalitis. The medical history, as best I can give it to you, is as follows. . . .

Quite honestly, I would like some independent, outside opinion as to whether or not he probably had the mental capacity and ability to make a will.

My attorneys tell me that he would be required to know that he was making a will, know generally who his relatives are, and know generally the nature and extent of his property.

NABHA, PUNJAB
INDIA

DEAR DR. HELPERN:

I have studied your book *Legal Medicine, Pathology and Toxicology* carefully, but find that my particular problem is not covered in your book. We have presently under investigation, a case involving the murder of a local Hindu merchant. He was struck several blows upon the head, seven to be exact, and sustained a fractured skull, after which he went on to die in about thirty minutes. An ornamental water-buffalo horn was found next to the man's body. It had blood on it in several places. Nothing else was found near the scene of the man's attack that would appear to have been used as a weapon. Our problem is to try to determine how and whether this water-buffalo horn was the instrument of murder. We would appreciate your advice in this matter.

ALBUQUERQUE, NEW MEXICO

DEAR DR. HELPERN:

We are writing to you in regard to the death of our daughter. Mr. Helpern, her death was passed off as a suicide. But we are not satisfied that it was a suicide. The whole inside of her left foot was black, and there were four or five black places on the front of her legs. I have a copy of the autopsy report, and these bad bruises are not mentioned. I asked the coroner what caused them and he said, "I don't know." We are devout Roman Catholics and the thought that our daughter could have committed suicide is horrible for us. We would deeply appreciate any help that you can give us.

ATTORNEY GENERAL
STATE OF NEW HAMPSHIRE
CONCORD

DEAR DR. HELPERN:

Thank you for sending me your observations on the death of the above-captioned individual, the young man who died from self-inflicted electrical energy. There were no pictures taken at the scene, but there were a few items of interest: A list of about one hundred juvenile female persons, giving their waist and bust measurements, and the sum of the measurements, and a description of the method by which each had committed suicide. There was also a newspaper with a prominently featured article on juvenile suicide. There were also twelve empty airplane glue tubes and a paper bag smelling strongly of airplane glue.

I enclose a copy of the form "View of Body." In addition to

what appears on this form, I am informed by the chief of police that the nylon cord from the pull-switch could be used to shut off the current as well as to turn it on. I am also informed that the magazines strewn about which indicated a "highly intelligent mind" were girlie books.

We are still at a loss as to how to classify the death. You will remember the body was found suspended from a beam in the basement of the house, by the wrists, which were tied with the cord. He lived with his mother and foster-father in a good suburban development. He had stripped off his clothing and donned a pair of women's panties, and a deep-cupped brassiere, in which there were two balls of sponge rubber covered with fragments of cloth. He had connected an extension cord to an outlet of the house current (110 volts), stripped the ends of the cord, and with adhesive plaster secured the bare wires, one to each nipple of his breasts. This arrangement would have sent the current through his heart, producing a cardiac arrest. He had also arranged a nylon cord from the pull-switch on the outlet to which he was connected so that after suspending himself from the ceiling beam, he could pull the cord to turn on the current.

I agree with you fully that the death is far more likely to have been caused accidentally during the victim's effort to obtain some type of bizarre sexual gratification, rather than an attempt at suicide.

CHICAGO, ILLINOIS

DEAR DR. HELPERN:

In our Department of Internal Medicine, we are attempting a survey in depth on the pros and cons of the effect of tobacco in cases of emphysema. We badly need the help of some active forensic medicine center which autopsies a great number of people whose deaths may have been caused from emphysema. Would you consider joining with us in such a research project? We hope that this may be the most thorough, exhaustive, and definitive study in depth of this particular disease entity that has yet been attempted.

SYRACUSE, NEW YORK

DEAR DR. HELPERN:

I would appreciate your opinion on the proper way to classify the death which resulted from the following set of facts. The deceased, while experimenting with LSD, slashed his throat with a razor blade, and went on to die a rapid death. Would you certify this death as being suicidal or accidental? My question is of more than passing academic interest. It involves not only the peace of mind of the deceased's family and relatives. There is also a double indemnity life insurance policy on his life.

PORTLAND, OREGON

DEAR DR. HELPERN:

I enclose the autopsy protocol on the above-captioned individual. Specifically, I would appreciate knowing your opinion on the number of hours between the bladder injury and death, and the manner of the bladder injury. Was this most probably a tear from a force against the anterior abdominal wall, or from an object inserted internally through the urethra?

The deceased was a thirty-eight-year-old, attractive white female with a long history of alcoholism and mental disorders. A state hospital psychiatrist described her as "sexually insane." Her sexual activity was predominantly heterosexual but apparently was widely varied and extensive.

She was found dead alone in her single jail cell at 8 A.M. Sunday, December 19th, 1965, and apparently had died at approximately 5 A.M. She had been booked on a "drunk" charge at approximately 2 A.M. the same day (three hours before). She was not examined by a physician then. On admission to the jail, she was intoxicated, but conscious and rational enough to give her name. She repeatedly requested drinks of water while alive in jail.

Her activities during the evening prior to her death were complex, confused, and not completely resolved. During the Saturday afternoon prior to that, she was in active good health, slightly intoxicated but carrying on her normal activities of walking, drinking, shopping, etc. Her early evening activities are unclear, but by approximately 11 P.M. she was wandering drunk and half-naked around a low-class hotel. Between 11 P.M. and 1 A.M., she was found in varying states of nudity in several separate rooms of the hotel. The occupant of the final room in which she was found, dressed her, took her into the hotel lobby, and called the police. At no time did she complain of any injury or trauma. The police have no witnesses to any event explaining the injury. There was no clinical evidence of recent sexual intercourse.

This unfortunate young lady comes from a very good family with strong political ties. Considerable pressure is being put upon our police department for a solution of this case.

ST. CLOUD, MINNESOTA

DEAR DR. HELPERN:

As pathologists in our area, we are called to the courts to testify as to findings and interpretations in many cases of suspected homicide or foul play.

One of the problems that we frequently run into is to assess a more accurate time (in hours) as to age of hemorrhage in body cavities or spaces (like subarachnoid and subdural hemorrhage). I am not familiar with any work with special reference to age of pre-mortem blood clots. The tissue response to these, of course, usually is described in terms of twelve hours or two days.

I would appreciate it if you would enlighten me in this subject and advise me about any studies which might have been published in reference to the *in vivo* formation of blood clots, and their time sequence of provable or detectable changes in body hemorrhages.

We recently had a case of a baby who died of subdural hemorrhage which followed what appeared to be suggestive of slapping the baby on the face. The assessment of age of head and skin bruises (measured in hours), as well as of subdural and subarachnoid hemorrhages, was very essential as to pinning down the verdict of "guilty." Of course, I could not extend myself as to that limit, rather than to be more vague.

St. Louis, Missouri

Dear Dr. Helpern:

We are presently involved in evaluating a case in which a thirty-three-year-old married woman, the mother of two children, died from a pulmonary embolism. None of the doctors involved, including the pathologist who did the autopsy and the woman's family doctor, can account for the development of this embolism.

Our only possible lead is that approximately four weeks before her death, the woman began taking one of the new contraceptive birth control pills, which is drug X.

I have read in the paper about two other cases involving this same oral contraceptive, in which the cause of death was a pulmonary embolism. We would like to know whether you have encountered any similar cases. If there is a connection between this oral contraceptive and the development of pulmonary embolism, it should certainly be explored and researched. If the pill is unsafe, it should be taken off the market.

Vellore
South India

Dear Dr. Helpern:

I have been in India as a missionary with the Methodist Church since March 1960. I expect to be here for five years.

My major problem is with forensic medicine. By law, all medico-legal autopsies must be done in a government hospital. The doctors in charge of the local government hospital will call on us when a medico-legal postmortem is being done, but only four to five per year are available. I would like some suggestions as to how to make my course in forensic medicine more interesting, worthwhile, and challenging to the students. I have no visual aids, but probably could obtain some if they are available commercially. I have even thought of assigning mystery stories by such authors as Erle Stanley Gardner for outside reading and reporting on the medico-legal aspects. Can you give me any suggestions?

GHENT
BELGIUM

DEAR DR. HELPERN:

We have a most perplexing case in which it is suspected that the victim, a twenty-six-year-old unmarried woman, was first manually strangled by her lover who then tied a rope around her neck and suspended the body from a rafter in the ceiling to make it appear that she had actually committed suicide. The pathological findings are as follows. . . . We would greatly value and appreciate your opinion on this particular case.

MANKATO, MINNESOTA

DEAR DR. HELPERN:

I have recently been confronted with the problem of what occurs to the ethyl alcohol in the bloodstream following death. In brief, I would like to know if the blood alcohol (ethyl) increases or decreases with decomposition of forty-eight hours or less. Also, if the blood alcohol level was elevated at the time of death, is this dissipated to any extent over that period?

I am awaiting your earnest reply, inasmuch as I will need this information by Monday, March 18th, at which time I have to testify in a manslaughter case in court.

TUCSON, ARIZONA

DEAR DR. HELPERN:

I have been authorized by the County Attorney of Pima County, Arizona, to contact you relative to the possibility of obtaining your services as an expert witness in the prosecution of a case of infanticide. I am therefore submitting for your inspection, detailed data including a copy of the autopsy report, microscopic sections of the lung, and photographs.

The following is a brief synopsis of the facts: On the morning of November 1, a professor at the University of Arizona, while seeking a box amongst the rubbish behind the girls' dormitory, came upon a paper sack. Thinking that this contained fruit, he turned it upside down, and a baby tumbled out head first (i.e., the baby was upright in the paper sack). A garment was knotted tightly around the infant's neck, as shown in some of the photographs. I took the body to a mortuary and performed a postmortem examination.

Upon further investigation, the girl who gave birth to the infant was found. According to her statement, she first noted abdominal cramps the day previous, October 31st, about noon-time. The time of birth was first stated to be 2 P.M., and then 5 P.M. that same day. She said that the child was born dead, but that to make certain, she knotted her undergarment around the infant's neck and drew it tight. She had cut the cord herself. The placenta was disposed of down the toilet bowl. She then placed the infant in a sack, and her roommate disposed of it in the manner described above.

The medico-legal problem is, of course, to determine whether the child was born dead, or was born alive so that death resulted from ligature strangulation. I know that you have had a great many similar cases in your experience.

ACKNOWLEDGMENTS

I am deeply indebted to:

Mrs. Milton Helpern for her collection of scrapbooks, letters, and numerous other data on her husband's professional career.

Dr. Charles J. Umberger, Chief Toxicologist, Office of the Chief Medical Examiner, City of New York, for his help with the subject of toxicology.

Assistant District Attorney Alexander Herman for his help in obtaining the last remaining copy of the trial transcript in *People v. Thomas G. Daniel and Leobaldo Pijuan*.

Dr. Michael Baden, Associate Medical Examiner, City of New York.

Dr. William Sturner, Associate Medical Examiner, City of New York.

Mr. John Foley, Statistics and Record Director, Office of the Chief Medical Examiner, City of New York.

Miss "Cavie" Cavanaugh, Chief Receptionist, Office of the Chief Medical Examiner, City of New York.

Mr. James B. Schafran, Curator, Milton Helpern Museum, Office of the Chief Medical Examiner, City of New York.

Mr. Daniel Porfido, Office of the Chief Medical Examiner, City of New York.

Mr. Sam Hicks, Temecula, California, for his help with the illustrations from the Warren Commission Report.

Dr. Frank Cleveland, Cincinnati, for his help with the transcript in *State of Ohio v. Domer*.